ADVANCED

INFORMATION TECHNOLOGY

ALASTAIR DE WATTEVILLE
SEAN NAUGHTON

Heinemann Educational Publishers,
Halley Court, Jordan Hill, Oxford OX2 8EJ
a division of Reed Educational & Professional Publishing Ltd

OXFORD FLORENCE PRAGUE MADRID ATHENS
MELBOURNE AUCKLAND KUALA LUMPUR SINGAPORE TOKYO
IBADAN NAIROBI KAMPALA JOHANNESBURG GABORONE
PORTSMOUTH NH (USA) CHICAGO MEXICO CITY SAO PAULO

© Alastair de Watteville and Sean Naughton 1997

First published 1997
2001 2000 99 98
10 9 8 7 6 5 4 3 2

A catalogue record for this book is available from the British Library on
request

ISBN 0 435 45259 2

Designed by Roger Denning and typeset by TechType, Abingdon, Oxon.
Printed in Great Britain by Bath Press

Contents

iii

Acknowledgements

Numerous people have assisted me before and during my writing. First and foremost I would like to thank my wife Joanne for helping me in many ways while I wrote – this has been a partnership effort and your commitment, love and support are outstanding.

Secondly and with equal importance, to my parents and sisters Melanie, Lianne, Shelly and Noëlle. Without your belief, devotion, love and support throughout the years I would not be where I am today. Thank you is simply not enough for what you have done.

I would also like to thank

Lindy, Jaime, Noëlle
Ron Bolzern
Noel Roberts
Simon Mann
Stephen Whewell
Steve Almond
British Steel
Coca-Cola Schweppes Beverages Ltd
Ford Motor Company Ltd
Karen Young
Marks & Spencer PLC
Paul Walters
Trevor Duckworth
Angela Smith at Virgin Management Ltd
Larry Hunter – University of Sunderland

In addition, I would also like to thank Rosalyn Bass, Margaret Berriman and Jan Nikolic at Heinemann Educational for their help, assistance and dedication in having the book published – and for tracking me down! Also to Mandi Noble for procuring information so quickly whenever it was needed.

Sean Naughton

I would like to express my gratitude to Rosalyn Bass, Margaret Berriman and Jan Nikolic at Heinemann Educational for their invaluable contribution to this book in particular for their high quality of editing.

Alastair de Watteville

The authors and publishers are grateful to the following for permission to reproduce photographs and other material:

Powerstock Photo Library
Stephen Oliver
ACE Photo Agency/Bill Bachmann
Ford
Chris Honeywell
ACE Photo Agency/CC Image
Microsoft
ACE Photo Agency/ John David Begg

Screen shots reprinted with permission from Microsoft Corporation

Introduction

Tutor introduction

Welcome to *GNVQ Advanced Information Technology*. The text is intended to help students obtain the GNVQ (Advanced) qualification in IT, based on the May 1995 revision of the specifications issued by NCVQ.

The authors recognise that centres delivering GNVQ (Advanced) in IT differ from one another in respect of their resources, cohort sizes, and the skills and experience that the teaching team can bring to bear on the task. They also realise that students may have come directly from GCSE programmes, or from Intermediate GNVQ programmes, or they may be mature; and that delivery philosophies vary between institutions. They have tried to provide accessible support for all these situations.

In recommending this book to students, tutors will want to emphasise that the qualification calls for knowledge, understanding and skill in the chosen subject area, as do all GNVQs. The book aims to assist students in these three aspects of learning.

We urge tutors, as students move forward into their course, to encourage them to plan their own progress, and to arrange their own visits and the accumulation of information by other means.

This GNVQ requires students to provide evidence which satisfies the specifications of 15 units; namely, eight mandatory units, four optional units and three key skills units. This book explicitly sets out to help students generate the evidence they need for obtaining the mandatory units, but it also identifies opportunities for obtaining evidence for the key skills units.

The 28 chapters of the book address the elements that make up the mandatory units, presented in the order in which they appear in the specifications. Within each chapter, the headings relate directly to the performance criteria and range statements.

Acknowledgement that the element is regarded by NCVQ and the awarding bodies as the main building block for GNVQ, for both delivery and assessment, is accorded to the chapters by offering *evidence indicator projects* at the end of each chapter. Students may work towards these projects throughout the chapter, in stages. Evidence collection points appear in the text when students should have completed criteria linked to specified evidence indicators. At these points it may be suitable for students to start working towards their project. If there is only one evidence indicator for an element, this is stated at the start of the element.

The *activities* presented in the text can help students acquire understanding, and may also provide evidence for their portfolios.

Seven of the eight mandatory units have external unit tests which must be passed before the units can be claimed. At the end of the last chapter for each of those seven units are sample questions which students can use in their preparation for sitting the external tests.

Key skills tracking sheets at the end of the book show you exactly which evidence indicator projects provide opportunities for students to achieve elements and particular performance criteria in key skills.

Much writing and teaching seeks to distinguish formally between the meanings of data and information. We have decided against trying to draw such a distinction. We have taken this decision partly because in some cases there is real doubt about which definition would apply, but more importantly because by forcing the distinction upon the attention of the reader we should have been introducing an unnecessary distraction. We believe it better for the context to imply naturally what is meant.

Tutors may find that parts of the 'Student information' and 'Student guide' sections of this Introduction are useful in reinforcing material presented to students during programme induction.

It is recommended that team members arrange the submission dates of projects they set to be co-ordinated so that there is no unnecessary bunching of work for students.

Student information

This book has been written to help you obtain the GNVQ (Advanced) IT qualification for which you have registered. GNVQ stands for General National

Vocational Qualifications. This means that each GNVQ is part of a scheme running throughout England, Wales and Northern Ireland to provide standard training and qualifications that will be widely recognised.

Our definition of information technology (or IT) is the acquisition, analysis, manipulation, storage and distribution of information; and the design and provision of equipment, and the systems required, for these purposes. The concept behind all GNVQs is that the students taking them collect evidence to show that they have the understanding, knowledge and skills that are required.

Advanced-level GNVQs are usually run by schools and colleges as two-year courses. Unlike GCSEs and A-level courses they do not work towards big examinations at the end of the two years. Rather, they provide for you to build up evidence of your progress as you go along.

You cannot fail a GNVQ. You simply cannot pass until you have collected all the evidence you need. If you do collect all the required evidence, you can be considered for a Merit grade or a Distinction grade. Your tutors will explain how this grading system works. There is also more information on grading in the 'Student guide' section of this Introduction.

The GNVQ (Advanced) in IT, like all other Advanced GNVQs, is made up of 15 units. They are

- 8 mandatory units
- 4 optional units
- 3 key skills units.

The mandatory and optional units are called vocational units. That means that in your case they are all concerned with IT. The key skills units are the same for all Advanced GNVQs: they are to do with writing and speaking ability, the use of numbers, and familiarity with IT. The aim of this book is to help you obtain all the evidence you need for the mandatory units and the key skills units.

Part of the thinking behind GNVQ is that the key skills should be made as relevant as possible to the subject area being studied. As far as practicable your key skills evidence will come from your work on the vocational units. In the chapters that follow you will find suggestions for developing key skills evidence from the work you are doing on the mandatory units.

Each mandatory unit is divided into elements. There are four elements in four of the units, and three in the other four units, making 28 elements in all.

As an example of this structure:

- Unit 4 is 'Communications and networking'.
- The second element of that unit is referred to as Element 4.2, 'Use electronic communications to transfer data'.

Every element has the same structure. There are

- *evidence indicators* which lay down the minimum evidence you have to collect;
- *performance criteria* which set out numbered points you will have to cover in order to satisfy the evidence indicators; and
- *range statements* which tell you about the area of the subject-matter that your evidence must cover.

This structure probably seems most bewildering to you. That is normal. You will be amazed at how quickly it all falls into place once you start work.

Student guide

The layout of this book

The eight main sections in this book relate to the eight mandatory units in the award. Each unit is clearly divided into the individual elements you need to cover. There is one chapter for each element.

Within each chapter you will find the following:

- The *main text,* which covers all the topics you have to know about. The headings and subheadings link to the element performance criteria and range of topics you have to cover.
- *Activities* designed to help you to think for yourself and work with your fellow students – these activities have been designed to help you practise and develop your learning. They are not assessed as part of your award.
- *Case studies,* to give you the opportunity to evaluate real-life examples and provide opportunities to link the theory to practice.
- *Evidence collection points* which will lead towards a main evidence indicator project at the end of each element. Your tutor may ask you to work towards, and complete, this project, or may have written a special project for you to complete. All assessable activities include details of the performance criteria, range and key skill areas covered.

This section of the Introduction tries to help you feel confident about the way you are tackling your GNVQ.

Assignments

Much of the evidence you need to collect will probably arise from tasks or assignments you are set. These assignments will have been designed to give you the opportunity of creating evidence for a particular element in the GNVQ, though sometimes there may be more than one assignment for an element, and sometimes an assignment will provide evidence for more than one element.

You should always try to hand your completed assignment in by the submission dates you will have been given. Doing so shows that you can plan your own time properly.

Throughout this book you will find *evidence collection points* which you can tackle to help you generate evidence. If that overlaps with other work you are set no harm is done. You will learn more as you go along, and no one will complain if you have too much evidence.

Other evidence

There are many ways in which you can get extra evidence to supplement that coming from your assignments. For example:

- You can demonstrate some skill to your tutor.
- You can give a short talk describing work you have done.
- You can explain some points in an interview with your tutor.
- You can obtain, and write up, information from books and from businesses or exhibitions you visit.
- You can gather facts and opinions from questionnaires.

The portfolio

When pieces of your evidence are complete they are filed in a binder called your portfolio. All your evidence must be on paper, either originated by yourself or else signed by your tutor as what is called a *witness statement.*

Your portfolio becomes increasingly valuable to you as your course goes on. Your school or college will probably look after it safely for you, but whatever the arrangements make sure it is kept safely. When you go for an interview for a job you may want to take your portfolio with you.

Be sure to organise the portfolio tidily so you can speedily find evidence for any unit or element.

Assessment

All your work will be assessed, or marked, usually by your tutor. The assessment is directed at gauging whether or not your work provides the evidence that is required. If it does not completely do so you will be asked to make good the gaps.

There will be someone called the *internal verifier* at your centre whose job is to see that assessors are all working to the same standards and are assessing fairly.

Normally pieces of work go into the portfolio only when they have been assessed.

Grading

When your work is assessed, once you are past the first few weeks of your course, it will probably be given a grading indication providing the evidence asked for is complete.

To achieve a merit or distinction grade for the whole GNVQ you need to have at least one-third of it to that level.

Grading decisions are made against four themes:

1 Planning.
2 Information seeking and handling.
3 Evaluation.
4 Quality of outcomes.

To earn the final grade all the four themes must qualify. Each theme is broken into two criteria. You must obtain the grade in each criterion to be awarded it for the theme. Let's look at each theme and criterion in turn.

Planning

The criteria are *drawing up plans of action* and *monitoring courses of action*. A plan of action is like a timetable for how you intend to tackle a problem. You create these all the time: 'I must wash my hair by 6.00 before leaving to be at the bus station by 7 o'clock to get the bus. If I arrive in Manchester by 8.00 then I can walk to the cinema by ten past.'

You will have to show that you can plan your assignments in the same kind of way. Then you will know what you need to do in the time you have available.

Monitoring

Monitoring your action plan is important, just in the same way you would keep checking your watch to make sure you were on time for getting to the bus station to get the bus for Manchester. Likewise, you must monitor your assignment plans and modify them if necessary.

Information seeking and information handling

The criteria are *identifying information and using sources to obtain information* and *establishing the validity of information*. The first of these criteria focuses on your use of information sources in compiling the evidence you need; the second is about looking critically at the information itself and gauging whether or not you feel it is valid.

Evaluation

The two criteria are *evaluating outcomes and alternatives* and *justifying particular approaches to tasks/activities*. This theme is the one that generally causes students greatest trouble. It is, however, as important as the others.

The first of the criteria is about looking back over work you have done and asking yourself if it meets all the requirements and whether there were other ways in which you could have tackled the tasks. The second criterion is focused on justifying the way you did, in fact, decide to do those tasks.

Quality of outcomes

The criteria are *synthesis* and *language*. Synthesis is the process of drawing upon all your relevant knowledge, skills and understanding in producing high-quality work. Make sure you include all important information, address all parts of the question, and make it accurate and easy to understand for you. Command of language is making sure the reader can understand the sentences. Keep them short and to the point. Do not say anything you do not understand, do not use slang. You are expected to be able to write good English and also to use IT specialist words accurately.

External unit tests

To help maintain uniformity across all areas where GNVQs are run there are centrally set tests on most mandatory units. For Advanced IT seven of the eight units are tested. You cannot claim completion of a unit that is tested until you have passed the test.

Each test consists of between 30 and 40 multiple-choice questions to be answered within one hour. To pass you need to score 70%.

To help you prepare for these tests you can work through the sample questions at the end of the last chapter in each of the Units 1–7.

Tracking progress

Finally, throughout the course you will want to know how you are progressing with collecting the evidence you need. The teaching staff will, of course, keep records; and they will also have a plan of what you should have finished by certain dates; but you would do well to keep abreast of your own achievements, and stay aware of the key skills performance criteria that you still need to complete.

Key skills tracking sheets are provided at the back of the book to show you exactly which Evidence indicator projects at the end of each chapters provide opportunities to achieve the particular performance criteria in the key skills.

This unit covers four distinct areas of IT. It can, of course, be studied as the first unit in a GNVQ Advanced IT course, but there is no need for it to precede all the other units. Three of the four elements follow on directly from three of the elements in GNVQ Intermediate IT, Unit 1.

As with much of your course, you will find it easier to acquire a full and balanced view of the subject matter in this unit if, alongside your supervised work, you read books and journals which refer to the topics in the elements. In particular, you will benefit when you tackle practical work in Chapter 4 (Element 1.4) if you have at least glanced at some computer magazines. You will also find it helpful to talk to people outside your school or college about their experience with using computer systems.

Chapter 1 (Element 1.1), asks you to describe and give examples of commercial and industrial systems, and to evaluate two of each. The element helps you to distinguish between the characteristics of systems devoted to commercial and administrative tasks and those devoted to controlling industrial functions and processes.

Chapter 2 (Element 1.2) introduces you to the items of hardware and to the types of software used in modern IT systems, and to the purposes of the hardware and software. It also lets you discover how the performance of a system is determined by the choice of hardware and software.

Chapter 3 (Element 1.3) explains the construction and operation of a micro-processor. Micro-processors find many applications today, not just in computers, but also in other equipment of the kind that you may easily encounter in day-to-day life.

Chapter 4 (Element 1.4) invites you to assemble a desk-top computer system, and to test that it is working as intended. This is a wholly practical element, for which you need to provide evidence that you have satisfied the Evidence indicators.

An external test form part of this unit.

Chapter 1

Investigate industrial and commercial information technology systems

To get us started in this exciting subject, we are going to look at commercial and industrial information technology systems. This may seem a daunting prospect at first, but it will be more straightforward than you may expect and, in fact, you will already feel at home with some of these systems in everyday life.

In order to gain as much knowledge from this element as possible, it is advisable to carry out your own investigations at local commercial and industrial businesses. To do this you will need to select some local organisations and write to them or speak to the manager in charge, explaining why you wish to investigate his or her work, and how you would benefit from it. Copies of any letters you write or receive should be kept.

After studying this chapter you should be able to:

1 describe and give examples of *commercial* and *industrial systems*
2 *analyse commercial systems*
3 *evaluate* the selected *commercial systems*
4 *analyse industrial systems*
5 *evaluate* the selected *industrial systems*.

Did you know?

Some very influential people have said all sorts of things about computers over the years. Some of the things they have said have been of great importance, while others, with hindsight, seem highly ironic and even amusing. Here are a few:

■ 'Computers in the future will weigh no more than 1.5 tons' (from *Popular Mechanics*, forecasting the advance of science in 1949).
■ 'I think there's a world market for maybe five computers' (Thomas Watson, then Chairman of IBM, 1943).
■ 'I have travelled the length and breadth of this country and talked to the best people, and I can assure you that data processing is a fad that won't last out the year' (the editor in charge of business books at Prentice-Hall publishers, 1957).

Introduction

In the Introduction to this book we suggest what is generally understood by the term *information technology* (IT). How you think about IT and its application in different circumstances depends

1

whether the emphasis is on the *information* or on the *technology*. In this chapter, as in some others the emphasis is on *information* – the types of information and the uses made of it. In the three remaining elements of Unit 1 we are more concerned with the *technology. There is a definition of Information technology,* and an explanation of the use of the words *data* and *information*, in the Introduction to this book.

Almost everything we do requires information. Shops keep records of sales and customers, doctors and dentists keep records of patients, and libraries keep records of the books on the shelves. The type of information organisations use has changed very little in the past 100 years. The volume of information has changed immensely, though – whereas in the past life was simpler and the number of records kept relatively small, nowadays there is so much information available (much of it is changing and increasing all the time) that we have to learn how to work with it – otherwise it would overwhelm us!

Information should be kept up to date. With the volume of information increasing each day this task becomes more difficult, especially when we consider that we are now so closely linked with other countries, particularly those in the European Union. With this in mind, there is a strong need to make sure information is looked after and used suitably. If information is to work for us it has to be kept safely and get to the right place at the right time; it has to be top-quality information – that is to say, it must be complete, accurate, timely, relevant and not redundant. If it is inaccurate and of poor quality then it is not just useless – it can be dangerous.

Successful use of information takes place around us all day long. Look at how quickly reports for newspapers and TV programmes are sent from the most hostile areas of the world into our homes. This is achieved through communicating, controlling and processing information. This is what IT is all about: the storage, control, manipulation and sending of data to achieve a goal.

It was only about 15 years ago when the very first home computers were introduced into the UK. The market had to wait for the reliability, compactness, and reduction of cost that were needed to make microcomputers suitable for home use. These characteristics, which every personal computer, or PC, shows, have continued to move rapidly towards the needs of personal and office users. The growth in sales, allied to growth in performance, has been strong and continuous, and now *you* are joining this vibrant world of IT.

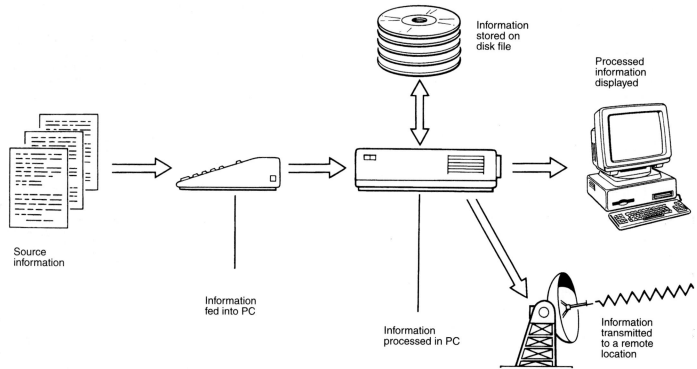

Figure 1.1 The flow of information

Commercial systems

Commercial systems are mainly those used by companies that sell products and services, but their use is not restricted to enterprises active in the field of commerce. Commercial systems can be thought of as administrative systems which are characterised by files of information which are routinely updated and used to obtain printed or other output. Such systems are used by central and local government, public corporations, and charitable and recreational bodies, as well as by businesses. The contrast with industrial systems will become evident. Contact a number of businesses in your area to see their systems for yourself.

The following are examples of commercial systems.

Booking systems

A good example of a commercial system is a hotel central booking system. A number of hotel chains operate such systems, whereby the customer can ring the central office and book a room in any hotel in the chain. The telephone operator asks the customer for details of which hotel and what accommodation are required and when, types them into a computer and waits. During the wait, the computer contacts the computer at the hotel of the customer's choice and checks to see if there are rooms available. As soon as there is a response the telephonist is notified and the customer can accept or reject it. If the booking is accepted, the telephonist takes the customer's name and a credit card number to guarantee the booking. In return, the customer is issued with a booking number.

All this is made possible by using the two computers, the right type of software, a telephone modem connected to each computer and a telephone line. The modems allow the two computers to 'talk' to one another. Figure 1.2 shows the interaction of the two computers in the system.

In some booking systems, such as those used for airline reservations, the booking file is held centrally so that enquiries about space on flights can be answered automatically and immediately.

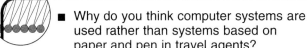

Did you know?

By using the Internet, it is possible to make your own bookings directly with the hotel of your choice – provided the hotel is connected to the Internet service. By sending details over the Internet email system, a booking can be made without having to talk to anyone – you can book a holiday in Florida without leaving your PC.

Activity

- Why do you think computer systems are used rather than systems based on paper and pen in travel agents?
- What advantages are there in using PCs for making bookings?
- Find another two examples of how computer booking systems are used by commercial businesses today. How do they affect the ways in which people work?
- List any disadvantages you can think of for computer booking systems.

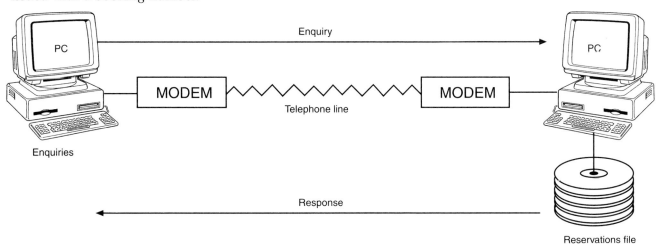

Figure 1.2 Making a booking enquiry

We now look at other examples of commercial systems.

Electronic funds transfer

Big employers have to pay large numbers of staff regularly. If this was to be done manually by handing them cash or cheques it would be an almost impossible job. It would also be very dangerous as anyone carrying large sums of money is setting himself or herself up as a security risk – especially if it is done regularly.

To ease these pressures, companies transfer salaries and wages to employees electronically. They pay wages from their bank account directly into the employees' bank accounts. The company's bank is given details of each employee's bank, his or her name, account number and sort code. When a payment is made, the company's bank computer debits the company account and the employee's bank account, makes a credit transfer. This system is known as BACS or the Bankers Automated Clearing Service.

There are, of course, many other applications of electronic funds transfer. The main financial centres of the world, including New York, London, Hong Kong and Frankfurt, send and receive enormous sums by electronic funds transfer every day.

Electronic point of sales system

This system is often referred to as EPOS. It is used in shops when customers buy goods using credit or debit cards. As far as the average user is concerned, each card is a piece of plastic with his or her name on it. In reality, each is more technical than this, and its use is governed by complicated agreements. Worldwide networks of computers and data communication links allow the use of these cards in millions of outlets in more than 100 countries (Figure 1.3).

When someone applies for a credit card, the issuing company checks his or her financial background. If the company is happy with this, they issue the card and thereby allow the customer to buy goods with it up to a set value. This is the credit limit.

When the customer uses the card to buy something in a shop, the card is *swiped* through an electronic magnetic reading device. This device telephones the computer of the card issuing company. At the same time it reads the information stored in the black

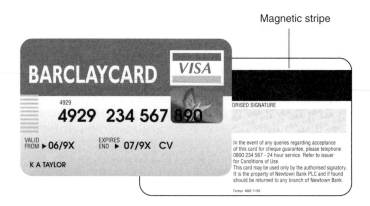

Figure 1.3 A credit card – front and back

stripe on the back of the card. This information is checked against the information stored in the main computer to see if there is enough credit left in the individual's account to make the purchase. If the credit is available, the cost of the purchase is deducted from the customer's account. If there is not enough credit left then the sale is refused. This cross-check is also a safety mechanism for all parties, as if the card in use has been stolen then the situation is recognised by the computer, and the sale is stopped.

EPOS does not necessarily need the presence of the credit card in order to work. It is common for transactions to take place over the telephone by simply giving the name of the card holder, the card number and the date it expires. If you have a multiscreen cinema near you will be able to reserve a seat and buy a ticket in this way. Simply ring up the cinema, tell them which film you wish to see and the time you wish to see it: your credit card details and a ticket will be waiting for you when you arrive. In the intervening time the cinema will have carried out the credit check with the card issuing company.

Did you know?

Tiny airships called *blimps* containing video cameras, microphones and loudspeakers may soon be linked in to the Internet all over the world. Conceived by Eric Pauulos and John Canny at the University of California, the far-fetched idea is that the blimps will be able to move around using electric motors and propellers. They will communicate with the Internet by radio links to computer workstations up to 50 metres away. But the greatest thing about blimps is that their operators could be on the other side of the globe! Internet users can direct the blimps anywhere they want. The inventors envisage them visiting art galleries, museums and shops – almost like a flying mobile telephone. If, for example, you are considering booking a hotel in Los Angeles, you would be able to contact a local blimp and send it to the hotel of your choice. The pictures you receive will allow you to check out its facilities. The fact that it would have a mobile telephone on board would allow you to ask guests already staying in the hotel what their views of it are. This is as close to *trying before you buy* as anyone could ever hope to get – and remember – all this would be possible without ever leaving your computer desk!

Stock control

Stock levels are often controlled in retail stores by IT systems. A good example of this can be seen in Virgin Mega stores, where many thousands of CDs and cassettes are sold each day. To ensure the shelves are always well stocked and up to date with the latest Blur, Status Quo and Oasis albums, an IT stock control system is used. Each music title is given a stock code, and this code is logged on the store computers. On the back of each piece of merchandise is a label with a bar code (Figure 1.4). This bar code is registered alongside the stock code and title of the music.

As soon as a CD, tape or video is sold, the sales assistant uses a bar-code reader to scan the bar code. The computer displays the price on a small screen, and prints a receipt for the customer. At the same time it logs the title and artist, and keeps track

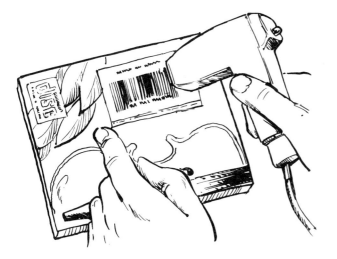

Figure 1.4 Bar-code scanner being used to check an item sold

throughout the day of every sale. At the end of the day the computer calculates all sales and compares the number of sales to the quantity of stock shown in the computer file. Any title no longer in stock, or below the reorder level, is immediately ordered. Not only is this IT system working in the record shops but, it also automatically places the orders over the telephone line to suppliers' computers.

This example illustrates the use of bar codes on merchandise. Bar codes are used by most shops now to help keep track of all stock – check out your local supermarket, they will probably be using a similar system.

By using bar codes, and getting the computer to subtract the quantity in each sale from the level of stock held by the computer file, the *order processing systems* keep track of all stock levels so that new stock can be automatically ordered (Figure 1.5).

Activity

Find out how stocktaking and ordering of stock was undertaken before computers were used and contrast the computerised system with your findings, showing the advantages and disadvantages of each method.

Payroll processing

Most companies use computers to calculate employee salaries and wages. This is more complicated than you would imagine as all employees have tax (PAYE – pay as you earn) and National Insurance contributions deducted from their wages before they are paid. These deductions go straight to the government. It is complicated further when you realise that tax to be paid depends on total income and on taxable benefits such as company cars. Extra payments such as overtime also mean that the payments are unlikely to be the same from one week or month to the next.

To make payroll processing simpler there are a number of standardised software packages available. Fed with the information just mentioned about each employee, they calculate the weekly or monthly payroll.

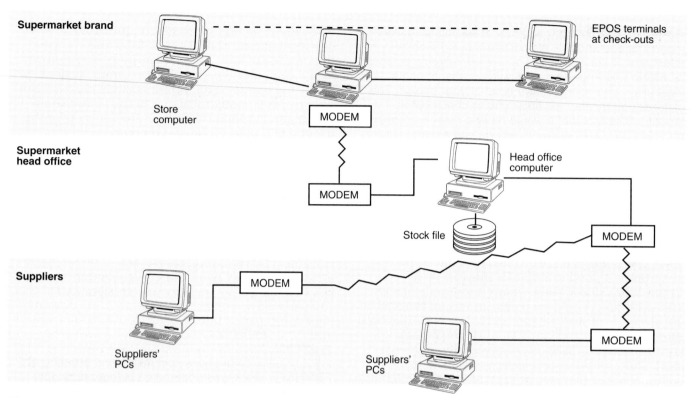

Figure 1.5 Order processing system for a supermarket

Industrial systems

Industrial systems sound a bit more complicated than commercial systems, but we actually use many of them ourselves each day. Examples are found in washing machines, central heating systems, traffic lights, car speeding cameras and photographic processing systems. Many other examples have roles in industry – the manufacturing of electronic circuit boards; control of processes such as refining oil and making paper; management of conveyor systems, in car assembly, for instance; the operation of wind tunnels and other test facilities; and very many more.

In discussing industrial systems we need to look at the concept of feedback. Feedback is an essential component of control systems which we shall study further in Chapter 8 (Element 2.4). Five areas of application of industrial systems are explored next.

Design

Until computers were widely available, products were designed using pencil, paper, T-square and slide-rule.

The people designing products were trained and highly skilled in their jobs. Once they had created a drawing of a new product, they would place dimensions and other details on it, including any angles necessary, measurements and the thickness of the materials required to make the product. If changes were necessary or mistakes made, they could be rubbed out and redrawn.

Drawing a design using computer-aided design, or CAD, software is relatively simple – it is very similar to drawing using Paintbrush for Windows or some other applications software package (see Figure 1.6). It can be done using either a mouse, or a special drawing tablet.

Drawing tablets work on an x/y co-ordinate grid that relates directly to what the user sees on the screen. These co-ordinates are just the same as the co-ordinates on a graph: the x co-ordinate goes across the bottom – giving left to right movement – and the y co-ordinate goes from the bottom to the top – giving up and down movement. If a mouse-pen is moved over the tablet to the right, the cursor makes a corresponding movement on the screen. If it is placed on a new spot on the tablet then the cursor also moves to the equivalent spot on the screen.

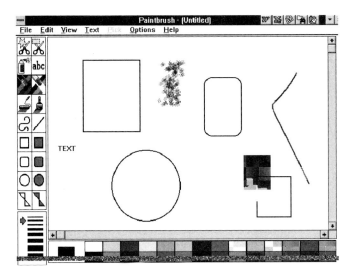

Figure 1.6 Design elements using CAD

Rather than have the designer draw directly on the screen, the tablet works as a virtual screen on the desk, in much the same way that a piece of paper worked for the drawing-designer in the past.

Computers changed the job of design for ever. By using CAD software, it became possible to create drawings on computer monitors. Once the drawing was completed the dimensions and other details could be added. Any mistakes were easily corrected by deleting them from the screen and inserting corrections. CAD made it possible to create designs in a fraction of the time it took to produce the drawings by hand. Not only this – further prints of the drawings could also be made without any effort, and without any loss of quality.

For many years, designers had been wanting to alter the designs they had drawn, very often by simply turning the design around on paper. CAD allowed this to happen painlessly. A drawing could be copied and turned without any effort. Figure 1.7 shows an example of this. The arrow drawing was made only

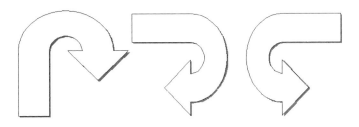

Figure 1.7 Rotations and reflections under CAD

once, then copied and rotated in different ways, all in just a few seconds.

CAD has other benefits too. By linking it up with other software applications, it is possible to test out the design. When petro-chemical companies want new refineries, they design everything using CAD. When complete, the computer puts all the drawings together in 3D, and allows the designer to simulate walking around the refinery. This way, it is possible to find out faults. For example, if a pipe is too low the designer would see on the computer screen that he or she would hit his or her head on it. Designs can also be turned to see how they look from different angles. Car designers use CAD to see how new cars will look, as well as how easy they will be to make and maintain.

CAD can be linked in to computer-aided manufacturing, (CAM), another computer-based tool. This allows the data produced in the CAD drawings to be downloaded into a machine to manufacture the part concerned. For example, if a new bolt is designed using CAD, the information can be sent to the appropriate machine tool and a prototype of the bolt can be made quickly and efficiently without having to employ skilled staff at short notice. This saves money and speeds the process up.

Did you know?

Formula One racing cars are now being designed with the help of CAD. The McLaren team was the first to design a car completely through the use of CAD in the 1995 season. Because all the features and detail of a car's design were held in a computer in a form that allowed instant processing, design changes could be incorporated quickly and safely.

Tom Baccei is a hippie. One day while staring at beansprouts, he thought he saw a picture develop. This gave him an idea – by putting a picture on to a computer and altering it so it looks like nothing unless you stare through it, he had developed the 3D Magic Eye pictures. Without computer graphic design, these pictures would never have been possible.

Process control

We all control processes each day. If you have a class starting at 9 a.m., say, you keep checking your watch to make sure you are on time for it. If you are becoming late you speed up. If you drive a car or motorbike you are constantly controlling your speed. Why is this process control? Because, by continually checking the time or the car's speedometer, and comparing the result with a standard that we calculate or know, we can alter the speed we do things.

Companies do this all the time. As there are strict environmental controls on the amount of certain exhaust gases companies are allowed to emit into the atmosphere, firms have computers to monitor their emission levels constantly. If levels go above the legal limits, they alter the volume being produced and reduce the emissions within minutes. You will find more on process control in Chapter 8 (Element 2.4).

Activity

Environmental laws at all major rock concerts in the UK state that noise levels must not rise above a set level measured in decibels. Environmental health officers attend some of the larger concerts and monitor the noise levels. If the they do go above the legal limits the promoters are forced to reduce the amplification. The noise level monitoring equipment can include hand-held devices as well as monitoring stations.

Draw a diagram showing the interfacing devices between the noise monitoring equipment and the computer that displays the noise level readings.

Robotics

Robots are machines controlled by computers. Robots have often been seen as a reflection of the human body, especially by toy manufacturers and cartoon makers. Thankfully, this has not yet happened in reality. Industrial robots are still fairly basic machines. They can only do as instructed by a computer program. They are often known as *robot arms* because the articulated levers that hold the tools, and grip and move parts, behave like automated arms.

It is possible for robots to be fitted with sensing devices so they can feel what is taking place around them. Robots are employed to do jobs that are unpleasant or impossible for people to do. For example, a robot can venture into the core of a nuclear reactor. If a human being did this it would no doubt kill him or her. Robots have been sent to collect rocks from planets that, as yet, people cannot visit.

Figure 1.8 Robots can afford to be more adventurous than people

The position of the working end of a robot's arm is specified on an x, y, z co-ordinate basis. When *we* draw graphs we use an x, y co-ordinate – this allows movement left, right, up and down. To make up the third dimension, we simply introduce a z axis. This allows the robot arm to move around. Next time you see a robot, on a TV advertisement for example, watch to see it move through the three dimensions.

Robots can be dangerous. The mechanical movements of robot arms are often capable of overcoming strong resistance, so should anyone get in the way the machine will prevail, possibly causing a serious accident. A number of workers, failing to anticipate a robot's next move correctly, have been killed in this way. Normally robots are separated from people physically, by putting the robots behind cages, or by making the people observe strict rules about how close they can go. There is further reference to robots in Chapter 8 (Element 2.4).

Environmental control

There is a good chance that your house contains a system of environmental control in the form of a central heating system. Even if it does not have one, you will probably have some other method of heating rooms. Even a thermostatically controlled fan heater is a good example of environmental control, as when the room gets too hot, it turns itself off. When the temperature falls slightly, it starts again to keep the temperature steady.

If the central heating system was to work without feedback, it would simply just heat water – like a kettle on a gas ring. The fact that information is fed between the storage tank, boiler and thermostat is crucial as this ensures the house is kept at the required temperature. If it falls below this temperature, the boiler is turned on to heat it up. When it goes above this temperature, the boiler is turned off – constant feedback.

There are other sorts of environmental control. They include monitoring and managing river levels; monitoring ozone concentrations with a view to influencing the behaviour which affects these concentrations; dealing with excessive speed on roads; excessive noise produced industrially and socially; noxious smells; and pollution of canals, rivers and the sea.

Did you know?

Feedback takes place with audio and video equipment as well as in IT systems. Have you ever been near a speaker with a microphone and heard a loud scream come through the speakers? This is the microphone picking up the sound from the speakers which in turn amplify their own sound. It gets louder and louder the closer the microphone gets to the speaker until finally the system breaks!

Traffic control

If you stand at a cross-roads and watch how the traffic lights work, you will notice that as one set of lights turns to red, another turns to green shortly afterwards. This is done evenly so there is no excessive build-up of traffic in any of the connecting roads.

What happens though if there is no traffic in one road? You may have noticed little black boxes on top of the lights pointing down to the traffic. These are sensors. If there is no traffic standing in the way of the sensor, it sends a message back to the controlling computer telling it the way is clear. There is little point in keeping a light on green if there are no cars to take advantage of it, so the computer turns the lights to red in this lane, and changes them to green

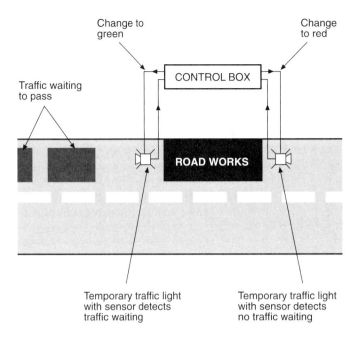

Figure 1.9 Traffic control

in another where there is traffic waiting to move (Figure 1.9). This is another example of feedback in an industrial system.

You may not live near a set of traffic lights with sensors, but there are other forms of control. On a pedestrian crossing, there is probably a box with a button that should be pressed when you want to cross. Pressing it sends a signal to the control system, informing it that someone needs the lights to change, which they do after an interval which is governed by how long it is since they last changed. Although this is not a very sophisticated form of system control, it does the job effectively and cheaply.

The systems needed to control road traffic and pedestrians efficiently and safely are simple compared with those needed for air traffic control. In the air each unit of transport may contain several hundred passengers, and the system has to cope with high speeds, limited fuel on board and three dimensions.

Activity

Think about the temporary traffic lights installed where there are road works which restrict traffic to flowing in one direction at a time. The lights, let us say, are on all the time, each showing either red or green. They change automatically. Is this an example of process control? What is the cycle of changes for each light?

Find an example of process control in your home. Work out how the process works. Show similarities and differences between your example and the traffic light example.

You should be aware that the processes we have dealt with here were not designed when computers were invented. They existed long before. The big difference computers made was to improve reliability and reduce costs.

Evidence collection point

At this point your tutor may wish you to start work on the project which will prove to your tutor and assessor that you understand this part of the element. If so, turn to page 21 and do Section 1 of the project.

Analysing commercial systems

Unit 5 (Chapters 17–19) covers the principles of systems analysis, and treats the subject in a formal way. Here we look at eleven aspects of systems to help you see the range of ways of thinking about them.

Why do we analyse? There are different reasons, but the main one is to see how and why things work, to see if there is any way of improving them. Do not worry if you cannot think of revolutionary new ways to improve something – just finding one small point for improvement is enough. For example, a notebook computer is great. However, it would improve it to have a trackerball built into it so you would not have to carry a mouse around with you all the time. It is a simple suggestion that cannot easily be carried out, but one that could make a useful difference to future models of the machine.

Purpose

Information technology can be used to help solve problems. During the Second World War at Bletchley Park, a computer called Colossus was built to break German codes. Although the codes could be broken by people working manually, it took so long that the decoded information was out of date by the time it became available. By using the computer, it is thought, the war was ended two years earlier than it would otherwise have been. Colossus' purpose was to handle and break complex data codes quickly and accurately. Although most IT systems won't be used for anything as critical as that, they still have purposes. The most common ones include the following.

Speed

IT systems are fast, giving the information as and when it is needed. Information not required is simply not used. If we think of BACS, it would not be possible to do the job manually at the same speed. If we *were* to do the job manually and had to cover the same volume of work each day, many more people would have to be employed in the banking industry to get the work done. This would make banking more expensive for all of us.

Accuracy

IT systems tend not to make mistakes once they have been set up correctly. Unless they break down, they work as accurately at 9 a.m. as they do at midnight and, unlike us, they do not need breaks.

Data handling

IT systems can handle large volumes of data. This is superb as we generally do not like handling data, and make mistakes due to tiredness, boredom – and getting confused! At last there is a machine that can do these tedious jobs for us.

Quality of output

Most systems produce printed output. The quality of that output must match the needs of the user. Documents for customers, or for promotional purposes, call for better presentation than those for some internal purposes.

Distance

Information can be accessed, sent and used over wide distances through the use of telephone lines and modems, local area networks and wide area networks.

Poor working conditions

IT systems work just as well in poor environmental conditions as they do in good as long, as the electronic components are protected against extremes of temperature and humidity. The traffic light system is a good working example of this. Robots are also useful tools for working in unhealthy conditions, such as car paint booths in assembly plants.

Hardware

The choice of hardware used in any IT system is very important for a number of reasons. It obviously has to be capable of doing the job it is there for. There is no point in buying a particular PC only to find it is not powerful enough to do the job. At the same time, there is little point in buying a computer powerful enough to launch a space ship if it will be used only as a word processor.

The rule of thumb is to buy only enough hardware to do the job you require it to do. Do not assume that in three years you will want more RAM and therefore pay out more money now to buy it. In three years RAM as we know it today may be totally

Figure 1.10 Not everyone needs a computer powerful enough to launch a space rocket

different and far cheaper. Buy as much RAM as you need for your most exacting working situations. Using Windows '95, 32 Mb of RAM is more than sufficient, 16 Mb is fine, but any less than this and your PC will struggle to run the software at a reasonable speed.

If you own two computers and want to share data between them, it would be a waste of money building a network for them. It is cheaper to transfer the data using diskettes, or connect the two machines using a simple peer-to-peer network or a cable link.

Similarly, if you need a printer, buy one that does the job and no more. There is little point in buying a Hewlett Packard colour laser jet for several thousand pounds if you only need to print letters on your home computer – it is simply a waste of money. Hardware acquired for any system must be compatible with the rest of the system, and it must be backed up by accessible advice and repair services.

Software

In many ways, the criteria for software analysis are similar to those for hardware. It is important to consider the jobs the software is expected to do before it is purchased. There is also a need to check that the hardware can work with the software. Buying Windows '95 while using a 286 machine is a waste of money as it simply isn't a powerful enough computer to run the software.

Similarly, if you only ever use a word processor once a month, there is no point in buying a powerful software package such as Microsoft Word for Windows 6.0 Professional. If you use a version of Windows 3.1 then the Write software included with it will do the job perfectly well for the number of times you need it.

Some companies may find that the software that can be bought from shops or mail order companies is not good enough to do the jobs required. To ensure a company's requirements are met, software contractors are able to write tailor-made programs.

In addition to being adequate, the software must be good value for money, robust so it does not stop if you make a small mistake, easy to learn to use and be well documented. And, of course, it must be free from any virus.

Data

All systems need data. If input data is flawed then the corresponding output will also be wrong no matter how good the processing steps. Data has to be relevant, accurate, complete and timely, and in a form that allows the user to deal with it.

People

Many people believe that information processing is all about computers. A system need never see a computer as long as people use information efficiently. Computers are brought in to speed the processing up, thereby bringing information and technology together to create IT.

It is a good idea to remind ourselves that IT and computers were developed by people to make jobs easier and their lives better, in just the same way that the vacuum cleaner was created to make cleaning carpets easier, and the car was designed and built to make it faster, easier and less tiring than travelling on foot or by horse. In business, though, the motivation for introducing IT has, in the main, been the search for greater competitiveness, usually bringing better working conditions with it.

Implementing IT in companies has not been without its problems. Although people are employed to run IT systems, in some cases fewer staff are being employed than before. The payroll processing packages mentioned earlier have enabled employees' wages to be calculated far more quickly and efficiently. Some supermarkets are introducing self-scanning shopping where the customer acts as the checkout person. This will mean fewer checkout staff but perhaps, initially, more staff within the store to help customers.

If we look back in history we find that all new inventions that made an impact on work also made an impact on the number of people employed. However, over a period of time the people who lost their jobs due to the new technology were employed elsewhere. If this follows for computer-related jobs, those people who have lost jobs due to advances in technology will be employed in other areas of industry.

Activity

Describe two commercial information technology systems. Find out how many people are employed to run the systems and whether there has been an increase or decrease in staff when compared to a corresponding manual system.

Processing activities

Processes take place all the time – they are the actions that take a set of inputs and turn it into outputs. Through the use of IT, it may be possible to make commercial processes more efficient. For example, rather than typing a letter out ten times, it could be word processed once, and printed ten times, saving considerable effort.

The design of the processing steps should ensure that the operation is, to the required degree, fail-safe; that processed data is saved appropriately; that the speed of processing is adequate; and that backup is available in case of equipment failure during critical work.

Inputs

The types of inputs (the data fed into the IT system) depend on the user's requirements. The examples used earlier in this chapter highlight inputs using bar code readers, magnetic strip cards (in the form of credit cards) and the mouse used in CAD. Consider the following case study and answer the questions that follow concerning inputs to IT systems.

Case study

Every Wednesday morning, Andrea Elinas goes to her local library in Cramlingborough. To gain entry to the library, she takes her library card with a magnetic strip on the back and swipes it through a card reading device in order to gain access.

Andrea places the books she is returning on top of the counter and the librarian takes a bar code reader and scans the bar code of each book in turn. This tells the library computer system that the book is now back in the library and is ready for loan again.

When Andrea has selected her new books she takes them to the librarian, who scans the bar code to tell the computer system that the books are being taken out. The librarian also has to swipe Andrea's library card to tell the system who the borrower is.

The computer system now has details of the loan – the title and ISBN of the book, the identity of the borrower, and the date the book was taken out.

1 Highlight the system inputs in the case study and describe how each of them works. What alternatives could be used for input to the system?
2 In what ways are information technology library systems better than the old manual system using tickets?
3 What benefits do 'swipe card' systems offer libraries and other such facilities?
4 Find out (using magazines or contacting companies) the costs of installing a swipe card system.
5 Visit your local library and find out if a swipe card system is used. Discuss the system with the librarians – is it a good or a bad system? If there is no such system, ask the librarians if they would like one introduced.

Outputs

A number of different types of outputs are available for commercial information technology systems. The choice of output device, the design of the visual display and of the dialogue with the user, where that is needed, all require care.

Screen output

This allows the user to see results on a screen. For example, automatic teller machines (ATMs) give the user detailed instructions on how to use them and what facilities there are available, such as money withdrawal or the ordering of a bank statement.

Supermarket checkouts use screens to show the price and description of each item as it is scanned through the machine. This allows the checkout operator to make sure the products are being added up, and it gives the customer the chance to check the prices as each item is added to the bill.

Every user of a computer system needs the screen to allow communication with the system itself, and for the display of output from application processing.

Paper prints

In the case of ATMs, paper prints allow the user to print the results of the enquiry, such as a bank balance or a receipt for cash withdrawal. Paper prints are often used by travel agents to give clients hard copies of details such as the cost, destination, flight numbers and dates of a holiday. Many applications such as billing, the issue of renewal notices by insurance companies and brokers, and payment runs and payrolls call for very large print runs.

Sound

If you use a telephone banking service such as Direct Line or the Royal Bank of Scotland, you will know about sound output. It is possible to use the service without talking to anyone – everything is done by keying in answers to computer-generated questions using the telephone. Typical questions include a customer identification number, a password and then details of the service that is required, such as paying a bill or getting a balance of an account.

Outputs from control systems

In the Andrea Elinas case study (on page 12), system output includes *physical restriction*. Banks and building societies sometimes use this facility. Banks with ATMs inside do not keep their doors open all day and night, but customers still need to use the ATMs. To keep everyone happy, customers can go into the bank if they swipe their bank card through a reading device. If the card is valid, then the doors are unlocked and the customer enters. This system physically restricts any non-banking customers from entering. In many companies, system output includes the *reordering* of stock using computers, modems and the telephone line.

Advantages

Each IT system will have its own set of advantages. Do bear in mind that what is an advantage to one person or organisation is not necessarily an advantage to another. IT systems are there for people. Their advantages and disadvantages can be individual or collective. The type of benefits an IT system may have could include the following:

- An IT system performs a job faster than a human being.
- IT systems are more accurate than people, particularly when it comes to doing boring, repetitive jobs.
- IT systems do not get tired whereas people do.
- IT systems reduce the number of people companies need to employ to ensure jobs are done.
- IT systems can be more efficient than people doing the same job – a computerised database of names and addresses can be printed directly on to envelopes more efficiently than someone can write them, as writing them involves finding out the name and address and then writing each line down in turn. The computer already has the data on file and so just prints it out.

Case study

In the last few years, national newspapers such as *The Daily Telegraph*, *The Times*, *Guardian*, *Daily Mirror* and *The Express* have undergone massive information technology changes to make them more competitive. The advantages for the companies that own the papers have been huge. They employ fewer staff and therefore pay out less in wages. Journalists write features by typing them directly on to a computer and downloading them to the editorial department where they are placed electronically into the paper's format. In the past, features were typewritten and, after editing, were handed over to a typesetter who typed the copy up on a machine that created the typeface in lead. This was issued to a printer who would put it on a printing machine for printing.

From this we can see that information technology is speeding up the process of producing a paper. It can improve accuracy as word processors check the spelling and grammar of the journalists' work. The information technology systems can also work 24 hours a day at the same rate – something that was only possible in the past by taking on extra workers in a shift system.

It may appear that the benefits were totally on the side of the employer. Although fewer people are employed, they now work in cleaner and safer conditions than before the information technology revolution – handling lead type was far from healthy.

Limitations

Even the best IT system in the world has limitations, although experts in the field of artificial intelligence are working to reduce their effect. Again, what is a limitation to one person is not necessarily a limitation to another. Consider the following limitations and see if you agree with them:

1 IT systems can only do as instructed in their programs.
2 They cannot think or apply logic to anything. They merely process information using hardware and software.
3 Information technology system users require training to get the most out of them – otherwise the information may be wrong or may never be found.
4 As with all information technology systems, security is an issue. Password protection and other security measures are needed to ensure information is secure so it cannot be used by anyone else. Security measures also stop people from using the system, and damaging or destroying the data held on it.
5 If the information technology system breaks down, it is difficult to get information as the

system works only with computers. If the job has to be done over the telephone, voice to voice, it is slow and cumbersome. It is even slower if letters have to be written and sent out to find the answers!

6   *When* mistakes are made by IT systems, they are not always easy to detect, and are rarely trivial! An example is the billing problems experienced by British Gas in the autumn of 1996, when customers received inaccurate bills, and final demands on non-existent bills.

Did you know?

There is an old saying in computer circles – 'To err is human, but to really foul things up requires a computer.' This refers to the fact that people make mistakes, but *when* computers make them, they tend to be major – usually due to a bug in the software. They are apt to be serious because they may be repeated a very large number of times as, for instance, when there is a mistake on all council tax demands in one local authority.

Companies exist that specialise in backing up IT systems and finding lost data in systems and putting it back together again. This seems like an almost impossible task, which is probably why they are so well paid for the job they do!

Impact on the environment

Computers and IT systems have had major impacts on the environment – not just the natural environment, but also the office and home environment.

Office

Computers make office work easier and faster. Rather than storing paper records, computers allow companies to keep records of data and letters in electronic format. This saves paper and saves space.

Travel

By using computers and modems, it is possible for people to work at home and communicate with the office. This reduces travel. In so doing, there is less fuel used by cars, buses and taxis, and less electricity by trains. This reduces the emissions put into the air and improves pollution levels.

Home

Computerised IT systems around the home include central heating systems which can provide improvements to the local environment. Similarly, department stores, office blocks, factories and even some cars, have computer systems to manage their own local environment.

Did you know?

Birthday cards that play tunes when opened hold more computer power than there was on the entire earth in the 1950s. Computers became relatively small only during the 1960s' space race between the USA and the USSR. The Americans realised that if they were to put a space ship into orbit, they needed computers and the computers of the day were too heavy to make this possible. They worked on miniaturising every part of the computer, and came up with micro-chips that took the place of large circuit boards. The weight problem was eliminated and their work paid off with the ultimate success of putting a man on the moon in July 1969.

Radiation

Many people are worried about radiation emissions. Absolutely everything emits radiation – even us.

Computer monitors emit a small amount of radiation. There have probably been more studies on this topic than on any other aspect of computer safety, but if you are concerned about this, you might like to know that it is possible to buy low-emission models. This may be of particular concern to a pregnant woman, as radiation can affect the unborn baby.

Paper

Although paper can be saved by using computers, it can also be used – quickly. Without thinking, people very often make prints of their work – prints that wouldn't be made if the work was being done by hand. This is a waste of paper and harms the environment.

Did you know?

An estimated 2.25 million people in Britain work from home using computers and modems to link in to computers at work. This saves the individuals time and money in getting to and from work, and there are savings for the country in terms of less environmental damage and fewer vehicles on the road.

Evidence collection point

At this point your tutor may wish you to start work on the project which will prove to your tutor and assessor that you understand this part of the element. If so, turn to page 22 and do section 2.

Evaluating commercial systems

Comparison with alternative systems

Before the use of computers became widespread there may have been few alternatives to the ways administrative tasks were carried out. Now that IT is used in most high-volume tasks the possibility of doing them by hand strikes us as absurd. Look at these typical examples. (Remember that some of the jobs that are now commonplace simply could not have existed without IT).

What alternatives are there for an *airline ticket price quotation service?* Instead of prices being obtained using a computer and a telephone line, all prices could be stored on paper, in files or books. This would not allow for any sudden changes in prices.

Consider again BACS. If computers were removed and people had to do the same tasks, banks would have to do one or both of the following:

- Give each person his or her salary or wages in cash personally.
- Make a withdrawal, and then deposit wages into each person's bank account on an individual basis.

The alternatives to using bar code readers and magnetic strip readers in *point of sale* systems is to keep paper-based records of every transaction that takes place. As this is time consuming, it makes it far more expensive for a company to run. The more information there is to collate, the longer it takes – especially when it is being done by hand and not by machine. It would also mean there would be a mountain of paper in the records department. Once the information was collated on paper, orders for new stocks would have to be placed over the telephone or by letter.

The alternative to *payroll processing* is to work out all calculations regarding pay, tax and National Insurance by hand. This would mean the process would take far longer to complete, more mistakes could be made and, in some organisations, more employees might be required to do the calculations.

There are, of course, alternative ways of using IT for commercial systems. For example, an alternative to the use of a network of PCs might be to use terminals linked to a mainframe. The service would probably look different to the user, but perhaps not radically so.

Costs

When we compare using commercial IT systems with completing jobs manually, we find the computer system far more expensive to set up and install. All employees require training to use the system properly, which is time consuming and expensive.

Once set up, however, the computerised system is far more economical to run than a paper-based equivalent, as a paper system always takes longer to process information and usually requires more people to work on it. Paper-based systems also need storage room for the mountains of paper generated.

What always has to be kept in mind when looking at the costs of an IT system is a simple question, *will the costs justify the improvement*? It is virtually impossible to know the answer to this for certain, but there are ways of estimating to get an answer. In Chapter 7 (Element 2.3) we look at *modelling data* using such methods as *simulation*. Modelling may help us to assess a system's advantages, and hence its cost benefits, but it will not be able to simulate all possible situations. There are other situations where even modelling is not the answer. What about ringing a hotel central reservation service only to find their IT system is not working and they cannot tell you if there are rooms available in any of their hotels? You may be happy to wait until the computer is working to find out, but there is a good chance that you would go to another hotel chain and book a room with them. The cost of losing customers in a situation such as this is huge. The mere nature of the business in this situation requires an efficient IT system – without one the company cannot function effectively.

Benefits

It is highly unlikely that any IT system worth its salt would be slower than the human equivalent paper-based system. We can therefore say that IT systems are *fast*. If one *is* slower, there's probably no point in having it!

As computers can work 24 hours a day without ever having to take breaks, they are highly *efficient* machines – certainly more efficient than people.

Did you know?

In Japan, supermarkets are restocked at night by computer-controlled robots. They calculate the goods sold each day (from the point of sale system) and stock the empty shelves with the right number of goods for sale. Just imagine leaving work from a half-empty supermarket at night, going home and coming in the next morning to find it has been cleaned and restocked – all by robot! In this example, commercial and industrial systems have been mixed together to create a better overall system.

The hotel booking system is faster, more efficient and more *accurate* than the manual method. It means that if bookings are controlled for a large number of hotels through one centralised IT system, each hotel does not have to build its own system and it can rely on a responsive, accurate service for enquiries.

The BACS system is more efficient than the manual method. Without it more people would have to be employed and, as the system is working with numbers all the time, the chances of expensive mistakes being made are reduced with the IT version of the system.

Before BACS was introduced all cheques had to be sorted, originally by hand and later by sorting machines. For the debits to be made, every cheque has to find its way from the payee's bank to the drawer's bank. That process represents literally millions of transactions a day. The impact made by BACS has been formidable, partly because it is centralised.

Many other systems have achieved striking improvements in speed, efficiency, accuracy and also in the *quality* of the service provided to users. The management of accounts in big organisations has improved greatly, with benefits to the organisations and their customers. Stock control is another area where there have been marked improvements benefiting firms and their customers, most conspicuously in the retail food and grocery sector.

Potential improvements

As we use computer systems more frequently, it becomes easier to see ways they can be improved. This is one of the reasons software and hardware are constantly being updated by suppliers and manufacturers.

No matter what type of system is used, IT or manual, there will always be room for improvement. Whether or not improvements to the system are carried out is a different matter as they may not be cost effective, but it is important to identify any potential improvements which can be explored further, and evaluated.

It is important to realise that technology is changing all the time. What was too expensive to implement in an IT system yesterday may be affordable today. With this in mind, it is desirable to keep records of all potential improvements system users identify because they may be of benefit to everyone – if not today then possibly tomorrow when the technology and cost allow it.

Case study

Every few months, supermarkets take stock checks – they find out exactly what stock is on the shelves at the end of a day's work so that the levels of physical stock can be compared with the computer stock records. This used to be done by counting the goods on the shelves, writing the numbers down and comparing them with the stock figures held in the stock control computer system.

This system has been greatly assisted by information technology. During a modern stock take, each employee is issued with Psion hand-held computers, or another similar hand-held device, and bar-code readers. They scan the bar code of each product *type* and count up how many goods there are. At the end of the stock take, all hand-held computers are taken to a central point and their data is downloaded on to the store's central computer, and the same comparison made.

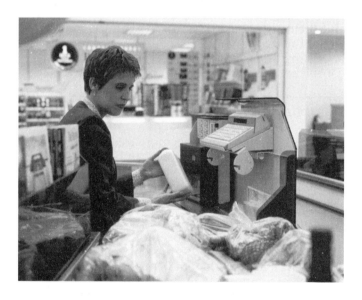

- The information technology method of stock taking is far faster and more efficient than the alternative of writing details down and then manually comparing them with either paper records or with data on the store computer. Not only does IT save time but, it also reduces the risk of errors as once the data is entered into the hand-held device, it is not interfered with again by other people.
- As the information technology method is faster and more efficient, it costs less to use as fewer wages are paid in the process. However, it costs more to set up as a central computer and software are needed; so too are the hand-held computer devices.
- It is hard to see how information technology can improve this system further, though it may be possible to have a robot with a sensing eye count up the goods at the end of each day and cross-reference them with data records. Ordering systems may also become 'cleverer' at forecasting demand.

Evidence collection point

At this point your tutor may wish you to start work on the project which will prove to your tutor and assessor that you understand this part of the element. If so, turn to page 22. If you have already started the project you may be ready to do section 3.

Analysing industrial systems

As we saw earlier, there are probably a number of industrial applications around your home. But if you can, make a point of visiting an industrial company to get an idea of how they use their systems.

Did you know?

Anyone who has checked the tyre pressure on a car or motor bike will know how messy it can be. ERA Technology in Surrey have developed a device that will transmit the tyre pressure reading from each tyre to the dashboard, via a radio transmitter. The car manufacturers Ford, Audi and BMW are interested in it and may be building it into their cars in the coming years.

Purpose

The industrial systems we looked at earlier in this chapter were

- robotic systems
- process control systems
- traffic control systems.

The purpose of using these systems is

- where the task can be carried out manually, to do it better
- to make life easier and more comfortable
- to make life safer

- to do jobs *we* do *not want* to do
- to do jobs we *cannot* do.

Hardware

If you look at any of the systems we have investigated, you will see that the hardware is durable – it has to be able to withstand the rigours of the job. How often do you see traffic lights not working because of the wind or rain? Whenever any part of the system does break down, it is generally a quick and easy process to sort the problem out, because it has been designed for speedy repair. If an industrial system fails to work then it can be uncomfortable, and could become expensive and dangerous to those around it. If a set of traffic lights break down, the chaos that ensues is generally short lived and there are unlikely to be many accidents. If the lights fail and are not fixed for a few days, the likelihood of accidents increases as the frustration of drivers builds up.

Although robots appear to move in a jerky, clumsy way, they can carry out jobs with great precision. And as we said before, always be careful in the vicinity of a robot.

The basis of each industrial system is a computer which is packaged to withstand whatever conditions it is expected to encounter. The whole system must be appropriately rugged.

Did you know?

As passengers dislike queuing at airport check-in desks, in July 1996 British Airways held trials of a new ticketless booking system that books them on to flights without having to queue. This is done by having kiosks where passengers type in the details of the flight and then choose the seat they want. If a passenger chooses to reserve a ticket over the telephone, a boarding pass will be issued to them as soon as their credit card is put into the kiosk machine.

Software

There are application software packages available to help run industrial systems, but it is common for the system designers and developers to write their own application software. This may be done in programming languages such as FORTRAN, ADA (a simulation language), or a 4GL, described in Chapter 20 (Element 6.1).

The programming team will work very closely with the team that is developing the industrial hardware so they know exactly how it works and what it has to do. The programmers design and write the necessary programs. They usually have a model of the hardware linked in to the software for program testing. We deal with software production in more detail in Chapters 20–22 (Unit 6), both in terms of what it is and how it is written.

Data

In comparison with commercial systems, industrial systems generally have small quantities of data to accept, process and display, transmit or print.

Typically the input data will be converted from analogue form, having originated at sensors or clocks; and outputs will be converted into analogue form to modify some physical device or setting.

People

Because data volumes tend to be low, and the processing fully automatic, few people are usually needed to oversee an industrial system, though a large number of customers or other users might have occasion to make use of an industrial system such as security gates or banking terminals.

As opposed to its actual usage, the design of an industrial system may require work by a fairly large number of individuals. This is because the effects of the system may be far-reaching, and consequently the system calls for extremely thorough design and evaluation before manufacture.

Processing activities

Chapters 7 and 8 (Elements 2.3 and 2.4) address the processing required of industrial systems. This processing is characterised by the adjustment of the computer model of the process. The inputs are presented to the model which works out the appropriate outputs needed to secure the modification of the process in the desired way.

As an example, suppose that a system had the task of controlling the viscosity of oil being sealed in cans. If the oil was found to be slightly thicker than it should be, the computer processing would set in motion the change needed to restore it to the correct value.

19

Inputs and outputs

Generally computers controlling industrial applications, no matter how simple or how complex, are alert waiting for input. The input will have originated in sensors, and have been converted to digital form on which the computer can operate through an analogue-to-digital converter. In some systems the sources of inputs are 'polled'. That is to say, the system keeps asking the input ports if they have a signal for processing.

When the computer operating system and applications program receives the input they carry out the intended processing, and generate the appropriate output. This output is converted into an analogue form, perhaps suitably amplified, and fed to the industrial equipment. Chapter 8 (Element 2.4) enlarges on this subject.

Advantages

The advantages of employing industrial systems correspond closely to the purposes of doing so, listed above. Such systems are acquired and installed in businesses to confer commercial advantage. Firms machining parts by hand could hardly hope to compete with one using versatile, numerically controlled machine tools.

In addition, users of industrial systems expect them to provide one or more of the following advantages. To:

■ to improve the quality of life by making tasks easier
■ to make activities safer
■ to undertake jobs we do not want to do
■ to perform jobs that people would be unable to do.

Limitations

Systems do not think for themselves – they only process information. If the information is incorrect or arrives too late to be useful, then the system doesn't work correctly. If there's a fault in your central heating system (the thermostat or thermometer breaks or starts to misread) then the temperature will not be kept at the level you expect.

Also, if the process is correct but runs too slowly for the job it is trying to do, the total system will not be controlled satisfactorily. Another limitation is the difficulty of testing how the software will handle any changes to the specification of its task in every possible eventuality.

Impacts on the environment

If a central heating system breaks down, the impact on the environment is local – it affects only the living environment of those in the house. To keep warm everyone simply puts on more clothes or goes to bed!

When a traffic light system breaks down, the local environment suffers in several ways – due to the hold up, there are more exhaust gases put into the atmosphere. It also means that surrounding roads become more congested and delays occur.

But if the software in the computer controlling, for example, the reactor in a nuclear generating station behaves in an unexpected way there may be exceedingly unpleasant environmental consequences.

Evidence collection point

At this point your tutor may wish you to start work on the project which will prove to your tutor and assessor that you understand this part of the element. If so turn to page 22. If you have already started the project you may be ready to do Section 4.

Evaluating industrial systems

Comparison with alternative systems

Before central heating systems in large office blocks were computer controlled, they were controlled by thermostats. The thermostat may have been sensitive to swings in temperature and may have automatically created cooler offices and warmer store rooms, but a computerised system anticipates when the clocks have been changed to British summer time and gives you the opportunity to phone the system to program it to come on earlier or later.

Before computerised traffic light systems were installed, mechanical lights were operated by 'time', a sort of clockwork clock. The 'clock' made no allowance for the volume of traffic and the number of pedestrians waiting to cross the road. The computerised traffic light system is so sophisticated that it can control traffic approaching from three directions, allowing an appropriate amount of traffic to pass from each direction, depending on the number of cars waiting.

Rather than use robots to assemble and paint cars, people could be employed to do the job. This is dangerous and dirty work for people to do, and robots would do it more consistently and probably more quickly.

It is a good idea to remember that where we stand today industrially is the result of many years of research and work by countless numbers of people. Without the benefits of robots, people would still be building cars completely by hand – Henry Ford's Model T was the first car to be built on mass-production lines. People stood still on the assembly line while the car was brought to them on a conveyor belt. If you aren't convinced of the improvements industrial systems have made to working life, ask your grandparents or an elderly relative to tell you what it was like 60 years ago.

Costs

As with commercial systems, the initial costs for setting up the systems may be high, though typically a computer of modest power, correctly programmed, can control processes in plants that have cost many millions of pounds to construct. Once fully operational though, the costs are fairly low – especially when compared to the benefits stemming from them.

It is very similar for traffic control systems. Placing someone in the position of controlling traffic instead of relying on lights is a long-term cost. It is more likely accidents will occur this way too, as people make mistakes when they get tired and bored doing jobs like this.

Benefits

Each of the systems we have dealt with is *faster* and more *efficient* than the human alternatives, and is *accurate* and works without breaks. They are also considerably *safer*. They tend to be reliable, with long working lives, and straightforward to repair. They may also be easy to upgrade. Operating costs are low. For example, car painting is almost done to order whereas previously this may have been a time-consuming and laborious process.

Potential improvements

The identification of potential improvements is always being done to industrial systems – some companies even pay employees for improvement suggestions! One example of this is can be seen from traffic lights – as technology advanced, traffic light systems improved.

Generally, industrial systems have been used to improve people's lives. They make light work of many onerous and boring jobs.

Evidence collection point

At this point your tutor may wish you to start work on the project which will prove to your tutor and assessor that you understand this part of the element. If so, turn to page 22. If you have already started the project you may be ready to do section 5 and the final stage.

Evidence indicator project

This project has been designed to cover all the evidence indicators related to Chapter 1 (Element 1.1). You may wish to complete the entire project at once or each section of the project at the appropriate point marked in the text.

Performance criteria: 1–5

Key skills:		
	Communication	3.2
	Application of number	–
	IT	3.1, 3.3, 3.4

Section 1
Choose four commercial and four industrial information technology systems and start to collect information about them.

21

Section 2
Select two of your chosen commercial information technology systems and analyse them. Your analysis should include information on their purpose; the hardware and software used; data used; people; processing activities; inputs and outputs; advantages; limitations; and impact on the environment. Keep all your notes for analysis on disk.

Section 3
Evaluate your two selected commercial information technology systems by comparing them with alternative systems: the costs, the benefits (speed, efficiency, accuracy, quality) and potential improvements.

Section 4
Select two of your chosen industrial information technology systems and analyse them. Your analysis should include information on their purpose; the hardware and software used; data used; people; processing activities; inputs and outputs; advantage; limitations; and impact on the environment. Keep all your notes for analysis on disk.

Section 5
Evaluate your two selected industrial information technology systems by comparing them with alternative systems: the costs, the benefits (speed, efficiency, accuracy, quality) and potential improvements.

Final stage
Collate all your information for both your commercial and industrial information technology systems. Read through the information and prepare a report on all your findings. Type out your findings on a word processor using suitable headings.

Investigate components of an information technology system

In Chapter 1 (Element 1.1) we looked at different IT systems. End-users make different demands on their systems and may need different components. In this element you will learn about what actually makes up an IT system. If you get the opportunity, remove the cover of a PC and look at all the hardware inside it. This way you can examine the components at first hand.

Also, collect magazines so that you have a permanent record of what things look like, what they do (and how much they cost!). Keep notes in a log or diary; you will need to refer back to these in Chapter 4 (Element 1.4) when you put a stand-alone system together yourself.

After studying this chapter you should be able to:

1 describe *types of hardware* and their *purposes*;
2 explain the effect of *system specification on performance*;
3 describe types of *software* and their *purposes*.

Special note

There is only one evidence indicator project for this element. It is at the end of the element, on page 42.

 ## Did you know?

The first computer was designed by an Englishman called Charles Babbage (1792–1871). He called it the *analytical engine*. It was intended to perform a variety of tasks. Punched cards were used to store data and to provide the sequence of instructions to be followed.

The idea was too ambitious to be realised by the mechanical devices available in the mid-nineteenth century, but within it can be seen the origins of today's electronic computer. Although Babbage did not live to see it work, it has recently been reconstructed. It does actually compute (although it does not have a monitor on which to see the results) and can be seen in the Science Museum in London.

Types of hardware

In our mind's eye we may see a computer as a monitor sitting on a box with a keyboard in front of it. As you work through this chapter, however, you will see that this is only one type of computer.

However, in most people's conception of a computer (probably a PC), a keyboard is used to enter data, and the monitor displays results. Inside the box will be the processor, diskette drive and hard disk; and at the back of the box are various sockets, or ports, for connecting cables to other devices. The storage devices inside the box allow data to be held, amended and retrieved at will.

Let us look at the main processor, input, storage and output components in turn.

Main processor unit

Taking the main processor unit first, we will investigate microprocessors and control devices.

Microprocessor systems

Chapter 3 (Element 1.3) deals with the components and functions of microprocessor systems. Here we give a survey of their main parts.

The microprocessor in all computers is known as the *central processing unit* (CPU). The CPU has three functional areas:

1 The control unit.
2 The arithmetic and logic unit (ALU).
3 The memory.

Control unit

The control unit takes program instructions, stored in memory, and decodes them. It translates the instructions, and sends signals to the ALU so that each instruction can be obeyed in turn. Some instructions will carry out internal steps, but others will initiate action on a printer or screen. Every storage location and every device has an *address* to which instructions can refer.

The range of program instructions available to a programmer is called the *instruction set*. There is a trade-off between the extensiveness of the instruction set and the processor's speed of operation. A reduced instruction set computer (RISC) has a greatly reduced instruction set, allowing it to run more quickly; it can perform complicated operations by executing a sequence of relatively simple instructions.

Arithmetic and logic unit

The arithmetic and logic unit (ALU) is the part of the CPU that carries out mathematical operations, such as adding and subtracting, as well as logical functions, such as comparing two numbers to find out which is the larger. For most purposes, the ALU in a standard PC is more than capable of doing the job the user requires. If the PC has to use software requiring a great deal of complex calculations such as computer-aided design (CAD), the ALU can be assisted by inserting a mathematics co-processor chip on the motherboard. This works alongside the ALU to speed up the arithmetic. (The printed circuit board on which the microprocessor is mounted is called the 'motherboard'.)

Memory

The term memory is normally used to refer to the fixed memory inside a computer. It is sometimes called *primary storage,* in contrast to rotating magnetic storage on diskettes, hard disks, and magnetic tape – any of which can be inside the computer or outside it and which are known as *secondary storage*. Memory holds software and data.

Bus Connections

The word bus means a high-speed connection for data, within a CPU, linking the control unit to registers holding storage addresses, to memory and to circuitry which executes instructions. The address bus, the data bus, and the control bus, which provide these data paths, are described in the next chapter which covers Element 1.3.

Memory refers to every kind of storage facility accessible to a microprocessor. There are two main types of memory: read-only memory (ROM) which preserves important, fixed information, including operating system modules that must not be overwritten; and random-access memory (RAM) which can be used by the system user. (Full descriptions of memory are given in Chapter 3, (Element 1.3.)

Activity

1 Find out the costs of buying extra ROM and RAM for a modern PC. Put your results in a spreadsheet table and show them graphically.

2 Find out the costs of buying extra ROM and RAM for a PC five years old. Put your results in a spreadsheet table and show them graphically. Make sure you show clearly the year the results belong to.

3 If there is a difference in the prices, what reasons can you put forward to explain this?

Did you know?

The German car company BMW claims to have built a car that contains more computer chips and equipment than the first space ship that took men to the moon. What's more, it can be bought from local BMW showrooms and not from NASA!

Bill Gates, founder and President of Microsoft, once said that 640 K of RAM was more than enough for any PC. His Windows '95 operating system software now requires a minimum of 8 MB to run (but at least 16 MB to run efficiently).

Control devices

In order for a computer to interface with its devices and the outside world, it has to use its control devices to interpret its information and turn it into a recognisable form for users for transmission to other equipment.

You will notice on the back of a PC a number of connection sockets. These are the *external* ports that connect to boards of micro-chips inside, and they allow the computer to control peripheral devices such as printers, scanners and communication channels. The sockets you can see are *normally* unique – there is usually only *one* type of *each* socket on each PC. However, some sockets may look exactly the same though on some recent PCs there are embossed indications to tell you the purposes of the ports. Some people say that plugging a device into the wrong socket will blow up the computer. This is very unlikely. It is more likely that nothing will happen – the device simply won't work and has to be unplugged.

The control devices housed within the case of a PC include the following:

- The hard disk controller.
- The diskette drive controller.
- Whatever cards are fitted into expansion slots, such as a video card, fax card, or music card.
- The connection to the parallel and serial communications ports, discussed in Chapter 13 (Element 4.1).
- The connection to the keyboard port.
- The connection to the mouse port.

Activity

Identify each lead/socket connection on the back of your PC. Attach differently coloured thread to each and in your notebook make a key – for example, a red thread for the mains lead, etc. Ask your tutor to check your identification.

Input devices: manual

Keyboard

The keyboard is used for text-based data input, for example, a mail order house entering client data or an author writing and amending a book. The keyboard is also used for giving commands to both systems software and application software.

Keyboards vary from one computer to another, although in the UK they all work to the standard QWERTY layout. The keyboard used on a notebook PC is small and compact (although there are one or two manufacturers who have created a keyboard that flips up and out as the notebook is opened, making the keyboard larger).

The standard keyboards used with PCs are generally referred to as the AT or PS/2 keyboard, because they emerged as standard layouts after they had been introduced by IBM for their AT and PS/2 models of PC.

In addition to the letters, figures and special characters of the QWERTY layout, the keyboard has 12 *function keys*. These are generally above the character keys. They start at F1 and go through to F12 and perform specific tasks for some software. For example, using WordPerfect word processing software, the shift and F7 key allows the user to select printing details, F10 saves the work and Shift and F10 together retrieve work from a disk.

Some keyboards have *number pads* on the side. These are far easier to use than the numbers on top of the keyboard. Someone working in an accounts department who enters lots of numbers would use one. It's possible to buy a number pad for a laptop computer, though it has to be carried around as a separate piece of hardware.

Mouse

The mouse is used for selecting data or icons (pictures), and for drawing and shading. Architects use the mouse to help them design buildings using CAD software. By moving the mouse around on a surface such as a desk or mouse mat you can control the

Figure 2.1 A mouse

movement of the cursor on the screen. The function that keys (normally called 'buttons' on a mouse) perform depend on the software in use.

If you pick up a mouse and remove the ball underneath it, you may notice that it is dirty. If so then remove the ball and wash it in soapy water. Using a cotton bud dipped in methylated spirit, clean the inner moving parts. Make sure the ball is dry before you place it back in the mouse.

Trackerballs

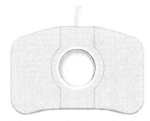

A trackerball is like a mouse turned upside down, and is an alternative to the mouse. Like a mouse it has two, or sometimes more, buttons. Some people prefer using a trackerball to a mouse, finding it more comfortable. On a trackerball the exposed surface of the ball faces upwards and the user's hand

Figure 2.2 A trackerball

moves it around. When this happens the cursor, or screen pointer, moves. Buttons, in easy reach of the operator's fingers, are used to make selections. It's not as easy to clean a trackerball as it is a mouse. The best way to keep a trackerball in good order is to place a dust cover over it when it's not in use.

GlidePoint

This is a new invention, intended to replace the mouse or trackerball. Instead of moving the device, you simply place a finger on the surface of the GlidePoint and the cursor on the screen automatically follows. It has three buttons that can be used in the same way as those on a three-button mouse (the third is programmable and can be set to do whatever the user wants).

Joystick

Joysticks are not commonly used with PCs any more, but are used on video games. They allow the user to point to objects on the screen in the same way as a mouse, but they are more convenient for following a moving target.

Bar code readers

Bar codes are read by bar code readers. These hardware devices are often used for point of sale input systems in supermarkets and other outlets. The bar code is scanned by a laser, which measures the thickness of the lines and the distances between them to decipher the code. Once read, the information can be transmitted to a computer. The computer cross-references the bar code with the price on the database held on the computer stock file. When the price is found, it is transmitted back to the checkout till and displayed on the screen and printed on the customer's receipt.

Other applications using bar codes and needing bar code readers include library book circulation systems, airport baggage handling, and some mail order operations.

Scanners

Scanners are used to detect a pattern on paper and to convert it into a data pattern inside a computer. Hand scanners are inexpensive (from about £80). Flat-bed scanners will accept images from A4 or larger sheets of paper, and generate a more precise representation than is possible with a hand-held scanner. The original document needs to be clean and preferably in black and white for best reproduction.

If the user has access to optical character recognition (OCR) software then any words that are scanned can be edited later on standard software such as a word processor. OCR software can be 'customised' to recognise particular character sets – which need not be English-language characters, of course – then read them and store them for subsequent processing. For example, OCR software can be made to recognise

Arabic script and convert it to a binary code which can then be fed to a translation program to create, say, an English version of the Arabic text.

Touch screens

If you have ever watched a TV programme about finance you might have seen people touching screens to obtain answers. They are using touch sensitive screens. A standard computer screen is covered by two very thin pieces of plastic. Embedded into the plastic is a fine wire and that is linked to the computer. When someone touches the grid, the computer can deduce exactly where the touch was made.

Activity

Test as many manual input devices as you can gain access to. In a group, discuss how effective each device is. Record the comments made by each member of the group and, together rank your preferences.

Input devices: automated

Telephone modem

There are times when we need information sent into our PC from elsewhere. We can achieve this by connecting the PC to a modem (which, in turn, is connected to the telephone socket). The telephone wires are used to transfer data into our PC.

Information from the Internet reaches a PC through a modem. (We will find out more about modems in Chapter 14 (Element 4.2).)

Magnetic ink character recognition (MICR) equipment

This is a piece of hardware that recognises characters, when the special ink used in some processes is magnetised. To read the characters the document passes through an MICR reader. Cheque sorting is the best-known application. (The use of MICR is discussed in Chapter 10 (Element 3.2).)

Magnetic card or magnetic strip reader

This type of device is commonly used with plastic cards (see Chapter 1 (Element 1.1)). *Swipe* and *credit* cards have black magnetic stripes on the reverse side, and it is *this* that the computer recognises. The black stripe holds information that can be accessed only by a special magnetic reading device. The reading device converts the information into a computer usable form (for example, at the automated teller machines found at banks and building societies).

Did you know?

Swipe cards were first used in private clubs to pay for food and drink. They were pioneered in America and were often used on student campuses. Students were bought swipe cards by their parents. They are now very sophisticated and can be programmed to pay for only healthy food (no crisps or burgers – but lots of apples!).

Activity

Why is automated data capture more efficient and reliable than manual data capture? Give an example of each to back up your findings.

Optical character recognition (OCR)

This process needs software as well as hardware. Its basic component is a scanner.

This makes a computerised copy of a page of text. The OCR software converts this image into digital data that is understood by computer software, so it can be stored, printed, manipulated and, in some systems, translated.

Optical mark readers (OMRs) are used to mark exam papers. Sometimes, in GCSE, GNVQ or A level, part

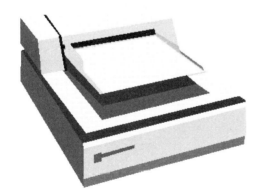

Figure 2.3 A scanner

of the exam is set as multiple-choice questions. The answers given by the candidates can be read by OMR.

OMR is also used by the utilities. Gas and electricity meter-readers mark cards with soft black pencils to show the latest meter readings. These are then processed automatically.

Data logging/sensed data

Computers are insensitive machines – they can't feel a thing! However, it is possible to link sensing devices into a computer system. We use sensing hardware components to measure changes for us when we are not available. The changes are monitored by the computer and actions can be taken if programmed into the computer (see Chapter 8 (Element 2.4)).

An example is a passive infrared detector (PID) in a house alarm system. If there is movement in a room after the alarm is set, and the PID detects it, a signal is sent back to the system computer and the alarm is sounded. Other examples include steam sensors in microwave ovens, water-level sensors in washing machines, and thermostats in greenhouses that open and close the windows to regulate the temperature.

Storage devices

We are all aware of different storage devices we use each day: filing cabinets, account books, card files and cupboards. In computer systems, data is fed into the computer, stored, processed, and stored again. Apart from magnetic tape described below there are three principal types of secondary storage devices for PCs. They are hard disk, diskette and CD-ROM.

Hard disk

Hard disks can store large volumes of data which, of course, includes software. This data can be accessed and retrieved quickly. Data is recorded magnetically on concentric circular tracks. Each track is divided into a number of sectors. A sector is the minimum amount of data that can be recorded or read back.

The hard disk is normally fixed in a PC, though removable hard disks have been marketed; and in some cases additional hard disks can be added externally.

Hard disk drives are precision devices operating in an environment of filtered air to fine tolerances. Their capacity is much greater than that of a diskette, and the speed of data transfer to and from the disk is also much greater. A hard disk drive is also an input device and an output, as data can be transferred to and from it directly.

Diskette

There are two types of diskette. They both do the same job – store information, allow it to be carried around and used in other PCs. The older type is a $5\frac{1}{4}$ inch diameter diskette, which now is not commonly used, except to maintain compatibility with earlier systems, and the newer $3\frac{1}{2}$-inch, more rigid diskette.

Figure 2.4 Diskettes

As with the hard disk, data is recorded on a diskette in concentric tracks divided into sectors. Although a diskette looks robust it is still a sensitive item that should be treated with care. Before you can use a diskette or, indeed, any disk storage, the sector boundaries and other areas not seen by the user have to be recorded on the surface. This operation is called formatting. To format a diskette in drive a: (the usual diskette drive) simply give DOS the command:

```
FORMAT a:
```

You may want to protect the information on a diskette by making it *read only*. This is done on a $3\frac{1}{2}$-inch, diskette by sliding the tab over to reveal the *write-protect* hole. On a $\frac{1}{4}$ inch diskette protection is provided by placing a small piece of tape over the write-protect notch.

The main characteristic of a diskette is its ability to make data in machine-readable form readily transportable – for example, by post. The contents of a diskette which is properly stored will stay unchanged for many years; it will not decay.

You should buy yourself one or two diskettes to store your work on. Always keep one in a safe place as a back-up disk.

CD-ROM

A CD-ROM is similar to a music CD. It holds very large amounts of data that can be retrieved very quickly by a equipped with a CD-ROM laser reader.

Figure 2.5 CD-ROM

Until recently, however, it has not been possible to record any data on CD-ROMs. They could be used only for specific purposes such as encyclopaedias or computer games. This type of storage device is known as *read-only*. Whitaker's *British Books in Print,* quarterly updates of legal judgments and various newspapers are put on to CD-ROM for reference.

Activity

Find out from your library which newspapers are available on CD-ROM. Look to see if any of them have a feature on a new area of information technology.

Now, however, it is possible to buy hardware that can write data to a CD-ROM, but these machines are expensive, which is why not many installations have one. Thus CD-ROMs can now be *read-write* devices. Business users may wish to write on to a CD-ROM when they back up a network file-server or hard disk containing important data. The CD-ROM will hold the massive volume of data the file-server hard disk holds.

CD-ROMs are also data input devices, as information can be loaded from the CD-ROM into the computer.

Magnetic tape

Just in case there is an accident and data is lost, it is advisable to make a copy of important files. The

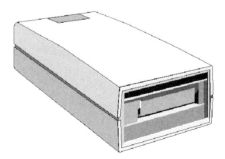

Figure 2.6 Magnetic tape reader

piece of hardware used for backing up data held on a PCs hard disk is called a streamer tape drive. As hard disks can contain very large files of data, streamer tape drives have high data transfer rates. The tapes themselves provide low-cost data storage.

Tape streamers are also referred to as *cartridge drives* as the recordable tape is contained in a cartridge that slots into a cartridge player.

Magnetic tape is an input device, as data can be put on tape on one system and reloaded on to another system.

Did you know?

One of the world's first laptop computers, the Grid Compass 1109, was used by NASA astronauts on the first space shuttle mission in the early 1980s. Its case was made of die-cast aluminium, it had an electro-luminescent display and 304 K of memory. It was said to be virtually indestructible. The CIA in the USA and the British Intelligence Services are thought to have used the machines and, in a bid to test its strength, it is reported that the machine survived being thrown out of an upstairs window in Whitehall in London. The Grid Compass 1109 was designed by Bill Moggeridge, a Briton. By modern mobile computing standards this machine is now virtually useless (it is less powerful than a mobile telephone). However, it was this machine that led to portable computing.

Output devices

Having input raw data and processed it, we need the results to be presented externally by one or more possible devices. There are four types of output device – screens, sound generators, printers and plotters, and physical control equipment.

Screens

Computer screens are also called 'monitors' or 'displays', even though, strictly, the screen itself is only the front of the device.

Did you know?

If you have a bad posture or are sitting in an unsuitable chair, using a computer monitor for long periods can cause sore eyes, headaches, sore necks and backs, and can lead to temporary eye problems. If you look at a computer screen for any length of time, you should make sure no harm comes to your eyes. Every forty minutes, say, take a break from the screen for ten minutes to let your eyes have a rest. If you use computers a lot, make sure you have your eyes tested regularly by a qualified optician. If you are meant to wear glasses for computer use, make sure you wear them! European Union computing directives state that if you regularly use a computer as part of your job, your employer may be partly responsible for regular eye checks. Should you need glasses for your job, your employer will contribute to the cost of them.

The purpose of having a monitor as part of a PC configuration is to provide immediate, clear, silent presentation of information about the PC's activity or the progress of an application. The contents of the screen, including the background, can often be in colours which the user can choose. The presentation is not permanent. Although this saves resources, it does mean that if you want to save what appears on a screen you have to store it or print it.

Sound

Sound has not been a particularly important function in PCs used by commercial organisations. However, it is starting to become more important for the home and educational markets as more and more PCs are bought with built in CD-ROM players – so-called *multimedia* PCs. CD-ROM disks can contain sound and spoken information, as well as video game sounds. For example, it is possible to buy a CD-ROM that shows pictures of the space shuttle taking off. Not only is this like the live footage of the first use of the shuttle, but the CD-ROM also has sound so that the user can more fully appreciate what it was like to be there at the time. This type of CD-ROM is revolutionising the way teachers teach.

Musicians can link their instruments into computers through a commercial format interface card called MIDI (*Musical Instrument Digital Interface*). MIDI is a world-standard communication interface that allows MIDI-compatible musical instruments and equipment to co-operate. This makes it possible to create MIDI instrument systems and equipment that offer far greater versatility and control than individual instruments have on their own. Sound signals are recorded digitally by MIDI, and then made available for processing and output by the computer. This allows music to be recorded on hard disk or on diskettes for playback and editing.

In order for us to be able to hear sound, speakers must be connected to a *sound card* inside the PC. This sound card takes the data from the CD-ROM and turns it into a signal. The speakers convert the signals into a sound we can recognise.

There is another use for sound in PCs – a more commercial one. It is now possible to *tele-conference* using a PC. Teleconferencing is a way of using telephone lines to talk to, and see, someone on a computer screen. This is explained in Chapter 13 (Element 4.1).

Printers

Whereas monitors show us on a screen what the PC is doing, printers record on paper the results of what the PC has done. A paper print is known as a *hard copy*.

The three main types of printer are *character, line* and *page*.

As the words used to describe them suggest, character printers print one character at a time, line printers a line at a time and page printers a page at a time. Page printers can also print addresses on to stacks of envelopes.

Page printers use non-impact technology: unlike traditional printing methods (for example, a standard typewriter), a non-impact printer does not employ 'keys' or 'hammers' to strike the paper. Character and line printers use both impact and non-impact. We shall not examine every combination of print methods in detail, but the following is a list of them:

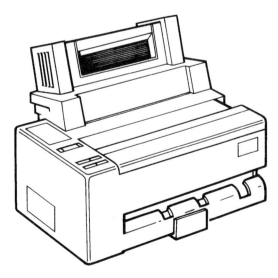

Figure 2.7 Ink-jet printer

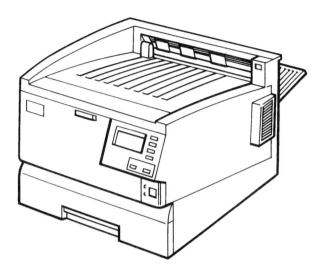

Figure 2.8 Laser printer

- Character impact printers (dot matrix and daisy wheel).
- Character non-impact printers (thermal and ink-jet printers).
- Line impact printers (drum and chain printers).
- Line non-impact printers (electrostatic printers)
- Page non-impact printers (laser, electrostatic, magnetic and xerographic printers).

In choosing a printer for a PC there are four main considerations:

1 quality of print
2 speed
3 noise
4 cost.

There is another form of printed output called *computer output on microfilm*. This is used to store data on microfilm or 'microfiche', such as is used in libraries.

Digital plotters are mentioned in Chapter 6 (Element 2.2).

Activity

You have been appointed by your Managing Director to select a new printer for your office. You will share the printer with two colleagues. Your work is mostly produced from a word processor, but occasionally Sabrina from accounts uses your PC, as does David from the design department with his CAD software.

Give your Managing Director an example of each of the three types of printers (line, character and page) and specify which printer is best for the jobs that you, Sabrina and David do.

Did you know?

The first *home* computer that was widely available in Britain was called the Sinclair ZX80. It was designed and built by Sir Clive Sinclair in1980, cost £99 and was available only through mail order. The ZX80 was shaped much like a door wedge, had a push-button keyboard and used a standard television as a monitor. It operated only in black and white.

Physical control

Output devices directly controlled by a computer can themselves control physical activity. Such activities are said to be 'on-line'.

Examples of on-line activities include

- some numerically controlled machine tools and robots;
- process control applications, covered fully in Chapter 8 (Element 2.4);
- any activity in which instant, automatic decision-making is needed to make a physical system behave in a desired way, such as the operation of lifts in a big office block or department store.

Purposes of hardware

Now we have reviewed types of hardware we can focus on the four main purposes for which the hardware is used.

Data capture

There are several ways in which hardware can capture data.

Manual

Manual data capture is any means by which the user places information in the computer system, using devices such as a keyboard, a mouse, a trackerball or a hand scanner.

Automated

Automated data capture is any means by which the system obtains information without any human contact. In Chapter 1 (Element 1.1) we looked at a number of different systems that feed information back from remote devices to a controlling computer including a central heating system thermostat and traffic light sensors).

Data logging

Data logging is a process whereby information collected at a remote site is recorded and stored, and only later put into the computer and processed. As an alternative to the use of OMR, some British Gas employees visit houses with hand-held reading devices. They take meter readings, type these into their devices and relay the data back to British Gas's central computer through modems on their home telephones.

Sensed

Sensed data capture methods are used in such computer systems as voice recognition and heart-beat monitors. Sensed data capture methods can be used when it is very difficult to establish readings through human methods such as observation or touch see Chapter 8 (Element 2.4)).

Processing

Automatic, program-controlled processing is the heart of information technology. Because the variety and scope of computer programs are unlimited, so is the range of processing possibilities. Throughout this book we encounter a large number of types of processing, and there arc plenty more not in the book. Processing can match the needs of users in every industry sector, and every government department and agency – for commercial and administrative purposes, for research, for control applications and to manage communications networks.

Storage

We have already looked at storage devices in this chapter. We can now consider them under two headings:

1   Permanent and temporary.
2   Primary and secondary.

Permanent

The permanent storage device inside the computer is read-only memory (ROM). It is part of the computer's fixed memory. It retains vital information about the computer even when the computer is turned off. A CD-ROM is also a permanent storage medium as once it has been created and the information stored, it cannot be rewritten except by use of special equipment.

Temporary

The main memory's temporary storage is random access memory (RAM). Part or all of the software being used will be stored in the RAM. In most systems, once the PC is turned off all data in the RAM is lost.

Primary and secondary

Primary storage is the name given to ROM and RAM together. They are fixed in with the computer, and operate at speeds greater than can be obtained from rotating or magnetic tape devices. Hard disk drives, diskette drives, CD-ROM and tape reading devices are known as *secondary* storage devices. They provide the computer with a semi-permanent method of storing data that can be retrieved and used later.

Output

Hardware produces output in a form most suitable for our purposes.

Screen display

Screen display is the most common method of output, although it was not the first. Text or pictures can be shown on screens, usually in colour. They are temporary methods of output.

Sound

Sound can be created by computers using a sound card. Computer-generated sound can be used to provide responses to enquiries; to give warning of out-of-line and potentially dangerous situations such as a robot about to start work; to give instruction, for example, to production line workers about the processes needed, or movement of the next component to arrive on their conveyor system; to give passengers information; and for recreational purposes.

Print

Printing from a computer can be very versatile. It can be produced from desk-top publishing software, or it can come from commercial or industrial applications. It can be in monochrome or in colour. It can be on multipart paper. It can be made to suit a wide variety of needs.

Physical control

The purpose of physical control by computer is to provide reliability, resilience, accuracy and cheapness in the control of some process or activity. We deal with this topic thoroughly in Chapter 8 (Element 2.4).

The effect of system specification

How do we tell the differences between one computer system and another? If we look in magazines, most computers looks virtually the same. However, we shouldn't buy a computer for its appearance – we have to examine the system specification to find out the differences and to see if one system performs better than another.

Microprocessor type

Generally, the first specification we see about a computer refers to the type of microprocessor it uses. It's common to hear people talk about having a 386, a 486 or a Pentium. The number 386, for example, is an abbreviation of the Intel 80386 integrated circuit (or chip). Intel is the main manufacturer of chips for IBM and IBM-compatible PCs. 'Pentium' is another Intel chip name.

As a rule of thumb, a 386 is twice as fast as a 286; a 486 is twice as fast as a 386, and so on. The 486 machines can be fitted with a number of different categories of microprocessors – the 486 DX is faster than the 486 SX, for example, mainly because the DX has a mathematics co-processor. If you set out to buy

a 486 be careful you know important points like this, otherwise you may be sold something you don't want.

Intel managed to build their chips so they could be removed easily and replaced with faster, upgraded versions. This is why so many computer advertisements display the 'Intel inside' logo, showing how easily the computer can be upgraded if required. The other main microprocessor manufacturer is Motorola. The first IBM machines were made using Motorola chips.

Number of microprocessors

Most PCs have a single microprocessor which obeys all the instructions in its programs one after the other. New developments are taking place to provide users with parallel processing in which two or more microprocessors run at the same time inside a single computer, greatly increasing the overall speed.

Also, subsidiary microprocessors are installed to fulfil specialist tasks, such as controlling the hard disk and the mathematics co-processor.

Microprocessor speed

Earlier in this chapter we looked at the control unit. The control unit's activities are co-ordinated by a clock. There are obvious dangers in referring to processor speeds in a book, as the march of technology provides continuous opportunities for manufacturers to offer machines with ever greater speeds. We *do*, however, discuss speeds in order to give you a feel for this dimension of PC design.

The clock is used to synchronise all the internal processes and data movements within the CPU. The unit of time used for these purposes is called a *cycle*. Thus, for example, fetching an instruction from memory would take one cycle; fetching an address from the address register would take another cycle. Designers arrange for activities to be overlapped where possible to reduce to a minimum the number of cycles taken to run a program. The clock's speed is an indication of computer processing speed. One megahertz is one million cycles a second. A typical PC may have a specification of 33 MHz – work out how hard it works each second!

When 486 chips were first released, the operating speeds were revolutionary – but the manufacturing companies went one step further. Over a short period of time they managed to make 486 chips with different operating speeds – from 25 MHz up to 75 MHz – and above.

Pentium chips, working at different speeds up to 130 MHz, or 130,000,000 cycles a second, are faster than 486 chips. They are now so fast that hard disks and other hardware can hardly keep up with them! Research into obtaining greater speed from disks, buses and other parts of PCs has to be continuous so that overall performance is increased. No doubt the speeds quoted in this paragraph will soon be out of date.

Did you know?

In autumn 1996, IBM incorporated remote control of household appliances into its Aptiva PC range. All that is needed is a small socket that the appliance plugs into, costing about £10. This in turn is plugged into the mains. Through the use of microprocessors, signals turning TVs and lights on and off will be sent from the Aptiva through the household electrical wiring system to the equipment.

Activity

Find out the difference between an Apple computer and a PC. Why can Apple computers now simulate PCs, and so run PC software?

Cache

Many people ignore the amount of cache available with computers, but it can play an important role in determining how fast a PC works. The cache is an especially fast part of the computer memory set aside to hold the most commonly used programs or data. This saves the computer time because when it needs such information it will first access the cache to see if it is there.

An example of the use of cache can be seen in modern word processing software. If the software is set to correct common spelling mistakes, the correct spellings are stored in the cache as it is faster to find them in this memory than from the hard disk.

Primary storage

As we have already mentioned, ROM and RAM are primary storage as it is in them that information is stored first — before it is passed to secondary storage devices, such as the hard disk, diskette or magnetic tape.

The size of RAM is measured in megabytes (MB). All information and software taken from the hard disk are stored in the RAM if there is room. The more complicated the software, the larger the RAM must be to hold the extra information and instructions.

It is the figure for the RAM that indicates how much memory a computer has. Windows '95 software requires at least 8 MB of RAM to operate properly. However, ideally it should have a minimum of 16 MB. If we think back to the Sinclair ZX80 having only 1 kilobyte (K) of RAM, we can see how much computers, and the demands of software, have moved on since 1980.

Very often the addition of more RAM will make a bigger difference to the running speed of a PC than changing to a faster processor.

Secondary storage

Hard disks, diskettes, CD-ROMs and magnetic tape are secondary storage devices. They are not part of the computer in the way that memory is. They are separate devices the computer calls on when needed to perform certain functions. All these store data reliably and relatively cheaply. Diskettes and magnetic tape have unrestricted capacity because they can be demounted and stored, possibly in large numbers. The disks, tapes or CD-ROM disks whose drives are attached to a computer can have their data accessed by the computer.

The capacities of these secondary storage devices used to be measured in kilobytes (KB). However, as

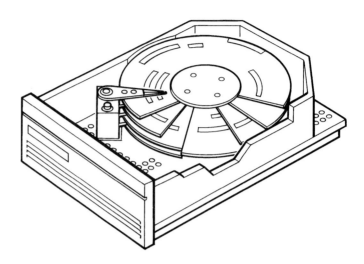

Figure 2.9 Hard disk

storage of all kinds has become cheaper and more plentiful it has become common for them to be described in megabytes: 500 megabytes is not unusual for a hard disk in a modern-day PC; 1.4 MB for a diskette (this is the smaller $3\frac{1}{2}$ inch disk, which corresponds to at least 120 pages of A4 typed script); and 500 MB or more for magnetic tape. Like processing speeds, these storage capacity figures are soon likely to be out of date.

Data capture

Although we have discussed the volume of data, we have not looked at the speed of information retrieval from each of the storage devices.

■ By far the fastest method of retrieving information is from a CD-ROM. It is now possible to buy CD-ROM drives that work at ten times the speed of a normal music CD-ROM.
■ Hard disk drives are the next fastest means of retrieval. The speed of information retrieval depends upon how much data is required and how full the hard disk is. There is big variation in read times of individual retrieval operations, depending where the read-write heads are in relation to the track where the data is stored.
■ Diskette drives are relatively slow – again the speed will depend on how full the disk is. We may have to wait a few seconds to get any information off a diskette.
■ Magnetic tape has to start at one end of the tape

and work its way through to find the relevant data, unless it is being used simply to reinstate backed-up files. The other information retrieval methods are faster because they are direct-access devices.

Devices

All computer devices, that is to say processors, drives, printers, communications equipment and anything else attached to and controlled by a computer, carry specifications. Storage media also have specifications.

You will find, for example, that modern monitors can display up to 16 million colours, have memories built in to help them work faster and have controls to allow the user to move the image around the screen – up, down, left or right. The intensity of the colours and brightness can also be altered. This illustrates the improvement in quality in monitors over the years. Monitors have running speeds (measured in MHz) – a typical value being 55 MHz. This shows us how quickly the monitor can reflect on the screen the changes the computer is making. For games use, the monitor's speed is important. There should be hardly any delay between the user's response and what is seen on the screen. For business computers, a fast monitor is essential for teleconferencing. All these characteristics are defined in the specifications.

Data capture

Data capture devices, such as scanners, have maximum speed limits at which they can capture data, for example, three pages every minute.

It is important that the specification for one device is compatible with the specification for other devices in the system, so that no device habitually keeps others waiting.

Data display

The principal ways of displaying data are on paper (by printing) and on screen.

Printer specifications include printing speed, declared in pages a minute (ppm), lines per minute (lpm) or characters a second (cps). Other specifications describe the resolution in dots per inch (dpi), the level of noise (decibels) and the electrical and space requirements. There will also be manufacturer's information on buffer size and data transfer rate.

Screen specifications mainly cover colour range and resolution. The absence of flicker, important to the user, is related to the *refresh rate* of the screen. The quality of remote display is partly governed by the specification of the intervening modems.

Modems have specifications that refer to *baud* rates. Most modern modems are *Hayes compatible,* simply meaning that they conform to the industry standard. Modems have to be set to transmit at a speed that can be safely handled by the telephone line. Typically, this is 9,600 baud, or bits per second.

Some modems allow for fast data traffic in one direction and slow in the other, thereby reducing cost. This acknowledges the fact that input from a keyboard is unlikely to exceed, say, 75 bits per second, which corresponds to a maximum typing speed of seven characters a second. (There is more about modems in Chapter 13 (Element 4.1).)

Keyboards, trackerballs and the computer mouse also have operating speeds, but, as they are set faster than the PC user can work, they are seldom important.

Did you know?

Company employees on the move can now take their notebook computers with them and still link in to the company's computer system. They use special credit card-sized modems and a mobile telephone. If either device runs out of battery power, it's possible to plug them into a car cigarette lighter and run them from that. Using technology like this, you can be in the office even when you're out!

Control

The user is not conscious of the control specifications which relate to the functioning of the CPU. They are, none the less, vital to the properly co-ordinated performance of the computer.

Performance

Speed

The working speed of a computer system depends upon the time it takes for hardware and software to interact with one another and to operate on any necessary information. If one or more part of the system as a whole is slow (for any reason), the entire system will slow down.

If we build a PC using a Pentium processor (130 MHz) but a hard disk drive that is five years old, the processor will be able to do its job at 130 MHz but, when data is needed from the hard disk, depending on the design of the application being run, it may be slow in comparison to the rest of the system.

Parallel processing

Parallel processing, using more than one CPU in one PC, was mentioned on page xx above. With a single CPU a PC can undertake multiprocessing when more than one job is executed at a time. This is achieved by the CPU switching between jobs whenever it is held up, for example, when waiting for disk access or for an input or output operation to take place.

Activity

In a group of no more than four, discuss the different aspects of computer performance. Is there a consensus of opinion as to what is the most important aspect of computer performance? Write down your views. In exactly one week, meet again as a group to see if anyone has changed his or her views. If someone has, ask him or her to make a short presentation to your group explaining why.

Quality

The quality of our work on a PC is likely to be judged by the quality of printed output. But there is more to quality than that.

The quality of hardware and its performance depends on how well the equipment has been made. Quality is part of what you are buying when you buy a well-known brand of computer, and not just the quality of the machine itself but also the quality of its components. If you buy equipment, be sure it is from a reputable shop and that it is made by a reputable company. If the equipment you buy is of poor quality, it won't last. Never be tempted to buy poor-quality diskettes. Not only will they break easily and lose data, but they may also damage the diskette drive itself.

There is an old computer saying that is well worth remembering when we think about quality – GIGO or Garbage in, garbage out! If poor information is fed into the computer, poor data will come out.

Did you know?

Many people bought Amstrad PCW8512s word processors in the 1980s. These were exceptionally good machines for the money, and had a reputation for being easy to use and for lasting. However, owners now want to upgrade from these machines to more modern PCs that use the latest software. The problem is that the Amstrad word processors use disks that will not work on any other word processor or PC. All work stored on their disks appears to be destined to stay there. Now, however, Locomotive Software have developed a piece of software called Locolink that will allow files to be copied from the Amstrad word processor to a PC in ASCII (American Standard Code for Information Interchange) format that can be read by most word processors.

Efficiency

Efficiency can be thought of in several ways. Is the equipment environmentally friendly and not wasting electricity or raw materials? On the other hand, do the components work fast enough for each other?

If you stand back from a PC to consider its efficiency, you'll think about the support you get from hardware and software suppliers, the ease of maintenance and upgrading, compatibility with other systems, the amount of training needed to make the system operational and, of course, its size and appearance. All these points matter.

Types of software

Without software a computer is only an inert mass of metal and plastic. The first computers were built to do one job, and it was only the hardware in these computers that was important. Now it's the software that is the brains of the machine. Without software the system simply would do nothing.

Operating systems

Every computer requires an operating system. It is this operating system that makes sure all the basic functions the computer needs to do are done. DOS, standing for Disk Operating System, is the operating system used on almost all IBM-compatible PCs. Windows, which is not an operating system, runs over DOS.

The earliest PC operating systems, before DOS and long before Windows, were awkward to run and manage. DOS was a leap forward; and Windows, with its graphical user interface (GUI), was a further marked advance.

Computers of all sizes have operating systems. Typically, their main jobs are

- scheduling jobs so that the machine does not stand idle;
- handling file allocation;
- controlling disks and input/output activity;
- overcoming and reporting malfunction;
- supervising external data communication; and
- communicating with the human operator.

Did you know?

When IBM were developing their first PC to compete with the computers the Apple Corporation were then selling, they did not have the time or expertise to develop an operating system. IBM executives visited two or three small software companies to discuss the possibilities of them writing an operating system for the IBM PC. One of the companies was Microsoft. Microsoft had no experience of writing an operating system and, indeed, had no operating system to show the IBM executives. Bill Gates tracked down a local company that had written such a system and bought it from them. Microsoft employees set to work to convince IBM that they could deliver the operating system IBM needed. Microsoft was awarded the contract and Bill Gates, as a result, went on to become the richest man in the world.

IBM realised that Microsoft were in a position to dominate the world of computers when Microsoft's operating system (DOS) became the world standard. To compete with Microsoft, IBM executives set about developing their own operating system – OS/2 (Operating System 2). OS/2 never captured a big enough market share for Microsoft to feel threatened.

User interface systems

To make computers more user interactive and convenient to use, Microsoft developed Windows. Most people find Windows far easier to understand and use than DOS. Windows provides users with a view of a desk-top, seen on the screen. It provides a GUI with icons showing the application and other software available to users. There are many other facilities provided by Windows, some of which you will use. *The Windows User's Guide* is 650 pages long, so you are not likely to use them all.

The recently released Windows '95 software provides a user interface *as well as* being an operating system. Its use eliminates the need to use DOS and Windows at the same time. It allows the user easy control over the PC, and makes the use of even the most complicated aspects of PCs within easy reach of most people. Its main drawbacks are its newness and its hunger for RAM.

To select software in Windows, move the mouse (and the arrow cursor on the screen) to the picture, or icon, of the required software, and 'click' twice. The computer brings in the software, ready to run.

Some applications software provides graphical user interface screens.

Network operating systems

Many companies link their computers, printers and other hardware together in a network so that the computers can *share* information, hardware and software. (Unit 4 is largely concerned with computer networks, and Chapters 15 and 16 (Elements 4.3 and 4.4) are devoted to this subject.) Businesses and other organisations take great advantage of networks as they save time and money. Much of their information is stored in one computer, the file server, and not in individual PCs. If there are two hundred PCs in a company and one file had to be found, it would be a massive task to search through each individual PC to find the file. If all files are on the one file server, the file would be found quickly. The file server controls the entire network of PCs and allows each PC to use the other hardware on the network.

The operating system for a network is very similar in its function to the operating system for a PC. The differences are in the number of devices on the network. Whereas a PC's devices are possibly all on one desk, the network can control many PCs, printers, modems and other devices located at different places in an office.

Network operating systems (seen again in Chapters 15 and 16 (Elements 4.3 and 4.4)), have to make provision for

- security, especially on the file server;
- data flow control;
- storage allocation on the file server;
- control of access to the network;
- handling the effects of configuration changes; and
- maintaining statistics of use.

The computers and other hardware devices are connected together by cable leading to a *network card,* slotted into the back of the computer.

Windows is available for networks as well as for PCs. As far as the user is concerned, a network version of Windows behaves in exactly the same way.

Communications

One way of establishing computer communication is through electronic mail, or *e-mail.* E-mail is a method of sending messages from one computer user to another. Once sent, the message sits in a file server storage area waiting to be read. When the receiving party next turns on his or her PC, it tells him or her that there is an e-mail message waiting.

E-mail is a fast, accurate, convenient, and inexpensive way of sending and receiving messages.

Did you know?

It is now possible to send messages electronically, by e-mail, to people all over the world. As long as your PC uses e-mail software, you are connected to a modem and you know the address of the person you are sending a message to, then you are all set. An example address is:

Wogan@BBC.Co.UK

This is the e-mail address for Terry Wogan's breakfast show on BBC Radio 2. If you e-mail a message on it, you may have a request or dedication played!

Communications take many forms. The term covers electronic file transfer, fax, voice and video. It covers all the different speeds and types of transmission, and all the control traffic needed to make communications systems work. Communications are dealt with in more detail in Chapter 13 (Element 4.1).

Programming languages

Computers can deal only with data and instructions in binary form. The first computer programs were written in binary, and then in machine code which was almost as difficult to use. In the 1950s assembly languages using operation codes and symbolic names appeared. Then, in the late 1950s, higher-level languages evolved: the principal ones were Cobol for financial and administrative applications, and

Fortran for scientific and mathematical applications. These, in turn, were superseded by other more versatile languages, although Cobol lives on.

In addition to the language processors these languages need to translate them into binary, there are now several special-purpose languages with their own translation software. If you are choosing a programming option in your GNVQ course, you will learn much more about different languages.

Applications

The software we have looked at so far has been responsible for controlling the computer. Applications software does tasks for the user, rather than for the machine. For example, this book was written using a word processor – Word for Windows 6.0. The word processor is a type of applications software. Other examples include spreadsheets, databases and desk-top publishing software. These are sometimes called *generic* applications because they are useful in every type of business.

Much generic software such as this is generalised – it can be used on many different computer makes and models. Usually there will be options a user can exercise. For example, an option can be set to save the work automatically every ten minutes by making changes in the menu system at the top of the screen.

There is also application software for almost every field of human endeavour. A few examples are banking, manufacturing, space travel, airline reservations, advertising, stock exchange operations and oil exploration. We describe a few examples of generic software here.

Word processors

Word processors allow the user to perform the following functions:

- Create documents of text and numerical data.
- Edit easily before the document is printed.
- Cut and paste information from one area in a document to another.
- Insert drawings, pictures and other files if they are in the correct computer format.
- Save documents and edit them later.
- Check spelling and grammar.

Spreadsheet

Spreadsheets are made up of rows and columns of cells. Each cell has a reference number. By using this reference number, the cell contents can be used in formulae to perform the following basic tasks, even if the contents of the cells change:

- Insertion of numerical data.
- Calculations using formulae.
- Create graphs with the data inserted.
- Structure data.
- Model data.

Integrated software

Rather than buying several different software packages, it is now possible to buy an integrated package that includes three or more generic applications, such as a word processor, a spreadsheet and a database. Integrated software allows data from one application to be used by another without conflict.

This is illustrated in Figure 2.10 where a graph has been *imported* from a spreadsheet into word

processed work. You may find this useful when you are creating a word processed report which includes graphs and charts showing figures.

Case study

Many British car firms have hit the headlines throughout the world – MG, Triumph, Austin Healey, to name but a few. However, one stands out above the others – Lotus. In the early 1980s, Lotus decided to produce a car for the cheaper end of the sports car market – at around £22,000. It was to be called the Élan. Sadly, Lotus had to stop production of the Élan because of high manufacturing costs. The firm had planned to make 3,000 models of the car each year, but only managed half that number. Part of the reason for this was that the manufacturing plant was made up of very high-cost computer-controlled equipment and the running costs for this stood at a total of £35 million a year.

A rival firm to Lotus, TVR, manufactured 700 cars a year. TVR made profits of £700,000 on sales of £15.4 million. This was achieved by *not* using the sophisticated computerised equipment Lotus insisted

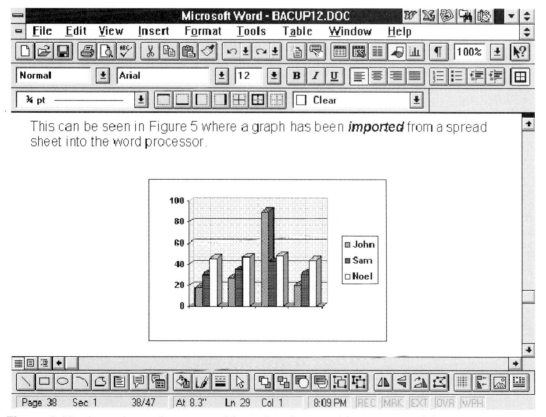

Figure 2.10 A graph word processed from data imported from a spreadsheet

upon in the production of their cars. However, TVR needed very expensive materials to produce their cars. The materials and labour together cost them £12,000 per vehicle – but even then they made a profit!

1 Using a spreadsheet, show the difference between the cost of building a Lotus against the costs of building a TVR. Illustrate your answer with a graph.
2 How much profit would Lotus have made on the Élan if it had achieved sales of 3,000 cars per year with no increase in costs? Work out your answer on a spreadsheet.
3 What percentage profit on sales did TVR make each year? Work out your answer on a spreadsheet.
4 Find a picture of a Lotus Élan. Scan it on to a disk and import it into your spreadsheet.

Databases

Databases are collections of data stored in an *organised* way. Most databases hold files of information in an index. Even though database management system (DBMS) software is now able to fulfil many functions, almost anyone can set a database up to make it a powerful and effective tool. The essential purpose of database software is to insulate the user and the applications software from the mechanics of using the physical storage media. DBMS software can perform the following tasks:

1 Hold large volumes of data.
2 Accept new data.
3 Handle communication with storage devices.
4 Reorganise the data.
5 Print reports showing specific requirements, such as a list of telephone numbers for all the people in the Windermere area with the surname 'Archer'.
6 Show trends from the information stored.
7 Make it easy for people to access the required information quickly. An example of this is a telephone directory enquiries operator finding a telephone number in a database rather than by looking through telephone directories.
8 Manage the data dictionary.

Chapters 23–25 (Elements 7.1–7.3) are devoted to databases.

Did you know?

Timex and Microsoft have developed a watch that works as a personal information manager. It can be programmed to keep track of appointments, birthdays and anniversaries, to keep lists and to sound alarms. This is made possible by the software – personal information is typed into Microsoft Data Link software on a PC, in much the same way as it is for other time management software. The watch is held next to the screen and the information is loaded into it in a matter of a few seconds. All data is displayed on the watch face as and when it is needed.

Purposes of software

System initiation

When the computer is switched on it starts its system initiation – the "booting-up" process when a computer loads the operating system software. During the boot-up the computer will

1 run a self-test to make sure all the hardware is working correctly;
2 load a set of instructions from the ROM to the RAM so that the operating system can execute them; and
3 configure the software so that it will work effectively and efficiently with the hardware in the system (for example, loading the correct file to run the mouse).

Simplify user interaction

Twenty or thirty years ago, computers could be used only by expert programmers. Programs were specific to the machine type – they could not be transferred from one machine type to another.

As already mentioned, modern PCs are much more user-friendly than the computers of the past. Apple Macintosh machines led the way in simplifying user and machine interaction, soon followed by DOS-based machines. Microsoft then developed Windows, which illustrates on screen the software available for use.

Activity

Make a comparison of Windows (Version 3) and Windows '95 software. Which is easier to use and why? Why do you think software such as Windows is upgraded regularly, if it is not necessarily easier to use the upgraded version?

Work group sharing

As already noted, companies and other organisations establish networks so that employees can share hardware, software and data. However, different departments will have different needs from others, and so the network differentiates between users. For example, estimating does not have access to, and therefore cannot interfere with, cost control's data. Each department is known as a work group. Certain software on the network may be dedicated to one work group only. For example, the design department may need to use CAD software, which can be put on the network file server so that only the design department work group can use it. Hundreds of work groups can be set up on a network if necessary.

Communicating

Using a physical connection link (telephone wires, fibre-optic cables, infra-red beams or radio/satellite transmission signals), communicating software can send data from one computer to another – even on the other side of the world. The most common method of communicating is over telephone lines. Through the use of modems and special software, PCs can connect with the Internet to send e-mail and can perform like fax machines, transmitting data on screen to a receiving PC or dedicated office fax. (For more information on communication, see Chapters 13–16 (Elements 4.1–4.4).

Whatever the media and the technology employed, the purpose in communicating is to transmit and receive information as quickly, accurately, and cheaply as possible.

Did you know?

Logitech have developed a mouse that doesn't need a lead to connect it to the PC. Instead it uses a radio link to work. If you have ever made presentations using software such as Microsoft PowerPoint, you will know that each time the display needs changing you have to press a key on the keyboard or the mouse (unless, of course, you have set it up to change the display at certain times). This means you have to remain close to the PC or at least close enough to hold a mouse. By using Logitech's Trackman Live leadless mouse, it's possible to move up to 10 metres away from the PC and still change the display.

Production of software

To simplify the production of software, computer programmers use programming languages or software development tools. These languages translate the programmer's code into the machine code the computer understands.

One example of this is an *assembly language*. Assembly languages allow the user to program using symbols rather than binary. The type of symbols used include ADD, DIV, MULT and SUB. Assembly languages and machine code are also known as *low-level languages*.

High-level languages were developed to overcome the difficulties people were having with low-level languages. They use words that are closer to English. There are three main advantages over low-level languages:

1 They improve productivity as they are easier to understand and write.
2 They can be used on different types of computer – low-level languages can be used only on one make of computer.
3 They speed the testing of programs.

Computers can turn program code into machine code in two ways. The first is to use an *interpreter*. This takes the high-level language and translates it line by line into machine code as it is run. The second is to use a *compiler*. This takes the entire program and turns it into machine code before handing it control to execute.

Programming languages are dealt with in more detail in Chapter 21 (Element 6.2).

Activity

Find out the advantages of using an interpreter rather than a compiler. Is there a difference in the time it takes to translate and run a program using one rather than the other?

File management

Information stored on hard disks and diskettes is in the form of files. Files are generally created when you save data. DOS applications software includes such facilities as File Save and File Open. DOS's own files run and manage the computer system.

Windows has File Manager software that allows the user to save, delete, change the names of files and copy them. This software is in GUI format. Using the mouse, the user can instruct the software what to do on screen rather than typing commands into the DOS environment.

Processing

Using applications software, computers allow users to process documents and data. Due to advancements in technology, it is now possible to manipulate data in ways that were impossible a few years ago. For example, using Word for Windows 6.0, it is possible to draw diagrams. Until recently this was only possible using graphics software. It is also possible to create graphs that used to be the prime domain of spreadsheets and graphics software. As technology improves, the differences between some groups of applications software dwindles.

Modelling

Modelling is a powerful analytical technique for using the computer to help with the visualisation of problems, (see Chapter 8 on (Element 2.3.)).

Controlling

DOS software, used direct or through Windows, controls the PC and all peripheral devices. Application software for controlling processes and machinery such as robots is widely used in industry.

Expert systems

Expert systems help users make decisions. An expert system does not itself make decisions; it helps people to do so by providing information based on the best knowledge and experience available. It will normally express its advice in terms of probability. For example, in a medical context, having been fed the symptoms exhibited by a patient and the characteristics and medical history of the patient, an expert system might display a message 'probability of food poisoning 60%, probability of appendicitis 15%'.

The accumulation of knowledge, called the 'knowledge domain' in an expert system, may be the sum of the knowlege of several internationally famous experts. All this knowledge can be saved on disk or CD-ROM and carried around the world to be accessed on any compatible computer.

Evidence indicator project

This project covers all the evidence indicators related to Chapter 2, (Element 1.2). It has been designed to be carried out at the end of the element.

Performance criteria: 1–3

Key skills:	Communication	3.1, 3.2, 3.3, 3.4
	Application of number –	
	IT	3.1, 3.2, 3.3

Scenario
Sports Life is a private sports club. It has eight squash courts, two swimming pools, a badminton court, two tennis courts, a multi-gym and sauna. As well as the sporting side of the club there is a thriving social scene: a large dance-hall, members' lounge and children's play area all help to make Sports Life a success.

The club now has over 550 members and Dave Granger, the club secretary, is wondering how best to keep track of records (such as addresses and telephone numbers). He is not keen on writing out 550 envelopes each month to send details of the latest club news to each member. Surely there is an easier way to do this? As well as his secretarial duties, Dave Granger looks after the finances. Until now he has been doing his accounts on paper, but this is becoming more and more difficult and time consuming. He wants computer software to help him do the job faster. He is also keen to know if there is a fast way of putting the details of each club member on to the computer. At the moment all details are stored on standard A4 forms.

The Sports Life committee know that club members have been taking friends into the club to play squash and tennis. Although they are allowed in the social areas, friends are not allowed in the sports complex. The committee have decided that some type of entry control system is required - possibly a credit card-style entry control barrier. Each member will be issued with a card that allows him or her access to the facilities.

Your task is to write a report to the Sports Life committee which researches the following:

1 Types of computer hardware and their purposes.
2 Types of computer software and their purposes.
3 The effect of system specification on the performance of speed, parallel processing, quality and efficiency.

Investigate the operation of a micro-processor system

How often do you turn on a computer without ever thinking about what it's doing inside? We all use computers every day and only really think about how they work when they break down! Apart from days when they are broken, computers are just tools that help us do jobs – like pens and pencils.

This chapter is concerned with the operations of a micro-processor system – what it actually does inside the machine. It follows on naturally from Chapter 2 (Element 1.2).

After studying this chapter you should be able to:

1 produce a block diagram showing the *components* of a micro-processor system
2 describe the *functions* of the *components* and the *characteristics of memory*
3 describe the main *elements* of the central processing unit
4 identify the *components* and *elements* used at each *stage in the machine instruction cycle.*

Special note

There is only one evidence indicator project for this element. It is at the end of the element on page 00.

Components of a micro-processor system

As well as reading about the components of a micro-processor, do your best to look at them so you have a good idea of what they are like. If you cannot see the components at first hand, look at pictures in computer magazines. This will be particularly useful when drawing a block diagram of a micro-processor, as you may find it difficult to think of a computer simply in terms of symbols, and you may need a picture in your mind.

If you think micro-processor symbols may cause you some problems, cut out magazine pictures and place them on a sheet of paper. Next to each picture draw the symbol that relates to it. This will help you to

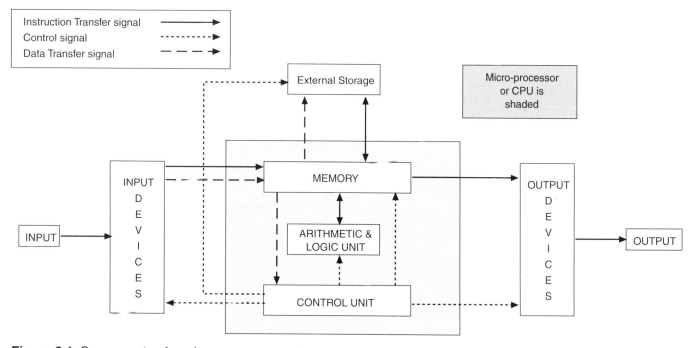

Figure 3.1 Components of a micro-processor system

remember and, if you forget, it will be easy to look up. We saw in Chapter 1 (Element 1.1) that the terms 'CPU' and micro-processor are identical in meaning in a PC. Figure 3.1 shows the components of a micro-computer system in diagrammatic form.

Activity

In a group, ask each person to select his or her own supplier from either computer magazines or *Yellow Pages* in your local area. In each case, find out the costs of buying a particular new CPU. Put the data together on a spreadsheet showing the different prices you found. Why do you think the prices differ from one supplier to another? From the data you have collected, which CPU would you choose and why?

Did you know?

Strange as it may seem, the human brain works in much the same way as a micro-computer system. We have a *memory* to remember facts and information, a *mathematical* and *logic* area that makes decisions, and a *control* area that takes the information from other parts of the brain and allows us to walk, talk and move our hands – outputs similar to those the computer makes.

We are constantly being bombarded by information from other people, the TV and radio, advertisements, papers, books ... the list is endless. These are all inputs to our brain, very similar to the inputs we put into a computer system. But do not try to press the analogy too far. It will soon break down under the weight of dissimilarities.

The components of a micro-processor are described in turn. Ensure that you are familiar with each component and what each does by checking the previous element, where appropriate.

Central processing unit

A central processing unit (CPU) in a computer is built on a single electronic silicon chip that contains the arithmetic and logic unit (ALU), memory registers and the control unit (CU), as illustrated in Figure 3.1. It is responsible for taking instructions from the memory and executing them. These instructions constitute a program. The operation of a CPU was dealt with in Chapter 2 (Element 1.2).

Within the CPU there are different types of information that flow between the component devices. We look at these types of information below.

Memory

The fixed memory within a PC is referred to as the *primary storage, main store, internal store* or *immediate access storage*. It stores programs, input data, output data and working data. It is made up of circuits that operate when the computer is turned on.

Memory is divided into two main sections – read only memory (ROM) and random access memory (RAM).

ROM

ROM is *not volatile:* it has instructions fixed into it at manufacture, and cannot be written to once inserted in a computer. ROM holds software instructions such as part of the operating system needed for booting up a computer and the programming software needed for basic operation of the computer. The only way to remove the contents of a ROM chip is to destroy it physically or by overloading it with electricity – simply turning the computer off will do nothing to the data stored in it. There are two variations of ROM – PROM and EPROM.

PROM (programmable read only memory) is a ROM chip that the manufacturer does not program – it is left to the user. However, once programmed it is set for life – it cannot be altered. It is not easy to do this, though, as special equipment is required for recording on PROM. Most computers do not come with PROM chips.

EPROM (erasable programmable read only memory) is also a ROM chip not programmed by the manufacturer. It too is programmed by the user, but unlike PROM, it can be reprogrammed by deleting any data stored on it and writing new data to it. EAROM (electronically alterable ROM) is very similar except the data already stored on it does not have to be deleted before new data is overwritten.

CD-ROMs provide large amounts of read-only capacity. A CD-ROM drive can be housed within a PC.

RAM

RAM is the memory to which the processing unit has direct access, storing any current programs or data there. The processing unit can read data from and write it to any part of the RAM at the same speed and in any order. In most cases when a micro-computer is turned off, the contents of the RAM are lost – it is a *volatile* part of computer memory. It's possible to expand the RAM by adding further RAM chips.

Processing

To speed up processing, program instructions are stored in RAM, or ROM if they are permanently needed on the system, rather than on secondary storage devices. In this way the delay that is bound to occur in fetching instructions from secondary memory is minimised.

Computers operate in code, which is made up of only two characters, 1 and 0. The data in the form of electrical pulses which circulates within a processor carries this code: when power is flowing, this represents the digit 1; when no power is flowing, this represents 0. Turning the power off thus fills volatile memory with zeros.

All data must be written to computer memory in binary digits, or bits, 1 and 0. *Bits* are stored together in groups of 8 to form *bytes*. A byte can represent any character in the character set of the PC, such as the letter A, number 2 or the symbol $. The letter A is represented in binary code by 01000001. There are 2^8, that is 256, possible arrangements of bits in one byte.

Did you know?

Modern business computers are using 16 or 32 bit processors to speed up their operations. A 16-bit processor is one in which the CPU data paths are two bytes 'wide'. That is to say 16 bits are moved in parallel to provide greater speed than would be possible with an 8-bit processor. Similarly a 32-bit processor has data paths 4 bytes wide.

These processors were originally put to commercial use by the Sega and Nintendo Corporations in their computer game consoles, allowing the games to have four different moving areas on the screen at once.

Activity

1 Why would the following people want to increase the RAM in their PC?
  - a business person
  - a college student
  - a ten-year-old child
2 Find out how many megabytes of ROM a typical business PC has. Do the same for a *multimedia* machine. If there is a difference in the machine specifications, find out why.

Bus

The term 'bus' means a physical route for transferring data. A so-called 8-bit PC has a data path of 8 bits in parallel, plus the *parity bit*. The parity bit is not part of the data: it is an extra bit in each byte set to a value which will make the total count of bits, including itself, either even or odd according to the local standard. If odd parity is the standard the parity bit is automatically set so that the total bit count is odd. Whenever the data is moved within the PC the parity is checked by the electronic circuitry.

The memory, CPU and input and output (I/O) ports need to communicate with one another in a computer. A group of parallel wires, known as a bus, connects the devices together. Designers of micro-processor systems always have high speed as a top priority. The 8-bit path, moving a byte in parallel rather than bit by bit down a single channel, increases speed. If the bus is increased in width to 16 bits, its speed is effectively doubled over an 8-bit bus. Nowadays, 32-bit machines and devices are becoming increasingly available.

There are three types of bus.

Address bus

Computer memory has a system of address locations. Data is stored and retrieved by addressing the required location in the memory. The address bus is the data path that is used both to carry the storage address for writing or reading, and to carry the data itself.

Data bus

Data transferred between the memory or input/output (I/O) ports and other components in the CPU is carried on the data bus.

Control bus

At times there are several instructions being sent around a computer. For example, we may be fetching an instruction, fetching an item of data, decoding an instruction, and passing a command to an I/O channel. Which activity is completed first? The control bus does the job by synchronising the data flowing around the micro-processor.

Input/Output

All systems are made up of three functions:

1 an input
2 a process
3 an output

The sequence of input–process–output is valid only if each step in the process has access to programs and data – which hence need to be held in some kind of storage.

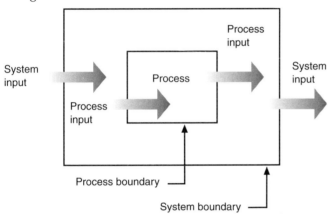

Figure 3.2 The 'process' within the system

Figure 3.2 shows this sequence, with processing taking place inside the double box. The inner 'skin' is intended to represent the discrete processing function, and the outer skin to indicate a boundary between the application and the processor. You may

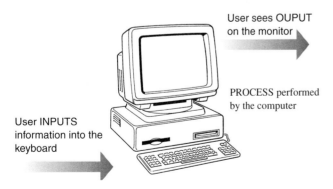

Figure 3.3 Input–process–output

find this a helpful distinction. Between the skins all the functions needed to turn a micro-processor into a PC take place. In a basic PC system, this input–process–output sequence is as shown in Figure 3.3.

A homely example of the same sequence is cooking, where a recipe defines the ingredients, the *input*. The ingredients are fed into the cooking *process;* and all being well there is *output* in the form of a prepared dish of food.

Activity

Draw a diagram showing the I/O signals for someone driving a car.

PC input devices include the keyboard, mouse and scanner. They are connected to the micro-processor through I/O ports in the back of the computer. Similarly, output devices such as monitors, printers and speakers are connected through I/O ports. Generally, the I/O port connections are two-way so, for example, information can be fed from the keyboard into the CPU, and any problems in the CPU will immediately stop the keyboard from accepting any more data.

Did you know?

A computer can sometimes stop working owing to an information overload in the chips. The computer tries to work its way out of trouble, but often can fail to do so. This is known as *crashing.* There are two ways of fixing this – both of which result in rebooting the PC. The first is to press **Ctrl**, **Alt** and **Del** at the same time. This is known as a *soft-boot.* The other method is to turn off your PC – a *hard-boot!* If you do have to turn off the PC, be sure to leave it 20 seconds for all the electricity to drain out of the circuits. This way, when it's turned on again the circuits will have been restored to the state they would have been in if the system had been closed down normally.

Component functions

Let us look more closely at some of the functions performed by a micro-processor. So far we have discussed the characteristics of the primary storage.

Instructions

Without instructions, few machines work correctly. For example, a car's engine may be running – the car may even be moving – but without a qualified driver giving it clear and precise instructions it is unlikely to behave in the desired way. Similarly, without a clear set of instructions a micro-processor cannot function correctly.

To issue the micro-processor with instructions, programming languages were developed to supply the micro-processor with instructions in a binary code.

A micro-processor's instructions are of three fundamental types. They transfer data, use mathematical and logical functions, and carry out tests:

- *Data transfer* is simply a case of moving data from one register or storage location to another.
- *Mathematical and logical functions* are performed in the arithmetic and logic unit (ALU), illustrated in Figure 3.1, where, for instance, two numbers may be added together.
- *Testing functions* are common in computer programs. Look at one written in BASIC and you will probably see statements like

IF A=20
THEN GOTO 240

This is telling the micro-processor that if the value held in the memory location A is 20, then it is to go to another statement called 240 in the program. If A does not equal 20 then it will proceed to the next statement and continue executing the program.

Calculations

We now know the ALU performs calculations for the micro-processor – in 1s and 0s. The calculations are performed in binary arithmetic. By binary addition, binary subtraction and shifting left or right, all the four arithmetic operations can be accomplished. In binary, the effect of shifting a number one place to the left is to double it; one place to the right halves it. Binary arithmetic can be carried out by electronic circuitry much more rapidly than arithmetic based on a decimal scheme of numbers.

Data flow

The flow of data within a micro-processor system is managed by the CPU, which carries out the following activities:

- *Set address* which establishes the destination address for a transfer of data, and places that address in the instruction that needs it.
- *Control* which oversees the timing and accuracy of the move.
- *Read* which obtains the data to be moved from its storage location.
- *Write* which records the data in its new location.

Storage

Micro-processors store instructions and data so they can be retrieved but also left undisturbed so that they can be used again. As we saw in Chapter 2 (Element 1.2), storage devices range from memory (primary storage) that the micro-processor uses before any other storage device to hard disk drives that store large volumes of data but take longer to access. CD-ROMs and magnetic tape reading devices are often used as external forms of storage, holding large volumes of data that can be accessed in different ways and at different speeds.

Activity

Find out the difference in access times/speeds for four different mass-storage devices. Put your answers on a spreadsheet and show the results graphically.

Memory characteristics

Read only memory (ROM): This is described on page 00. As this memory is *non-volatile* it is not lost when the PC is turned off.

Random access memory (RAM): This is described on page 00. This memory is volatile so the memory contents are lost when the computer is turned off.

Read-only: Read-only storage devices do not allow any data or information to be recorded on them. This is covered on page 00.

Read/write: Read/write storage devices allows us to read information from them and write information on to them.

The main elements of the CPU

There are four main elements in the CPU.

Program counter

In any program the instructions are held in memory. To ensure that the program runs correctly, the microprocessor uses a program counter to point to the instruction that is next in line for execution. Once an instruction is being executed the program counter moves to the next instruction due to be executed. This is illustrated in Figure 3.4.

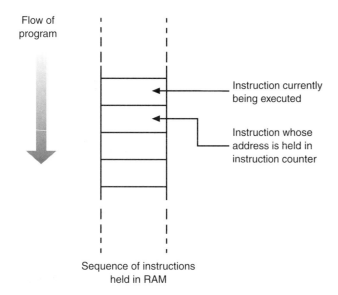

Figure 3.4   Program counter

Memory address register

This is the register that holds the address of the location to be accessed for reading or writing on the next machine instruction cycle. For example, if a program was proceeding from one instruction to the next one in program code, the memory address register (MAR) would obtain the address that it expects to need in order to be able to execute the next instruction. But if the program made a jump out of sequence, as it could have done in the BASIC code example (see above), the MAR would have to obtain the address needed by the next instruction to be executed, which would not then be the next in the sequence in the program text.

You should note that some computer instructions need two addresses, as in an instruction to move data from 'A' to 'B'. The MAR has therefore to be able to accommodate both addresses.

Memory buffer register

If you have ever typed in an instruction to a computer while it was busy, but it showed the characters after it stopped the previous job, you will have used a *buffer*. It's an interim storage device that feeds data from the keyboard into the computer, and from the computer to, for example, the printer. The memory buffer register works in much the same way: it is the buffer lying between memory and the CPU for temporary storage of the contents of a memory location.

Current instruction register

This register in the processor holds the machine instruction that is currently being processed during the current machine instruction cycle.

The components and elements used at each stage in the machine instruction cycle

The three stages of the machine instruction cycle are *fetch, decode* and *execute.*

Fetch

If you decide to play a game of cards, you need to *fetch* them first. In a similar way, if a computer has to do a job, it has to fetch from memory the next instruction it needs before it does anything else. The instruction, which can be up to three bytes long, is read from memory and placed in the instruction register.

Decode

You choose to play poker with your deck of cards. You know how to play the game without thinking. In reality, though, when you make your mind up to play the game, your brain decodes the name of the game and fetches relevant game instructions from past records – only then are you really ready to play. This is the same for the computer. It has to decode instructions. An instruction will normally contain an operation code, such as add, compare, move or jump; one or two addresses; and possibly an absolute value. An absolute value is either a quantity used in

Operation	Input	Control Unit	ALU	Memory	Storage	Output
Fetch	✗	✔	✗	✔	✔	✗
Decode	✗	✔	✔	✗	✗	✗
Execute	✔?	✔	✔	✔	✔	✔?

Figure 3.5 PC components active during a program instruction cycle

Operation	Input	Why used in machine instruction cycle?
Fetch	✗	The cycle is internal to the CPU
Decode	✗	There is nothing for the computer to decode
Execute	✔?	Data *may* be wanted from an input device

Operation	Control unit	Why used in machine instruction cycle?
Fetch	✔	Controls the equipment to find and retrieve the required data
Decode	✔	Tells the ALU and other decoding circuits to perform the task
Execute	✔	Makes sure the tasks are executed, as required, by the right system components

Operation	ALU	Why used in machine instruction cycle?
Fetch	✗	Has no job until the instruction has been fetched
Decode	✔	Makes decisions and calculations during the decoding of information
Execute	✔	Used for decisions and mathematical calculations during the execution phase

Operation	Memory	Why used in machine instruction cycle?
Fetch	✔	Stores instructions and holds data to be decoded once found and fetched
Decode	✗	No role for memory during decoding
Execute	✔	Data and program instructions for execution need to be retrieved or stored in memory once decoded

Operation	Storage	Why used in machine instruction cycle?
Fetch	✔?	Data is stored on disk or in memory. Data has to be retrieved from some storage device, though there will be a substantial delay if the data is not in RAM
Decode	✗	No role for storage during decoding
Execute	✔?	Data too big to be held in RAM will ultimately have to be written to secondary storage

Operation	Output	Why used in machine instruction cycle?
Fetch	✗	The fetch operation is not used in the output operation
Decode	✗	The decode operation is not used in the output operation
Execute	✔?	The instruction *may* require data output

Figure 3.6 Why components are used during the machine cycle

the processing, or an actual storage address (as opposed to a symbolic address). Electronic circuitry in the CPU decodes the instruction last fetched extremely quickly, and sets up the processes for obeying the whole instruction.

Execute

When you begin your poker game, you are executing. Likewise, when a computer uses instructions to perform a task, it's executing them. Execution of an instruction in a computer may consist of carrying out an arithmetic operation and storing the result appropriately, or it may involve doing a test on stored values, or it may initiate activity through the I/O ports.

So what components are used at each stage in the machine instruction cycle? Figure 3.5 shows this. A tick means that the component has a role to play, and a cross means that the component has no role to play. A tick with a question mark means that if an instruction causes an input or an output operation to occur, the component will be active, but not otherwise.

We must now investigate why only certain components are used during the various stages of the machine cycle. This is shown in Figure 3.6.

Evidence indicator project

This project covers all the evidence indicators related to Chapter 3 (Element 1.3). It has been designed to be carried out at the end of the element.

Performance criteria: 1–4

Key skills:	Communication	3.1, 3.2, 3.3
	Application of number	–
	IT	3.1, 3.2, 3.3

Scenario

You are the Technical Director of Computer Memory Systems Ltd. A local firm of solicitors has asked you to write a detailed report to assist in a court case between one of their clients (Mr John Smith) and a computer company that sold him a computer. The computer company claims the computer was in perfect working order when it reached Mr Smith. He claims it was faulty. The computer was sent to Computer Memory Systems Ltd for evaluation to check each of the components. The computer is fine as far as Computer Memory Systems Ltd is concerned. Your task is to help to classify the issues, by writing the following report:

1 Draw a block diagram showing how all the components of a micro-processor link (include the CPU, memory – ROM and RAM, bus – address, data and control, and input and output).

Use

_____	solid lines for data transfers
....	dotted lines for control signals between components
- - - - - - -	dashes for instruction transfer

Think carefully about what each component does and what it needs to 'know' to function correctly.

2 Describe the functions of the components and the characteristics of memory types you have mentioned.

3 Describe the main elements of the CPU.

4 Identify the components and elements used at each stage in the machine instruction cycle of the micro-processor system.

Install and configure a stand-alone computer system

In Chapter 2 (Element 1.2) we suggested that you collect pictures of hardware components so you would know what they look like when it came to putting a stand-alone system together. Now your hard work is about to pay off – it's time to put your system together at last!

After studying this chapter you should be able to:

1 connect *hardware components* together to meet the *specification*;
2 *configure* the operating system software to meet the *specification*;
3 *install* applications software;
4 *test* the computer system;
5 *review* the system and make recommendations for improving the *specification.*

Special note

There is only one evidence indicator project for this element. It is at the end of the element, on page 62.

Connect hardware components together to meet the specification

A stand-alone computer system is a computer or PC that is not attached to any other computer or network. It works with a monitor, keyboard, printer and mouse and any other peripheral devices that may be attached, but it is *not* in a network!

If you are worried at the thought of getting a PC up and running, there is one very important thing you should do as soon as possible – prepare. There are plenty of computer handbooks about your machine. They can tell you what to do to make the PC run. However, you don't want to be reading books while you are being assessed. You must be sure you know what you are doing without having to refer to books.

Until you are absolutely certain how to connect your hardware components together, it is always worth going about the task in a methodical manner. That way you should not be left with any loose leads. Remember the function of each component and this will help you to check it is connected to the correct parts:

- *Keyboard* This is connected to the main processor unit by one lead with a plug at the end. The lead is generally curly so the keyboard can be moved around without being strained.
- *Mouse* The mouse has a thin, long wire with a plug on the end to connect to the PC. The plug is round, with a number of pins, and generally fits into the PC socket in only one way.
- *VDU* This *may* have either one or two cables that need plugging in. The first one will *have* to go into the PC. This carries the information from the processor and shows it on the screen. Most modern PCs have another lead, which is for power. It generally goes into the electricity socket in the wall though it could go into an electricity outlet socket on the back of the PC.
- *Printer* This is connected to the main processor unit by one lead, and to the power source by another.

Be sure all cables look safe and don't have any wires hanging out. Make sure you have a plug attached to the mains power lead. If there isn't one on the mains power lead, you will have to fit one. If you have not done this before, check with your tutor before you do it. If the cables go in the wrong places you may well do damage or possibly even electrocute yourself.

Once you think all the cabling is attached, check you have no loose ends. You should have two, or possibly three power leads to plug into the electricity supply. You can now plug in and switch on. Then switch on both the monitor and the main processor units. You must switch on in this order.

If you are ever worried about getting an electric shock from a computer or any other piece of electrical or electronic equipment, don't use it before it has been checked by an electrician. It's a good idea to use a circuit breaker on expensive equipment such as computers. If there is a fault with the wiring, it will cut out before anybody is hurt.

Did you know?

To protect a computer and its user, it's a good idea to fit a circuit breaker in the electrical power supply line. The circuit breaker will react very rapidly to any power surge, above a safety threshold level, by interrupting the supply before people or equipment get hurt. Circuit breakers come in two different types. The first is plugged into the fuse box in the building. The other is plugged into the wall socket and the cable from the computer. This type has to be set and tested each time it is used.

Be careful to place the right plug in the right socket. Some of the plugs look similar, but forcing the mains electricity plug into a parallel port may have some nasty effects – both from the computer and from your tutor. In fact, it is very difficult to force a plug into the wrong socket because there are differences in shape. If you find the plug will not go in easily, and you have it the right way up, check that you are trying to put it in the right place.

It *is* possible to plug a computer system together correctly, but when it is turned on, it doesn't work as it should even though it is *not* broken. Computers have something called *DIP* switches. They are very small and not always easy to find. There are normally eight of these little switches together, and they need a pencil or other sharp point to change them. You should not touch them until you have been taught how to alter their settings. If the computer is not responding as it should, generally on the monitor or at the printer, ask your tutor if the DIP switches are set correctly.

The computer manual will tell you the different orders the DIP switches can be in to configure the computer to do different things. For example, there are two families of monitor standards used on PCs called EGA and the more recent VGA. The letters denote the type of graphics adaptor card used to produce the displays, and they imply the need to have different signals. The VGA standard has been developed to super-VGA (SVGA) which provides higher resolution. If the monitor is a VGA monitor, the switches will be set one way. If it is an EGA monitor they will have to be set another. You may find that the printer also has DIP switches that need changing to meet the computer's specifications.

Specification

This is the standard the computer system must meet to function correctly. There are various aspects it must cover.

Purpose

What job is the computer to do – is it to be used in an organisation's office doing business-related jobs,

or as a learning tool for children using CD-ROMs and educational software? Alternatively it could be used to write programs for applications software or simply as a games machine in someone's home.

These are all considerations that have to be taken into account when a PC system is being put together as the applications it will be used for may make a difference to the types of hardware bought with it. Some PCs don't come in a single box any more. The customer may decide the specification, and the relevant hardware and software are acquired so that the system can be put together. If the machine's purpose is not known then this is a fruitless task.

Input

The system specification will highlight the ways in which data is to be fed into the PC – either manually or using automated methods. Whichever is chosen, it must be capable of working with the software the system will use. For example, if a bar code reader is required, database software that can work with it will be needed. If only word processing is to be carried out then a keyboard is required, but which one – a standard IBM or IBM-compatible PC keyboard, or an ergonomically designed Microsoft keyboard?

Processing activity

The processing steps that are taken in a particular program constitute the activity for which the program is being run. The equipment must be capable of running the program correctly, and fast enough to be useful. The specification must provide for enough computing speed and memory capacity to meet this requirement.

If features such as a mathematics co-processor, or high-speed cache memory, or an additional online hard disk are needed to make an application run well they have to be ordered, and fitted. This is discussed below.

When data has been entered into a computer, it is processed in one way or another, whether it be data in a database or spreadsheet, or text-based data in a word processor. Once data *is* entered, it's important to make sure it is processed and used in the correct way. There is no point in entering it once and then having to carry out processing steps all over again in a different software package.

Output

Output specification is just as important as the input specification. The output might be provided for the user through printing on paper, through display on a screen, by plotting on paper or by the use of special output devices. Printers and VDUs are discussed below.

Hardware (components, system performance)

Main processor unit

This is the most important part of any computer system, and its specification has to be considered carefully as it is the most expensive. Areas for consideration may include the following:

- The type of micro-processor being used – a 386, 486, 486 DX or a Pentium processor? These terms were explained in Chapter 3 (Element 1.3).
- The speed of the micro-processor – 25, 75 or possibly 130 Mhz?
- The type and size of hard disk drive the system uses – is 500 Mb enough or would 1 Gb be better?
- Is an internal CD-ROM needed, or a tape drive?
- The type of diskette drive required. (It is more common to use high-density disk drives rather than low density.) Also, is a 5.25-inch diskette drive required, as well as a 3.5-inch, for compatibility with earlier systems?
- Are the I/O ports and their related internal cards of the required specification for the jobs they will have to do?

- Can the system be upgraded easily in the future when new technology is introduced?
- Is local technical support available?

Keyboard

Keyboard layouts differ between countries – the keys don't represent the same letters and numbers and therefore the specification must clearly state the county it will be used in. The size of the keyboard is important – is it necessary to have a full number pad as well as the standard QWERTY arrangement? Is a built-in tracker ball needed in the keyboard, and if the specification requires a notebook computer, is an extra keyboard needed, or is the built-in one suitable?

Mouse

Each computer tends to come with a mouse. However, the standard model of mouse may not be good enough for the tasks the mouse has to perform. It may be necessary to install a more sensitive one for tasks using graphics. A mouse may not even be needed if a tracker ball is built in to the keyboard.

Did you know?

The 3.5-inch diskettes was developed to hold more data than its 5.25-inch forerunner. Students were also considered during development – putting a 5.25-inch disk in a pocket bent it, making it useless. The 3.25-inch disks are harder and more durable, as well as being physically smaller.

VDU (visual display unit or monitor)

The size and shape of the VDU is important. A small screen size (for example 12 inch, measured on the diagonal) is harder to read than a larger one (such as 16 inch). CAD systems tend to have large VDUs to make working with technical detail easier. Typists sometimes prefer to use VDUs shaped more like an A4 piece of paper, showing the page in portrait format rather than the standard landscape format.

Monitors have different levels of resolution. Super video graphics adaptor (SVGA) monitors have clearer definition than video graphics adaptor (VGA) or EGA devices. However, in order to take advantage of high-resolution monitors, the correct type of output video card is needed for them.

Printer

The specification will have to include the type of printer, such as a dot matrix, laser or ink jet. This will depend on the type of work being done – office-based work is not likely to need a colour laser printer, or an HP Designjet used with CAD systems. As well as the quality of the printed output, cost, noise, flexibility, speed, and the weight and size of printer have to be considered.

Ports (serial and parallel)

The quality of ports is important – cheap models may not carry information as reliably as more expensive models, and may even cause errors in data transmission. Ports provide the interface between the inside of the computer and equipment outside.

Cables

Like ports, cables should be of good enough quality to provide dependable connections. Plugs on the ends of cables are also important – the wrong plug on a cable simply will not connect to an I/O port making the peripheral device useless to the computer system.

Did you know?

Plugs on the ends of cables and I/O ports are known as either *male* (having connecting pins sticking outwards) or *female* (with space to house the male connecting pins). If you ever have the wrong plug, it's possible to buy a converter plug to go on the end of a male socket to turn it into a female one, and a convertor to turn a female socket into a male one.

Software (operating system, applications)

As IBM and IBM-compatible computers are the ones most commonly used throughout the world, there is more software available for these models than for any other. On the other hand, Apple Corporation computers are widely regarded as being the easiest to use, and more people would buy Apple machines if it wasn't for the fact they use IBM machines at work. Emulation bridges this gap. Although Apple machines have their own operating systems there is now software available to allow Apple PCs to run like IBM machines. This process of making one PC behave as if it were another, different type is called 'emulation'. This means Apple Mackintosh machines can use the software designed for IBM machines. Most stand-alone computers in the world are IBM compatible: Apple Corporation computers are the principal alternative.

IBM-compatible computers can use a number of different operating systems – DOS (there are a number of different versions such as Microsoft's MS-DOS, and PC-DOS), IBM's own OS/2 and now Windows '95 (which, unlike earlier Windows products, is both an operating system and a graphical user interface).

Ultimately, the specifications for the operating system will depend on the jobs the computer system will be doing – Apple computers are used more for graphical work whereas the IBM compatibles are more likely to be chosen for business, educational and home recreational use. Computers using software such as CAD might require special operating systems like, for example, the one used in Sun computers.

Applications software will depend to some extent on the hardware – a computer primarily used for CAD may not be chosen to run word processor software because the machine specification is unnecessarily high. Users will want to run applications that meet their needs. Those applications will dictate the minimum hardware specifications of the computing equipment.

Configure the operating system software to meet the specification

Just before you install and configure your computer, your tutor will give you the required specifications. These will indicate how the system is to perform. Your tutor will decide if you are to use DOS or Windows on your system.

Display

Make sure your VDU and video card are compatible. If you have a SVGA monitor but only a VGA video card, ask for help. The SVGA monitor will behave like a VGA monitor. However, it won't work the other way around: an SVGA video card can never work with a VGA monitor, because there are signals generated by the SVGA card that are not recognised by the VGA monitor.

Memory

Modern PCs have four different types of memory. *Conventional* memory is the basic 640 K of memory all PCs use. *Extended* memory is the extra memory needed to run Windows, as Windows needs Memory Manager to organise its system. *Expanded* memory, as its name suggests, is extra memory cabled to the system should the user need it. Expanded memory needs extra software to run it. *Virtual* memory is the space on the hard disk Windows uses as if it was actually memory. If only parts of a program are needed, they can be put into virtual memory while the other parts are stored. This way, more programs can be used at one time.

The amount of memory your system has determines how many applications you can run simultaneously, and how much information those applications can store in memory, at a time. It can also affect the speed at which Windows performs. Windows runs more slowly when there is little available memory.

Altering the amount of RAM is easy – simply add extra RAM chips to the spare slots on the processor board in the computer. There is nothing to configure once they are in place, and they may make a great improvement to system processing speed.

Devices

Let us consider the attachment of common devices and the installation of DOS and application products.

Mouse

Although the mouse is simply plugged into the appropriate socket, it will not work until the computer recognises it. To achieve this recognition, the operating system runs a small file when it is turned on. This is in DOS, and it ensures the mouse is ready for use when the software is loaded.

Printer

If Windows is being used then a Print Manager must be installed to make the printer work with the software. Before the printer will work, a software file needs to be installed so that the CPU recognises the printer.

Ports

You may find that some of the ports don't work when the computer is turned on. This is probably because certain vital functions of the PC, controlled by a Set-up program, are missing. Use this program to make sure everything you need is active. Do not, however, set anything you do not need as this wastes system resources. The Set-up program also activates the time and date.

DOS

DOS should already be installed in the computer. When the computer does its self-test it will notify you if any part of DOS is missing or is corrupt. Watch the screen for any such messages.

Initialisation

When the system *boots,* the memory settings have to be correct, as do instructions, for example, telling the PC that it is to work with an SVGA monitor. The optimisation of memory allocation is a specialist activity which becomes increasingly important with an increasing number of concurrent processes – that is, simultaneously running applications – in the PC. There are extensive sections in both the DOS user's guide and the Windows user's guide on memory optimisation. The initialisation settings are controlled by DOS. It is possible for the user to change them but, once set, DOS automatically runs them when the computer is turned on. For example, the computer set-up file enables the date and time to be programmed in, after which they will stay correct.

Applications

Whether you are using Windows or working directly with DOS, your system cannot perform useful work without an application installed and able to run. An application will be provided on diskette – perhaps a large number of diskettes – which need to be loaded in the correct order.

Date and time

Configuring these details in a PC is easy (and necessary when the clocks are changed twice a year or the battery that provides continuous power for these functions has run out). You simply have to enter the set-up program and make alterations. This can either

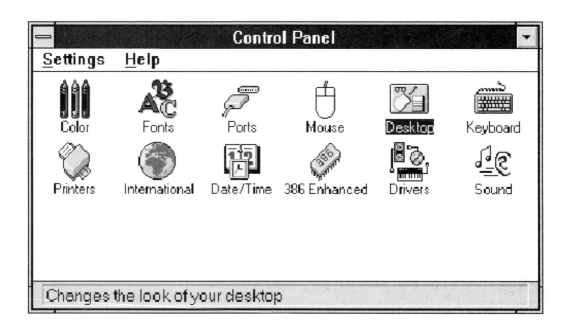

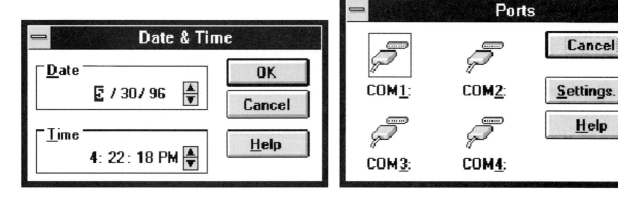

Figure 4.1 Control Panel window with Date/Time and Ports options

be accessed when the PC boots up, or, in DOS, by pressing the Ctrl, Alt, S keys together. In the set-up program a number of different system specifications can be configured such as informing the PC what type of monitor is being used. The alternative way of doing this is to enter the Windows Control Panel software and make changes there. Figure 4.1 shows the Control Panel window and the Date/Time and Ports changing options – far easier than DOS and shown in a graphical user interface way. Changes may also be made in the Windows Control Panel software. By

clicking on the Ports icon, the options available are shown and similarly the Date/Time options. Once your PC is correctly configured, you're ready to install applications software.

Install applications software

Applications software may be installed using Windows or DOS. Let us take these in turn, first Windows.

Windows

There are applications that have been written to run under Windows, and those that have not. Applications written for Windows are designed to take advantage of Windows features, specifically the graphical user interface and the co-operative use of memory shared with other applications.

Applications written to run under DOS will not enjoy those advantages, but will still run.

Creating a directory

If you use paper files, there is a strong chance that you use file dividers. They work as separators between subject areas in the file. Directories do much the same thing on computer disks. In creating a directory, we can save files so that their names are grouped as we wish.

To create a directory in Windows, enter the File Manager option that accompanies Windows software. The screen is divided into two areas. The left-hand window shows the root directory: in the case of PCs this will be the C: or A: drive. The right-hand window shows the subdirectories or files that exist in each of the parent directories (see Figure 4.2).

To create a new directory, we select the File option from the menu at the top of the screen and move the cursor to the Create Directory option.

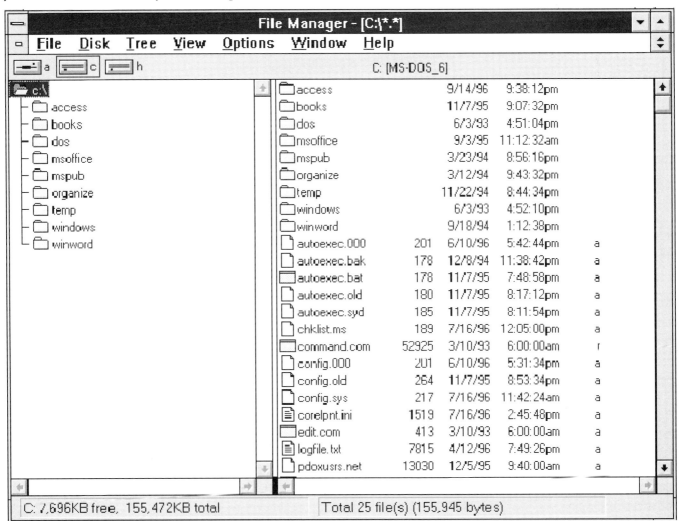

Figure 4.2 Creating a directory in Windows

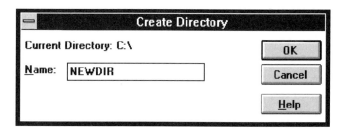

Figure 4.3 Creating a directory name

A small window appears in which we can assign a name to the directory we wish to create. Except in the case of Windows '95, directory names can be only up to eight characters long. In the example shown here, the directory has been called NEWDIR (see Figure 4.3).

The result of this operation can be seen by checking the C: drive – the directory NEWDIR now exists.

Installing applications in a directory

Windows software assists the user to install applications software in directories. Using the File Manager, we select the File option, and then Run (see Figure 4.4).

A new window appears, asking for a Command Line. This is the instruction the PC needs to start installing the application. Although you *may* know what this instruction is, there is a strong possibility you don't.

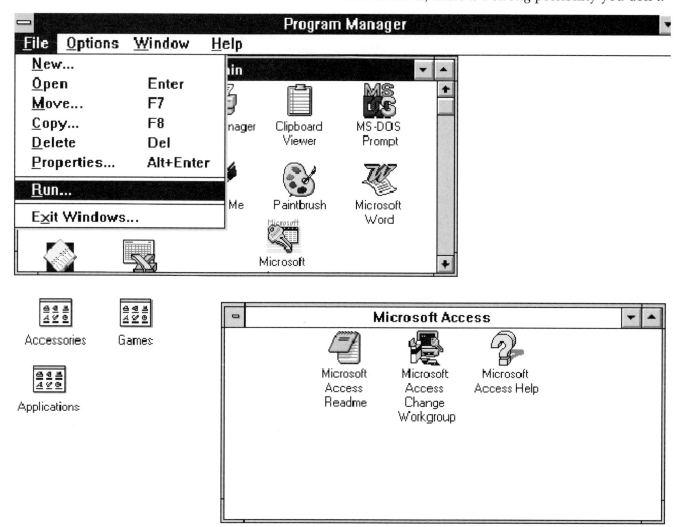

Figure 4.4 Installing an application

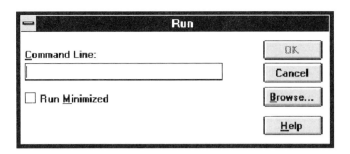

Figure 4.5 A Command Line

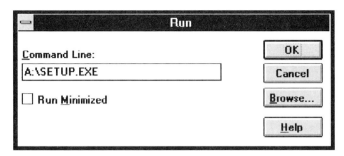

Figure 4.7 The Run window

This being the case, select the Browse option (see Figure 4.5).

A number of file names may be presented as in Figure 4.6, each one covering different options in the installation process. If you are unsure as to which one to choose, select the Setup.exe file. Remember to choose the directory the installation software is being used on – it is unlikely to be the hard disk if it has not been installed before.

The selection made is then transferred back to the Run window, Figure 4.7. When OK is selected, the installation procedure is followed through by the PC.

Generally, the installation software creates a directory and places the application files in it. Sometimes the user is given the option to name the directory the applications files will be placed in. No matter which option is used, the applications files are transferred on to the hard disk.

Setting defaults

There is a program information file (PIF) called DEFAULT.PIF located in the Windows System directory. DEFAULT.PIF contains default values for memory allocations, video memory, display usage and other values.

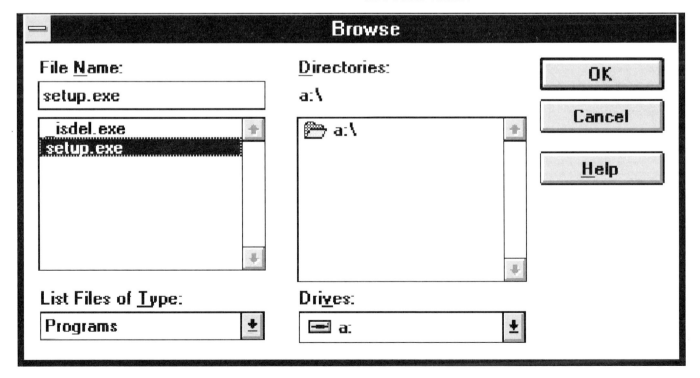

Figure 4.6 The Browse option

If you want to change these default settings use the PIF Editor which has an icon in the Main group.

Installing device drivers

You can install most device drivers by using the Drivers option in the Control panel, but for the drivers for the keyboard, mouse or monitor you must use the Windows Set-up screen.

Let us now turn to installing applications software under DOS.

DOS

Creating a directory

To create a directory in DOS you use the **md** command, standing for 'make directory.' This is

illustrated in Figure 4.8, where we have created a new directory called NEWDIR, and then instructed the PC to show all the directories to check that NEWDIR now exists.

Installing applications in a directory

This is done with the DOS Copy command to copy the application files from diskette into the newly created directory.

Setting defaults

In DOS, the default settings are held in system files called **CONFIG.SYS** and **AUTOEXEC.BAT**. It is unlikely that you will feel the need to change the default values, but if you do, first take a copy of the files, using the **SYS** command, then use a text editor on the system to make changes.

```
C:\>md newdir

C:\>dir/w

 Volume in drive C is MS-DOS_6
 Volume Serial Number is 20CA-88E5
 Directory of C:\

[DOS]        [WINDOWS]     [TEMP]       [BOOKS]       [MSOFFICE]
[ORGANIZE]   [NEWDIR]      [WINWORD]    [ACCESS]      [MSPUB]
CONFIG.000    WINA20.386    COMMAND.COM    CONFIG.OLD
PDOXUSRS.NET
VGAMODE.EXE    AUTOEXEC.000    AUTOEXEC.SYD    AUTOEXEC.OLD
LOGFILE.TXT
AUTOEXEC.BAK    CONFIG.SYS    AUTOEXEC.BAT    EDIT.COM
CHKLIST.MS
CORELPNT.INI
     26 file(s)    155945 bytes
               4915200 bytes free

C:\>
```

Figure 4.8 Creating a directory in DOS

Installing device drivers

To install a device driver you must include the appropriate device command in your **CONFIG.SYS** file. For example, include

```
device = c:\mouse\mouse.sys
```

to load **MOUSE.SYS,** the mouse device driver, into memory. The driver then becomes part of DOS systems software, and stays in memory.

Test the applications software

Power up

When you have successfully set up your hardware and installed your software, you will need to test the computer system. As we already know, the PC will not work unless the self-test procedure works correctly. You may find that the self-test works but there are still problems using peripherals which have not been configured correctly. This is because changes made to operating system files can alter the configuration the computer assumes it has. Go back and check methodically each step you made to be sure you did everything correctly.

Did you know?

Whenever you test hardware, software or indeed anything else, you must always use the same test data for successive tests, so that you can check the system is working as it should. You should not include randomly generated numbers in your test data as you won't know what the results are meant to be. Test data should be carefully planned so that you know for certain exactly what you have tested.

Access software

If you manage to power up the PC without any problems, the next step is to access software. In Windows this is done by double-clicking on the icon, or picture, of the applications software you need.

In DOS, you need to display the directory the software is in, and then select the file to start the software working. This file generally ends in **.EXE** which means it is an *executable* file. If you don't know which file to choose to make the software

work, look for the one with the **.EXE** on the end, type the name and press Return.

Enter data

To make sure software works correctly you will have to enter some data. If, for example, you have loaded a word processor, type up your notes on setting up the system, installing software and setting defaults. Make sure that all the functions in the software work to your satisfaction. There may be some parts of the software that can be altered to your preferences. It may take you some time to find out how you like to use the software best.

Save data

Using both the hard disk and diskette, save the notes you have just typed on the word processor. It may also be an idea to close the file, and then open it up again to make sure you are happy retrieving the document in your new software package.

Print

Print out the piece of work you have completed and keep it in your portfolio as evidence. Word processor software generally allows work to be printed easily. However, it is possible that your work will not print because the hardware has not been configured correctly. You may need to check that the right printer driver for your printer has been installed. Don't worry if you have to install the driver, as it will have accompanied your printer when it was bought, and will be easy to install.

Review the system and make recommendations for improving the specification

While you are gaining your evidence, make notes reviewing the system. That is, make notes as to how easy it is to put together – both the hardware and the software. At the end of the exercise you will be able to make recommendations to improve the system specification. Your notes will be invaluable here – the more detailed they are the better. You may want to think about the following areas:

- Speed of the CPU.
- How much RAM the system uses.
- The size of the hard disk drive.
- How big the monitor is – is it big enough to see clearly?
- How well the printer works.
- Ease of plugging the PC together.
- If you use DOS, would Windows be easier for you to use?
- Were the ports working without you having to make changes?

You might like to produce a chart like the one in Table 4.1. This will need your comments included in it.

Action	Easy/difficult to Install	Comments
Connect PC to monitor	Easy	1 cable used
Connect PC to electricity supply	Easy	1 cable
Connect monitor to electricity supply	Easy	Cable already connected to monitor – just plug into wall
Connect mouse to PC	Easy	
Connect printer to PC	Easy	Use clips on both ends of cable
Connect printer to electricity supply	Easy	1 cable
Connect keyboard to PC	Easy	
Turn PC on	Easy	
Load operating system	Difficult	Hard – takes a long time. Easy to make mistakes
Configure PC	Difficult	Mistakes easy to make
Load applications software	Difficult	But Windows helps
Test PC – power up	Easy	
Access software	Easy (Windows)	Much easier than DOS
Enter data	Easy	Don't be too ambitious
Save data	Easy	
Print data	Easy	

Table 4.1 Reviewing the system

Don't feel that these are the only comments you can put in your table – anything you feel is important should be noted down.

Evidence indicator project

This project covers all the evidence indicators related to Chapter 4, (Element 1.4). It has been designed to be carried out at the end of the element.

Performance criteria: 1–5

Key skills:	Communication	3.2, 3.3
	Application of number	–
	IT	3.1, 3.2, 3.3, 3.4

When you have been given the selection of components, and the specification, by your tutor, you can start this practical project. Make sure that you know what operating system software and application software you will have to load, and that you are clear about the configuration requirements.

When you feel confident about setting up and installing a stand-alone computer system ask your tutor to watch you and talk him or her through what you are doing.

1 First, you must connect all the following hardware together:
   - main processor unit
   - keyboard
   - mouse
   - VDU
   - printer
   - ports (serial, parallel)
   - cables.
2 You must then install the system, configure the software to meet the specification and ensure the system is tested.
3 You will also need to prepare notes on reviewing the system and making recommendations for improving the specification. You can type these notes on your PC when it is up and running allowing you to show your tutor that you can print data successfully.

Information technology systems: Unit test 1

1 Which of the following is an electronic point of sale system?
   a A bankers card taking money out of a bank account
   b The use of a credit card in a store to purchase goods
   c A shop using a bar code reader to scan details of items sold into a computer
   d Direct banking

2 Sales order processing includes
   a A computer ordering stock via a telephone line
   b A company employee ordering stock over a telephone line
   c Replacing old PCs
   d Producing invoices

3 The advantages of payroll processing include
   a More money for staff
   b Reduced National Insurance payments
   c Automatic payment of wages through banks
   d Improved cheque transfer accuracy

4 An example of an industrial system is
   a A bank's computer system
   b Traffic lights
   c A quality control system in a company
   d A computer network in a manufacturing environment

5 An example of a commercial system is
   a Traffic lights
   b A bank computer
   c The Teletext computer database system
   d Robots manufacturing cars

6 One advantage of using a robot is
   a They are easy to use in all jobs
   b Robots are always cheaper to employ than their human equivalent
   c Robots never break down
   d They can work 24 hours a day without a break

7 Which of the following is an example of environmental control?
   a A greenhouse window that opens when it becomes too warm inside
   b Computer-controlled motorway LED signals
   c Stock control order processing
   d Global warming

8 Which of the following is an example of hardware?
   a A spread sheet
   b Data on the Internet
   c A printer
   d A printed invoice

9 An example of software is
   a Data typed into a computer
   b A printer
   c A computer program
   d Computer equipment

10 Which of the following is an example of a processing activity?
   a A database management system creating a report
   b The information displayed on a computer monitor
   c A computer RAM
   d ROM

11 Which of the following is an example of an output device?
   a A bar code reader
   b A computer keyboard
   c A computer monitor
   d A computer receiving information via modem

12 Negative impacts of computers include
   a Improved efficiency in the work place
   b Possible eye-strain for operators
   c They work faster than people
   d Computers do not get tired

13 Why are computers said to be more accurate than humans?
   a They are more intelligent than humans
   b Computers work faster than humans
   c Computers cannot get tired and make mistakes
   d Humans cannot handle large volumes of data

14 A computer's CPU is situated on the
   a ROM
   b RAM
   c Motherboard
   d Monitor

15 Which of the following is not an example of a control device?
a A monitor
b A video card
c Serial output card
d Parallel output card

16 The capacity of a storage device is measured in
a Bytes
b Bits
c CPI
d MHz

17 Hardware capable of automated data capture includes
a A mouse
b A printer
c A sheet feed scanner
d A keyboard

18 The RAM in a PC is used to
a Store information even when the PC is turned off
b Store the operating system
c Start the computer system operating
d Hold working data while the computer is running

19 Which of the following can be used to record data for permanent storage?
a A CD ROM
b A hard disk
c A diskette
d RAM

20 An example of an operating system is
a Windows 3.1
b A word processor
c File management software
d DOS

21 Which of the following is not an example of a programming language?
a FORTRAN
b BASIC
c Turbo Pascal
d Expert system

22 Applications software includes all but one of the following
a Microsoft Excel
b Lotus Smart Suite
c DOS
d Foxpro

23 In a PC, one job of the Operating System is to
a Control the printer
b Interface between the PC and the printer
c Make printing faster
d Manage the allocation of memory

24 Programming languages are used to
a Run the computer
b Run the computer instead of DOS
c Create new applications software
d Control the hardware and software

25 Computer modelling can be used for which of the following?
a to control machine tools
b to view models in 3D before they are created
c to control robots
d to build graphical user interfaces

26 Expert systems are used because
a Computers operate more accurately than humans
b Computers calculate answers faster than people
c They never become obsolete
d They allow computers to stand in for human experts

27 The motherboard contains the
a Hard disk drive
b Printer socket
c Modem socket
d CPU

28 The job of the address bus is to
a Fetch and store data
b Act as an I/O device
c Link terminals to a computer
d Connect a modem to a PC

29 The Bankers Automated Clearing Service makes it possible to
a Pay debts without the need for cheques
b Use telephone banking facilities
c Automatically pay debts through the use of cheques
d Send cheques through the banking system quickly

30 Windows '95 is an example of
a An Operating System
b A graphical user interface
c An Operating System and graphical user interface combined
d A word processor

This unit addresses, through its four elements, four areas of study which are all important and which together lay the foundations for understanding a wide tract of computer usage. Chapter 5 (Element 2.1) introduces you to the way computers can be used to process commercial documents. The purpose of each type of document may be new to you. You should nonetheless accept that in every kind of business the use of these documents is essential. If you can visit firms and see how they rely on their paperwork, even in an age of high technology and widespread automation, you will grasp the importance of the various forms you will encounter here.

Chapter 6 (Element 2.2) is about the use of graphics. There are many fields in which a well-chosen diagram or sketch is often the most effective means of conveying an idea. Sometimes, as when an architect wants to present the plan of a building, there is little alternative to showing a drawing. You will have opportunities

throughout this GNVQ course to harness your new skill in getting your PC to produce illustrations for you.

In Chapter 7 (Element 2.3), the construction and uses of computer models are discussed. The accuracy, versatility, and speed of a PC make it ideal for modelling. You will learn how to use computer-based models to handle changes in linked sets of figures; how to get answers to questions of the 'what if' kind; and how to predict outcomes from trends.

Control systems are the subject of Chapter 8 (Element 2.4). An understanding of the nature of negative feed-back, which is a feature of almost every control system, will stand you in good stead. Control systems, varying from straightforward to exceedingly complex, abound in everyday life. You will be well placed to recognise them, when you have completed this element.

An external test forms part of this unit.

Chapter 5

Process commercial documents

Unit 1 included an investigation of commercial IT systems. In this element of Unit 2 we shall be looking at one aspect – the use of commercial systems. This is an important part of office life and is one of the major uses of IT in the commercial world. You will find it helpful if you can collect a variety of commercial documents either from your work placement or from colleagues at work. Be careful though as some documents are sensitive or confidential. Use these documents to compare different styles and layouts and the uses of different documents.

You will find it helpful to look at a standard typing or word processor book to find out about layout conventions, and a business administration textbook will give you more details about the function of different documents.

After studying this chapter you should be able to:

- create a corporate style *specification* for *commercial documents*
- create templates with appropriate *page attributes* and *layouts* for commercial documents
- enter *data* and import data files
- *edit documents* and use *software tools*
- apply appropriate *accuracy* and *security checks*
- produce documents.

Special note

As in the rest of this book, we shall be using Windows-based software to illustrate important points. This doesn't mean that you have to use this software too. The illustrations are examples of the *type* of evidence you will have to produce. The software *you* have to use will do the jobs just as well – but in slightly different ways. If you run into difficulty, ask your tutor for help, or consult the handbook that accompanies the software. Modern software generally has a Help facility. This can assist in the same way as the handbook or manual. If you feel you need to, call up the Help and print it out so you can follow the instructions carefully.

Create a corporate style specification

Commercial documents are used by companies that wish to make an impact or impression with customers. You will generally find that each of the documents used externally has the company logo, address, telephone number, fax number and email address (if appropriate). *Some* companies with pages on the Internet will also have their Internet address displayed.

Businesses use their commercial documents to develop or reinforce their house style. They take the opportunities provided by customers, prospective customers, suppliers, and others reading the documents to create a particular impression and thus build an image of the business.

Every type of business document has a distinct purpose, but companies will probably use the same colours, logo and type styles on all of them in order to help establish their corporate identities.

There are no rules as to how the corporate logo appears unless the business is a limited company. If this is the case, the notepaper and all other commercial documents must by law display its name in legible characters. The company must also show the company's place of registration (England, Wales or Scotland), the address of its registered office and the company registration number.

Activity

Contact a company and ask for copies of their official notepaper, memo paper and business cards. Find out their email addresses and contact them. Is the company logo used in the email system? What benefits does email have for the company you contact over and above the more traditional methods of communication?

Type of document

There are a number of different types of document – some of which are for use inside an organisation,

Internal documents
- Memorandum (or memo)
- Newsletter (or house magazine)
- Agenda
- Minutes
- Planning information
- Financial reports

External documents
- Business letter
- Quotation
- Invoice
- Statement
- Financial and legal returns
- Annual report and accounts

Figure 5.1 Examples of types of internal and external documents

where only its employees see them, and others that are sent outside the organisation. Figure 5.1 lists examples of these types of documents. It is unusual for the same documents to be used both internally and externally.

Purpose

Internal documents are often less formal than external documents. External documents have to be carefully worded because each one is sent on behalf of the company. Care must be taken in drafting such documents not to commit the company to any obligation that has not been agreed, and not to use words that could diminish the reputation of the company in any way.

Let us now look at the main purposes of these documents:

Memorandum

A memorandum gives information, makes requests, agrees arrangements, asks for comments. Memos can be addressed, or copied, to several people, with the originator keeping a copy (see Figure 5.2). This is a straightforward memo which addresses just one topic clearly, and without formality. CC means that a copy is to go to Rosemary Wright.

MEMORANDUM

Date:	02/04/XX
To:	John Holmes, Ian Wright, Chris Pole, Steven Coventry, Jason Beeches
CC:	Rosemary Wright
From:	Mike Smith
Subject:	Canteen

For those of you not already aware, the new canteen equipment has now arrived. It will be installed next Wednesday. This may cause some disruption to us all due to the noise the engineers will make while drilling, etc. Please bear with us for a few hours – it will make lunch times so much more enjoyable in the future!

MS/SN

Figure 5.2 Example of a memo

Newsletter

A newsletter is a regularly produced periodical telling employees what the organisation is doing. It may, in part, be lighthearted, with competitions and correspondence columns. Try to find a copy of a company newsletter and identify the layouts that have been used.

The more existing documents you look at the more confident you will become at deciding a layout and building your templates for producing them.

Agenda

An agenda is a list of the items to be discussed at a meeting, in the order in which they will be taken. An agenda is usually distributed with the notice of the meeting, giving the place, the day, the time and a list of those to attend (Figure 5.3).

Minutes

The minutes record what was said at a meeting, and what was decided.

Planning information

Any document setting out the plans to be followed for a given activity.

Financial reports

Financial reports let managers and others know the extent to which a business is achieving its financial targets.

Business letter

These can be to any firm or individual on any matter to do with the functioning of the business. Companies may wish to have the layout of their letters like the example in Figure 5.4, with the body of the letter fully justified and everything else left justified.

The address block of Stuart Thomas Ltd could have been centred at the top of the page, on the right, or even placed along the bottom of the page. Microsoft Word allows you to keep details of your layout in a table.

Weekly Status Meeting	
	02/04/XX **2:00 PM to 2:55 PM** **Building 1, Conference Room**

Meeting called by:	Simon Norcross
Type of meeting:	Weekly Status Meeting
Note taker:	SN
Attendees:	Simon Norcross, Joanne Naples, Melanie Jones, David Mercer, Cathleen Turner
Please read:	Last week's notes
Please bring:	Last week's minutes of meeting

Agenda topics

Apologies for absence

Minutes of last meeting

Matters arising

Meeting overview

Allocation of rooms

Office move

New telephone numbers

Arrival of new equipment

Next meeting

Any other business

Special notes:

Figure 5.3 An agenda

Quotation

A quotation gives the details of prices to be changed, and other terms of business, that would apply in meeting a particular order. Quotations are normally sent in response to inquiries about the supply of goods or services.

Stuart Thomas Ltd
11 Glebe Street
EDINBURGH
EHXX 6XX

4 February 19XX

Denise Prior
11 Cavendish Road
SOUTHPORT
SPX 6XX

Dear Denise

The body of the letter goes here, fully justified

Yours sincerely

Stuart Thomas
Managing Director

SN

cc: John Wilmslow

Figure 5.4 A business letter

Invoice

The single most important document, many businesses would say, is the invoice – a bill for goods or services supplied. If no invoices are issued no money will come in (Figure 5.5).

This is a simple form of invoice. All the products and services offered by Woolacoombe Fine Art attract the same rate of VAT, so there is no need to state the rate for each type of item. If the firm also sold books, which are zero-rated, there would have to be an extra column for VAT rate.

WOOLACOOMBE FINE ART

INVOICE Ref: Your order 1234/yz/5 of 1 Feb XX

Invoice address Invoice No. **452**

Accounts Department
Artists' World
17 Station Road
Withenshaw

Delivery address Date 8 Feb XX

Artists' World
Deansgate
Manchester

No. of copies	Title	Unit price	Cost
12	Paint Boxes, W & N, Model 7a	22–50	270–00
5	Sets of Brushes, Squirrel (000–9) BB	32–00	160–00
Gross cost			430–00
Discount 10%			43–00
Net cost			387–00
VAT @ 17.5%			67–72
Total due			319–28

Terms of Please pay Woolacoombe Fine Art by 8 Mar XX.
Business Additional 2.5% discount if payment made before 21 Feb XX.

Please pay WOOLACOOMBE FINE ART.

PO Box 57, Woolacoombe Bay, Devon, EX19 8UA
Tel: 01271 831190 Fax: 01271 738151
VAT No. 315 843271

Figure 5.5 An invoice

Also, as the business is not a limited company, there are no registration details to be carried on the invoice.

Statement

This is a summary of invoices sent to a particular customer, usually over the previous month. It will show any unpaid older invoices.

Financial and legal returns

Various bodies such as the Inland Revenue, Customs & Excise, and the CBI routinely need information from businesses.

Annual report and accounts

For a limited company this is often a prestige document for shareholders as well as the formal report of trading.

Page attributes

Page attributes are the sizes of paper being used, the orientation of the paper, and the way 'widows' and 'orphans' are to be handled.

The most common paper sizes used in business are A4, which is 210 mm × 297 mm, and A5, which is half the size of A4 – 148 mm × 210 mm. Orientation can either be portrait or landscape, as shown in Figure 5.6.

'Widows' and 'orphans' are small amounts of text that overflow on to the top of the next page, or appear after a blank line or area at the bottom of a page. Software can help users to eliminate them.

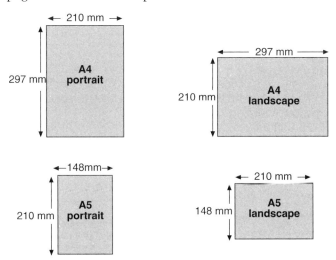

Figure 5.6 A4 and A5 portrait and landscape

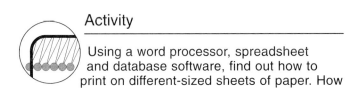

Activity

Using a word processor, spreadsheet and database software, find out how to print on different-sized sheets of paper. How easy is it to change the orientation from portrait to landscape?

Layouts

The layout of a page determines how it looks, and how well it meets its purpose. For example, if you look at a page of print in a book you will see the width of the margins, the column layout and any indents of lines or blocks of text. You can also note the font used, the line spacing and the numbering of the pages.

All these features of the printed page constitute its layout.

Justification

Justifying text means changing the distances between words so that each line of text aligns with the right margin, in the same way as it starts at the left margin. This may be referred to as fully justified. If text is lined up on the left, but ragged on the right, it is left justified. Similarly, text can be right justified.

Indents

Negative indent and hanging indent are two examples of indented text. These are illustrated in Figure 5.7.

The negative indent has text inset from the left and right margins whereas the hanging indent has text inset from the left margin only. Indents are common in numbered lists and glossaries.

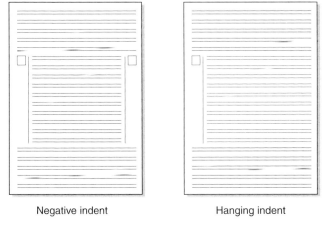

Negative indent   Hanging indent

Figure 5.7 Indents

Tabulations

Tabulations or tabs are standardised distances across the page, usually every $\frac{1}{2}$ inch, where you can insert text. Using tabs ensures that text inserted at different points across the page all line up correctly. When using a word processor, it is possible to specify whether the tabs are left, centre or right aligned.

Line spacing

Line spacing is the amount of vertical space between each line of text and the next. The standard line-spacing options are single, one and a half and double with double-line spacing being twice that of single-line spacing. Most text-based software defaults to single-line spacing.

Fonts

Font is another word for typeface. There are many different fonts on a word processor or desktop publishing system, but the use of fonts should be guided by clarity. Commercial documents must be clear and easy to read. Fancy typefaces are best left for posters and design work. Fonts come in a range of sizes from around 8 point to 72 point. The most common font size used in commercial documents is 10 or 12 point.

Page numbering

The instructions for page numbering on a word processor vary by preference. The page number can be inserted at the bottom or top of the page, in the centre, left or right aligned. You can also include text with page numbers, for example, 'Page 4' or start numbering on a page other than the first page of your document.

Headers and footers

A document header is the zone at the top of a page, before the first line. It can be used to repeat text information such as a document or chapter title as shown at the top of this page. A document footer is the zone at the bottom of the page after the last line. It is usually used to show information such as page numbers as in this book.

Column layout

Word processing or desktop publishing systems enable you to arrange text in newspaper columns.

This is when the text flows from the bottom of one column to the top of the next. Creating columns in tables enables you to display text in a clearer format. Most word processing and desktop publishing packages create two or more columns of text on a page. Within each distinct column, margins and tabs may be adjusted without affecting the style of the other column(s). It is most useful in newsletters or newspapers. Have a look at a national newspaper to see how the text is laid out.

Document notes

Document notes include such things as footnotes, endnotes and summaries. If you wish to make a statement but need to back it up with a reference, the word processor will allow you to place a reference point (generally a number) next to the statement and a back-up quote at the bottom of the page.

Did you know?

Footnotes tend not to be used in formal letters: they are more common in textbooks and manuals. It is possible to have a footnote reference on a page but no footnote at the bottom of the page. If this is the case the reference will be at the end of the chapter.

Activity

- Why are the settings on a word processor so often in inches?
- Why are border measurements included in word processors?
- What standard page settings are used for A4 word processor pages?
- What is justification used for when word processing?

Evidence collection point

At this point your tutor may wish you to start work on the project which will prove to your tutor and assessor that you understand this part of the element. If so, turn to page 79. This covers the first evidence indicator for this element.

Create templates

A template is an electronic file that holds basic outline data about a document. This may be style

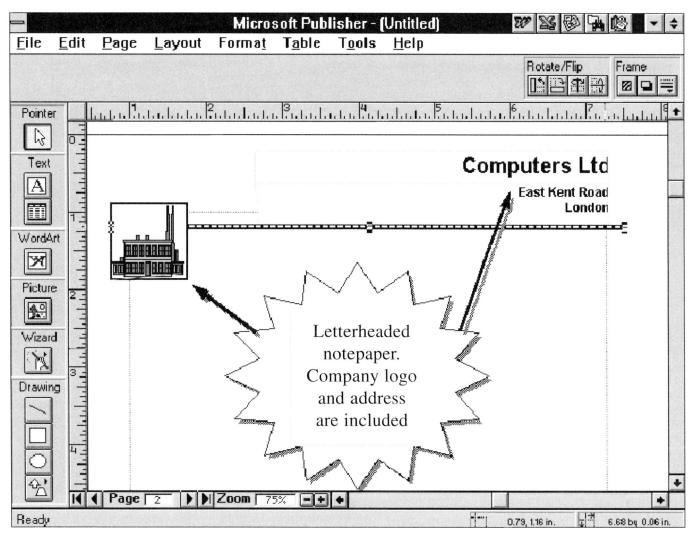

Figure 5.8 Part of a company letterhead design

data such as the type of font that will be used in the document. With some word processors, the date can be inserted into the page once, and each time the document is opened and printed, the date is changed to the date of printing. *Macros* in word processing are similarly preset document arrangements. An example of a macro is a letter type – the position of the references and the location of address details.

Did you know?

If you don't have a computer to create your own letter headings and business cards, some printing companies will do it for you to your own specifications.

This book was written using templates. At the start of the book, the page number was inserted, along with the time and date. Each page that was written then had these basic details included without having to re-enter them. The details were used for editing. Each time a draft was printed, it carried the date.

Once you have created your template you will be able to save it and call it up at any time you wish to prepare and send out the document to which it relates. All you will have to do is add the details of the contents to it and much of the work is done for you. Your address and other details are already there so you don't have to type them in again. Word processors are now able to provide the time, date and address. Each time the template is used and printed, the time and date are updated.

Some software can help you design the page layout you want. Microsoft Publisher has this facility, called Page Wizard. It takes the user through the process one step at a time, allowing names, telephone numbers and company logos to be put in (Figure 5.8). There is nothing wrong with using this type of software to gain your evidence. However, always remember that one day you may need to design a document without this help.

Did you know?

In most business organisations it is more common to send a memo or an email about a topic than to send the message over the telephone. This is because there is a record of the information for future referral, kept by the sender.

Evidence collection point

At this point your tutor may wish you to start work on the project which will prove to your tutor and assessor that you understand this part of the element. If so, turn to page 79. If you have already started the project you may be ready to do Section 2. This covers the second part of the evidence indicator for this element.

Enter and edit data

To improve the layout, emphasise bits of text, add or delete material in a document you have to edit it. A number of tools are available to you on the word processor that allow editing to take place quickly and efficiently. These tools come for the three different types of data:

Text   Delete, insert, copy, move, enhance
Tables   Insert (row, column, item), delete (row, column, item)
Graphics Size, rotate, copy, move, manipulate

Text

Text probably makes up the majority of data on most commercial computer systems, traditionally in the form of word processed and desktop published documents, and sometimes in databases, spreadsheet and organiser software documents. The great advantage of using word processors and desktop publishers over typewriters and hand-written

documents is that text can be manipulated easily – any mistakes can be corrected in a matter of seconds through tools included in the software.

Most programs offer several different ways to perform the same editing functions. Most systems offer the facility of being able to delete text by highlighting the selected words and pressing the delete key.

Inserting text can usually be performed by moving the cursor to the required position and typing the required text.

Text may be copied and or moved by highlighting a selection and dragging it into position or by copying it to a clipboard, moving the cursor to the insertion point and pasting it in.

Text may be enhanced by selecting the relevant icon on the screen and editing the data. Enhancing facilities include emboldening, underlining, changing the font size and use of italic.

Software tools

Search (and replace)

If you ever write a book or a long essay, you may want to find a particular topic or word you used. Reading through the entire text is time consuming and annoying. Modern software can help – by using the Search facility in word processing software, it's possible to enter a word or number of words and tell the computer to search through the entire document until it finds a match from your input (Figure 5.9). In Word for Windows, the search facility is called 'Find' in the 'Edit' menu.

Figure 5.9 Searching for 'word processor'

In a similar way, the search and replace option allows us to tell the word processor to find a word and change it for another (Figure 5.10).

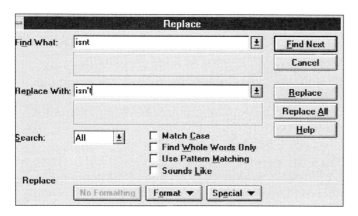

Figure 5.10 A 'search and replace' operation

There is further reference to the use of these tools in Chapter 10 (Element 3.2).

Mail merge

Mail merge allows the creation of a personalised document that is to be sent to possibly hundreds of people. The mail merge facility allows the user to combine data such as names and addresses in a secondary file with information in a master file to produce multiple documents, each containing the same master information but addressed to a different person (Figure 5.11).

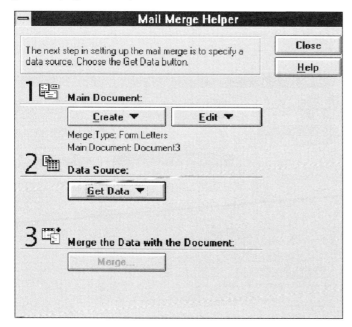

Figure 5.11 Setting up a 'mail merge' run

Mail merge is particularly useful for businesses writing to all their clients with news of new products, or for clubs and societies writing to all their members – using the mail merge technique, everyone in receipt of the letter thinks it has been written only to him or her!

Activity

Using a spreadsheet, create a template for a company accounts system. The page attributes and layouts are just as important as in a word processed document.

Create a document using the template and edit it. Use any software tools available to you on the spreadsheet software you use.

Is it easier or harder to create templates in a spreadsheet than in a word processor?

Tables

Tables are useful to illustrate data. They can be created in spreadsheets, word processors and sometimes databases. They are made up of rows and columns.

Until quite recently, it was only possible to create tables in software such as spreadsheets and import them into the word processor. Now it can all be done using a word processor software package such as Word for Windows which allows tables to be created in Table Editor.

Did you know?

Public limited company annual reports use tables and graphs to show shareholders details of the number of items sold in the past year, the size of the markets the company operates in, the number of people working for the company and profits compared to those of the previous few years. Some organisations even forecast future profits in tables, comparing them to the figures from previous years.

Once a table has been created, inserting text is simple – place the cursor, using the mouse or arrow keys, in the cell you want the text in and type. The cell size will adjust itself to the amount of text you want to enter. To delete text, move the cursor to the required cell and use the backspace key or the delete button.

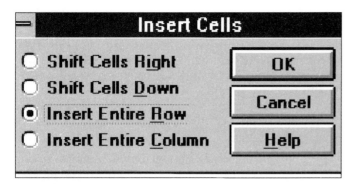

Figure 5.12 Insert cells

Once created it is possible to insert or delete extra rows or columns as and when required. This is done by highlighting the required row or column and using the software menu system to make adjustments as required (Figure 5.12).

Cells may have different heights and widths depending upon how much information is placed in them – there is no standard size. If there was a standard size, the data would have to fit into the table (not very flexible) instead of the table fitting around the data.

Graphics

Graphics can cover a number of different areas. Data from tables can be put into graphical form to show their results more easily as illustrated in Figure 5.13.

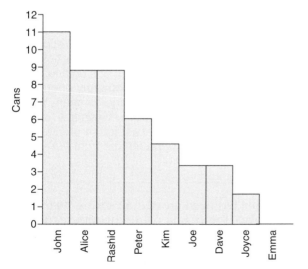

Figure 5.13 Graph showing weekly consumption of Cola

Possibly a more exciting area of graphics comes in the ability to create a drawing but then edit it in different ways. For example, an object may be copied, moved, rotated and the size altered.

Graphic packages usually include rotation and flip features. You highlight the object and select the degree of rotation you require. Rotating 180° is the same as turning the object upside down, which you can usually do with a flip command.

There are small squares or circles on the line that surrounds a graphic object, called handles. By clicking and dragging these handles you can size an object.

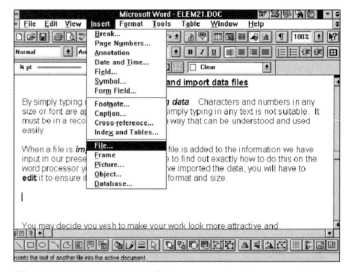

Figure 5.14 Inserting a file

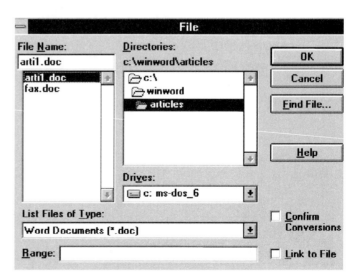

Figure 5.15 Selecting the file to insert

Import data files

When a file is imported, data from this file is added to another file. Once data has been imported it may have to be edited to ensure it's all in the same font and point size. Figure 5.14 illustrates the initial procedure for inserting a file into a word processor. Figure 5.15 shows how the file to be inserted is selected from the disk. Once the user presses the Return key, the software does the rest of the work.

Clipart

You may decide you wish to make your work look more attractive and interesting. One way of doing this is to import Clipart. Clipart is a computer vector picture (more about this in Chapter 6, Element 2.2) – but not a true picture that has been scanned into the PC (Figure 5.16).

Clipart can be changed in size by selecting it with the mouse and moving the corners to the size you require.

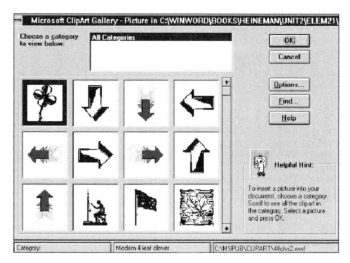

Figure 5.17 A Clipart gallery

Did you know?

It's possible to create your own Clipart by either taking a drawing and placing its image into the Clipart gallery or by scanning a picture you have taken into a file and placing it in the same gallery. An example of a Clipart gallery is shown in Figure 5.17.

Evidence collection point

At this point your tutor may wish you to start work on the project which will prove to your tutor or assessor that you understand this part of the element. If so, turn to page 79. If you have already started the project you may be ready to do Section 3. This covers the third part of the evidence indicator for this element.

Accuracy and security checks

Spellcheck

Other editing facilities include spellcheck and grammar checks. The software holds the correct formats for spelling and grammar, and when requested cross-references the data in the present working file with that in the software grammar file. *Generally* the software won't make a change without asking the user if the change will make the word correct – otherwise it may change a word that is right into another one, making the sentence mean

Figure 5.16 Examples of Clipart

Figure 5.18 Spellcheck

something totally different! Similarly, the user can over-ride the advice given on grammar.

When using the spellcheck facility you must also be aware that proper names are not recognised unless in the dictionary and that the computer may use American spelling.

Did you know?

Writing was invented when countries started trading with one another. In order to remember what and how many goods had been traded, and for what price, it became necessary to have permanent records. Ensuring they were accurate was equally important then. Inaccurate written records are at best useless, and at worst dangerous because they can be used as evidence that something happened when in fact it didn't, although the record said it did!

Proofreading

As well as having the word processor make checks on your work, it's always necessary to check your work yourself both when it's on the screen and when it's printed. This is known as proofreading. Computers can make mistakes at times without you noticing. Imagine you are typing a business letter and key in £100 by accident when you meant to key in £1.00. Although this is an error, the spellcheck facility on a word processor wouldn't pick it up because it could be perfectly correct. This type of error could cost a lot of money.

There are many opportunities in English for creating words that a spellchecker will not warn you about but which, due to a single transposition of a character or a missed character, can make rubbish of your text. For instance: 'to' instead of 'too'; 'for' for 'form'; and many more.

Security checks

Confidentiality

If you ever create a file that holds data or information that should not be seen by others, it's possible to put a confidentiality number or password on the file. Different computers do this in different ways and you should find out how it's done if you are working on a confidential document.

Some documents may be so confidential that if someone walks in, you can't allow them to see it on screen. Rather than turn off the computer, Windows software allows the user to switch to another software package or the main menu by simply pressing the ALT and Tab keys at the same time.

Regular file saving

A part of computer security that is often overlooked is regular file saving. It's vitally important to save your work regularly in case it's lost or corrupted. Most computer software can now automatically save work whenever the user wants. It's also a good idea to save important data in a number of ways (such as on a hard disk *and* a diskette) so that if one method fails for any reason, the data is safe on the other. This procedure is known as *back-up* filing. It's vitally important to keep at least two copies of all your course work just in case one is lost, misplaced or damaged. Ideally, leave the copies in totally different places. But, remember that if you keep two copies of

work in two different files, whenever new work is put into one it must be put into the other at the same time to keep them identical and up to date.

Activity

Why is it necessary to use security checks on software and files containing data?

If you ever find that the electricity supply is cut or your computer switches on and off quickly and your work is lost, there is a good chance that all is not as black as it seems! The computer *should* save work in a *temporary* file. These files end in **.TMP**. They are placed in different directories according to how the PC is set up. By finding the right **.TMP** file and loading it back into the software, it's possible to get your work back at the place you last saw it.

Although it's highly unlikely that you will lose two sets of files, it's a good idea to *retain source documentation*. This means keep hold of original data, and once the information is printed, you should keep hold of that as well. If the files are lost, the printed data *can* be reloaded into the word processor by *scanning* the image and using OCR software.

Theft

It's a sad sign of the times that we must be careful of all items – and that theft is widespread. As well as putting password protection on files, it's possible to make sure software can't run on hardware without the permission of the software owner. This is achieved by using a *dongle* on the back of the computer. The dongle is plugged into one of the I/O ports. When the software starts, it checks the dongle is plugged in. If it's not, the software won't work.

Did you know?

Financial institutions in the City of London and in the USA have paid out millions of pounds to international gangs of 'Cyber terrorists' who threaten to destroy their computer systems and data. They have used *logic bombs* that once in the computer system can be detonated remotely, by *high-emission radio frequency guns* that send large currents of electricity through the computers to destroy them. Banking institutions have agreed to pay the ransom demands because if news broke out that their security systems could be defeated, confidence in banks could be lost and they could go bankrupt. If you

want to make a lot of money in IT, design and develop a security system that cannot be accessed by anyone without authority.

Hardware theft is a problem too. To stop this there are a number of precautions we can take:

■ Lock the PC or laptop in a desk or cupboard when not in use.
■ Place a password on the PC so when it *boots up* the user must type in the correct password, otherwise the computer won't work. This won't affect the ROM or RAM as the password is stored in a file in part of the *set-up* program on the hard disk.
■ Always use the *key* on the side or front of the PC. As long as the PC is locked when not in use, it can't be used.
■ Buy a computer security cage that locks the PC to the desk or the floor. This way, nobody can get to it without a key. Such devices cost around £150.
■ Place a lock in the diskette drive door when the PC is not in use.
■ Protect the PC with a cablelock – cable fits through mounting plates fixed to the PC, monitor and the desk.
■ Fit a PC theft alarm such as The Wobbler. It fits in a spare expansion slot inside the CPU. If the PC is moved it triggers off a 105 dB (very loud) siren for up to an hour – if the PC is taken out the building by anyone, they will be noticed by the noise.
■ Thieves are no longer simply lifting up a computer and running away with it. Due to increased costs and demand for RAM and processor chips, thieves are starting to open up PCs to take the micro-chips they require. They

can simply be put into a pocket and nobody knows until it's too late.

■ Change all the screws on the PC to *alun-key* screws. This way, a normal screwdriver won't be of any use to a thief who wishes to take the top off the PC to steal the micro-chips.

Did you know?

Computer viruses are small programs passed from one computer to another, generally by diskette, but also on networks and now the Internet, that destroy software and data files. There are a number of different types of viruses – those that simply annoy and those that positively destroy. The annoying viruses play tunes every ten minutes or make words drop off the screen. They do no real harm. Deadly viruses are those that format the hard disk or mix all data on the hard disk up so it can't be read.

If you find a computer has a virus you must act quickly to stop it spreading and doing any further damage to other machines. You are unlikely to work out where the file is on the hard disk as viruses generally attach themselves to other software files so they can't be detected. Special anti-virus software is needed – the market leader is Norton Anti-Virus. Not only will it eradicate the virus but it will also regularly scan the computer and make sure no other virus gets into the system. If it does then it notifies the user and action is taken.

NEVER assume that a virus is harmless – they are written to cause damage and chaos in the world of IT – the further they spread the more fun the writers have, so **stop them immediately before they get out of control.**

There is a form of security check that many people forget about. This is a *copyright* check. Anyone who writes software, a book or any information or data of any sort owns the copyright. This means that without the permission of the author, it's illegal to copy or use the information. This is just as relevant to software and data as it is to information in books or other publications. Whenever you see the sign ©, this means that the information is protected by laws on copyright. Anyone copying copyrighted © information is breaking the law. You shouldn't copy software from a friend's machine and install it on your own. Not only is it illegal but it also increases the risk of spreading viruses to your computer – it's simply not worth it.

So if you find any of this book copied, ask if permission has been granted!

Did you know?

Security laws exist to make sure information is not disclosed to people not entitled to know about it. Anyone who works with confidential information may be required to sign a *non-disclosure* agreement. Once signed, the individual is committed not to discuss any information with anyone outside the organisation.

Computer manufacturers often tell prospective customers about future products to try to dissuade them from buying competitive products. There will always be a requirement to sign a non-disclosure agreement.

The Official Secrets Act is one law that legislates and covers the disclosure of secret information.

Evidence collection point

At this point your tutor may wish you to start work on the project which will prove to your tutor or assessor that you understand this part of the element. If so, turn to page 79. If you have already started the project you may be ready to do Section 4 which covers the fourth part of the evidence indicator for this element.

Evidence indicator project

This project has been designed to cover all the evidence indicators related to Chapter 5 (Element 2.1). It is divided into four sections. Tutors may wish students to complete the sections at the appropriate points marked in the text. Alternatively, tutors may prefer their students to do the entire project at the end of the element.

Performance criteria: 1–6

Key skills:	Communication	–
	Application of number	3.1, 3.2, 3.3
	IT	3.1, 3.2, 3.3, 3.4

Scenario: Computers-Are-Us
Nigel Masterson is starting his own computer company. He realises that he must have a corporate style (or *house style,* as Nigel often calls it) designed to be sure that information is simply presented, is easy for customers to assimilate and, though including a

company logo, creates an image of the company that improves awareness and provides positive publicity.

Nigel's company is to be called Computers-Are-Us. Not only will he supply well-known brands of computers and computer-related equipment but he will also configure computers to customer requirements. He will be employing his friend Indira who is a technical wizard with computers, and a secretary, Chris.

Section 1

Create a corporate style specification for four documents likely to be used by Computers-Are-Us. Remember the market that the company will be working in – computers are hi-tech and he must have an image consistent with this. In your specification for each document you must include the following:

■ the purpose of each document
■ the page attributes (sizes and orientation)
■ the page layouts.

Section 2

As your work was so good for him last time, Nigel Masterson has decided to come back to you! This time, he needs you to create some templates with pages and layouts set up correctly. He needs you to work on your chosen four documents.

For each of the templates you create, you will need to provide evidence that your template caters for the following:

■ margins
■ justification
■ indents and tabulation
■ line spacing
■ font style, size and enhancement (or emboldening)
■ page numbering
■ headers and footers
■ column layout
■ document notes – footnotes and summary.

You may want to print the documents you create several times showing changes and evidence of your editing

work. Remember to spellcheck your work so there are no errors. If the software you use has a grammar check facility, you can use this as well. Take screen dumps (press the 'Print Screen' key in Windows) showing these features in action – this way you have evidence for your portfolio.

Section 3

Nigel Masterson would like to see an edited version of the text, tables and graphs you have already produced. Go back into your files and use some enhancing facilities on all the documents which have been created. Keep both versions so that Nigel Masterson can decide which one he prefers.

Section 4

You have created a specification for a corporate style, or house style, suitable for all types of commercial documents for Nigel Masterson's company; and you have built templates for four of those types of documents.

Now, to complete the collection of the evidence you need for this element, you should produce examples of these documents, if you have not already done so.

Each document must use at least two types of data (text, tables, graphics); at least one document must be more than three pages in length; and one must include columns and document notes.

You should keep print-outs or other evidence showing how you entered text, tables and graphics; how you edited the text, tables and graphics, using 'search', 'search and replace' and 'mail merge'; and how you applied appropriate accuracy and security checks.

For this last point you should consider spellchecking, confidentiality, saving and backing up, and protection of copyright – and apply these as you think appropriate, giving your reasons.

Chapter 6

Process presentational and technical graphic designs

In Chapter 5, Element 2.1, we looked at processing commercial documents. In this chapter we shall be investigating presentational and technical graphic designs. As you work through the element you will become more aware of design applications. As well as creating your own, try to find as many examples as you can – this makes it more practical, more fun and gives you more ideas.

After studying this chapter you should be able to:

1 describe *graphic design software* and give examples of how they might be used
2 identify the *components* of *presentational graphics* and *technical drawings*
3 produce *presentational graphics* according to *design specifications*
4 produce *technical drawings* according to *design specifications*
5 save and output graphic images.

Special note

There is only one evidence indicator project for this element. It is at the end of the element, on page 88.

Graphic design software

Graphic design software has taken over a job that was traditionally done on paper. It literally allows people to design equipment, diagrams or anything else using graphics, so everything can be seen easily and clearly.

Did you know?

Internet users can download presentational resources, graphic designs and sound to their computers as well as straight data. There is even a radio station that broadcasts only on the Internet. These facilities can be used on a PC only if it uses a suitable video and sound card to interpret the data into usable formats.

Activity

In small groups, discuss the advantages of designing and using computer software rather than using paper and pens.

Bitmap

A bitmap is an electronic file where each tiny item or dot in the picture is represented by a single bit of information in the file. In Figure 6.1 a drawing has been created – note the freckles! In Figure 6.2 a *section* of the drawing has been *zoomed* in on – it is actually the freckles on the right cheek. As this drawing is in bitmap format, individual dots can be altered – if there are too many freckles, we can change a few back to the colour of the skin. This is made possible by the gridlines going from left to right and top to bottom – by using the mouse and clicking, the colours can be altered. This allows us to have very detailed control over the graphic. The only disadvantage with bitmap files is that elements of the bitmap graphic cannot be edited as an entity – for example, if we want to change the colour of the hair to bright pink, each dot on the screen would have to be altered rather than simply telling the computer to change all black hair to pink.

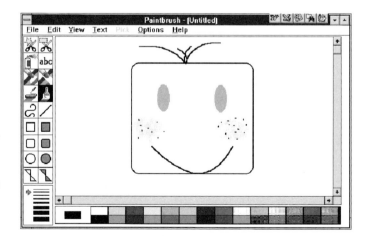

Figure 6.1 A bitmap graphic

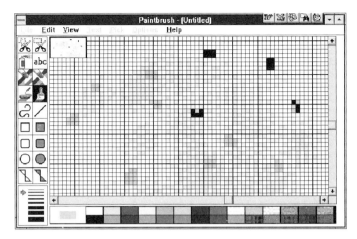

Figure 6.2 Part of the Figure 6.1 graphic greatly enlarged

Bitmapping can be used to touch up photographs. If the photograph is scanned into the computer, and perhaps someone's eye isn't quite looking straight at the camera, it is possible to alter individual dots in the picture to make it look as though the eye is correctly positioned. Alternatively, the colour of the eyes could be changed.

When the bitmap file is complete, it can be saved and imported into other applications.

Vector

A vector is an electronic graphic file where the elements are in vector form – that is, the elements are defined using co-ordinate geometry, enabling them to be scaled each time they are used. Look at Figure 6.3 – the first arrowed line was drawn and a copy of it taken to make the second line. The second line was edited to alter its thickness – nothing else changed. It is still pointing the same way at the same angle and is the same line except for the one change made. The resolution of the line is not altered at all when this is done.

Clipart is an example of a vector-type graphic. If Clipart is selected, it is placed on the screen in a

Figure 6.3 Changing the weight of a vector diagram

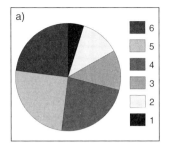

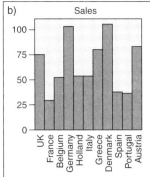

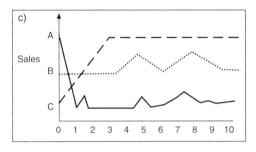

Figure 6.4 (a) pie chart; (b) histogram; (c) straight-line graph

certain size. If the size isn't suitable, the user can change its shape by moving the cursor to one of the edges of the illustration.

Charts

Many graphics and spreadsheet packages provide facilities for producing charts such as organisational charts, pie charts, histograms and bar charts. Organisational charts generally show the structure of an organisation. *Pie charts, histograms* and *straight-line graphs* may be used to show sales comparisons, accounts, analysis and marketing analysis (Figure 6.4).

These representations are typically used to show the following types of information:

■ *Pie chart:* fractions or percentages, such as the standing of political parties at some moment, or the different markets by value for an organisation's products.
■ *Histogram:* the distribution of heights of a group of people, shown at perhaps two-inch intervals of height, or the record of sales revenue over years or quarters for a business.

- *Straight-line graph:* shows conveniently the programme or schedule of activities for some project, or the achievements of a sequence of tasks.

 Activity

A mobile ice-cream seller has the ice-cream sales below over a 12-month period (figures represent packs of 100 single portions).

	J	F	M	A	M	J	J	A	S	O	N	D
Vanilla	1	1	1	2	2	3	10	20	25	3	1	4
Strawberry	1	0	1	3	4	10	15	25	30	15	2	0
Chocolate	1	0	1	2	5	10	10	15	10	0	0	1
Peach	0	2	2	3	3	4	5	5	4	3	2	3

- Draw a straight-line graph to show the sales of one flavour over the year.
- Draw a histogram of sales of each flavour by quarter.
- Draw a pie chart of annual sales to show the proportion of each flavour.

Slide show presentation

Traditionally, when lecturers or speakers give a presentation, they have used blackboards, whiteboards, handouts, OHPs and acetates. Each of these methods can be difficult for the presenter as it requires a lot of thought during the presentation to create the graphics he or she requires. A slide show presentation can overcome all this. By using presentation software, such as PowerPoint for Windows, it is possible to create in advance all the text and design details you require for the presentation on the screen. This includes *Clipart* and other pictures and data that can be imported from files. An example of this can be seen in Figure 6.5.

During the presentation, the computer is linked into a special *power tablet* or *power viewer* that is placed on top of an OHP. The image displayed on the computer screen is also projected through the OHP and on to a wall or screen.

The presenter can either move from one slide to another by pressing the Return ⏎ key on the computer, or by setting a time for the slides to change. One further advantage of using presentation software rather than other methods is that the information used in the presentation can also be interpreted as handouts that can be given out to the audience. To do this, the software analyses all the data in the presentation file and converts any text into word processor format – which can then be printed.

Did you know?

If you are connected to the Internet and have access to Net Search software, it is possible to find animation, Clipart and pictures that can be used for presentations. Some animations cannot be used for presentations, though, as they belong to companies and have copyright restrictions, despite the fact that they are on the Internet. One example of this is the Walt Disney Corporation. There is a dedicated Disney area with promotional still shots from films such as *Pocahontas* and *The Lion King*. These shots are in full colour and look fantastic on the screen!

Activity

A group of GCSE students who are about to take their exams. They all want to go on to further education, but some are unsure of which subjects to choose.

As an outstanding GNVQ Advanced IT student, the Head of IT has asked you to make a 20-minute presentation to the GCSE group, telling them why *you* think it is a good idea for them to study the same subjects that *you* studied. Your presentation should include the following:

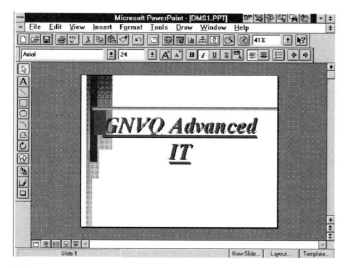

Figure 6.5 Presentation software

1 The use of presentation software to produce OHTs, *or* the use of presentation software with a power tablet on an OHP. If you can use a power tablet with the software, make sure the presentation screens 'come and go' from the screen in as many different ways as possible to make it interesting.
2 Handouts for everyone watching, giving them a brief breakdown of your thoughts.
3 A short period for questions from the audience (and answers from yourself).
4 Feedback and comments sheets to be given to and filled in by the audience so that *you* get feedback on how your presentation went.
5 If possible, make a video of the whole session so you can watch it later to see how you did.

Presentational graphics

Slide show

Presentational graphics are graphic images which are used to represent artwork-type information such as pictures or electronic artwork. Presentational graphics include the slide show we have already looked at, and charts and pictures. PowerPoint is a good example of slide show software. It can be used by the novice (with assistance from the software in the form of Wizard assistants) or experts (who knows how to use the software to best effect). The options available when creating a new presentation are illustrated in Figure 6.6.

From here, it is possible to select the type of look the presentation slides will have. This comes from

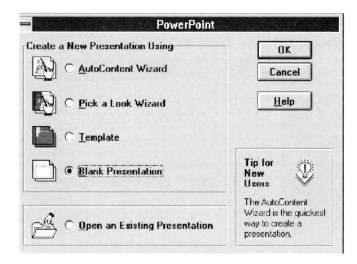

Figure 6.6 PowerPoint opening screen

combining a *template* (with the slide background) and *layout* (a choice of introduction slide, Clipart, graphs, etc.), illustrated in Figure 6.7.

Once the layout and template have been chosen, the software automatically shows the user the slide with the features in place in order for it to be worked on – text, graphics, data, Clipart, tables and charts can be built and placed anywhere the user wants. An example of this is shown in Figure 6.7.

Chart

As with many other software packages, presentation software includes the ability to create charts –

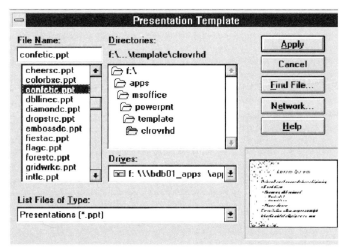

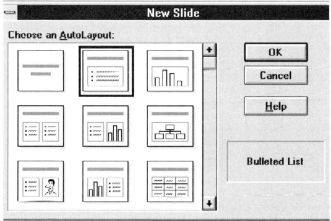

Figure 6.7 PowerPoint template and layout screens

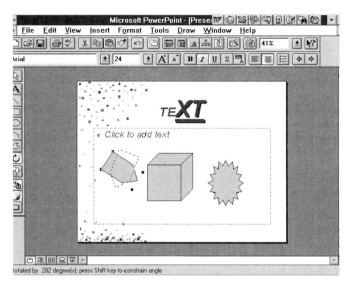

Figure 6.8 Development of PowerPoint combined screen

organisational and numerical charts such as bar charts. By selecting the right option, the software interfaces directly with other appropriate software, such as a spreadsheet, so that charts can be created.

Once in the spreadsheet, the user is assisted by the software to enter the required numeric values and to select the chart required – the software does the rest. In Figure 6.9 we have a spreadsheet in which two sets of data have been inserted. The software even gives the option to change the type of chart required using the same data.

Did you know?

The first spreadsheet ever developed was for an Apple computer in the early 1980s. It was the basis for all spreadsheets and if compared to a modern one such as Excel, Lotus 123, Quattro or Supercalc, it would not look much different.

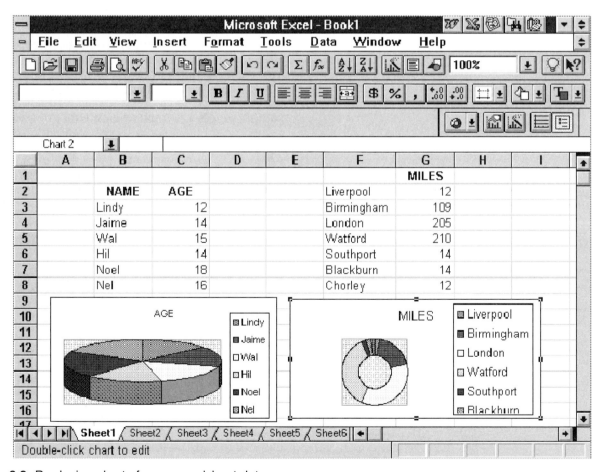

Figure 6.9 Producing charts from spreadsheet data

The software writers could have made enough money to retire ten times, but they decided not to register it as a product and so anyone is able to create a similar product. You might expect them to be annoyed at themselves for this, but they are not. They are happy to see that the idea has been put to good use and that so many people have benefited from it. In their eyes they were successful in making it popular: the money is unimportant!

Picture

Unlike Clipart, pictures generally do not come with software. There are a number of ways they can be obtained. CD-ROMs can be bought holding many thousands of pictures (NASA, for example, has CD-ROMs with pictures of early space shuttle missions). It is possible to have your own pictures put on to CD-ROM at a local high-street shop. You could use a diskette camera to take pictures and download them into the PC, or pictures can be scanned and stored on disk as files. This is probably the cheapest and most convenient method, providing you have access to a scanner and relevant pictures. Figure 6.10 is an example of a scanned photograph saved on a diskette and loaded into a word processor. To make it stand out more, a border and shading were added.

Figure 6.10 A scanned photograph

Technical drawings

Technical drawings have been created on paper for many years by trained draftsmen. They needed to be very accurate and required the use of protractors, set squares, rulers and fine pens. It was very skilful work. Technical drawings now, however, are graphic representations produced using vector-based software of layouts of buildings and detailed drawings of products used for manufacture. The technicians use computers with dedicated software allowing them to do on the computer screen everything that used to be done on paper. They then print off copies of their work. This allows changes to be made easily and quickly, and also allows as many copies of the drawings as required, without any loss of detail or quality.

Layout

The layout of a technical drawing refers to the production of drawings using vector-based drawing software. This gives a *plan*-type view of the objects. Examples include railway maps, road maps, house plans and the arrangement of car parks. They must be scaled so that each item on the drawing is as true to life as can be expected.

Product design

Product design refers to vector-based drawing software that determines how products are to be manufactured. An example of this could be the manufacture of telephone cases, window frames (as in Figure 6.11) or tennis racquets. Materials, thickness and size are defined. Details are included through the use of arrows and lines. This particular type of drawing is one of product design, as it gives dimensions.

Figure 6.11 Setting out the design for a window frame

Activity

Visit a local architect or kitchen showroom and look at some layout plans. If possible, keep copies of these plans for future reference. When you next use a computer, try to copy these plans to create your own technical drawing.

Block schematic

Block schematic refers to the use of vector-based drawing software that produces an image to illustrate any system flow or organisation. We could use a block schematic to show the workings of a microprocessor with boxes representing the components or to create an organisation chart. The next time you visit a DIY shop such as B&Q, look out for their instruction leaflets on how to fit a tap or fix a burst pipe – the chances are that the diagrams they use as an illustration are in block schematic form – very often showing three dimensions.

Activity

Redraw the diagram you produced for Chapter 3, Element 1.3, showing the components of a microprocessor. This time you should produce the diagram using vector-based drawing software.

Did you know?

The Nintendo Corporation of America sold their one billionth video game in October 1995. This is equivalent to a non-stop sales rate of three every second for twelve years. And it is all just moving images created by a computer!

Graphic components

Look at Figure 6.12. It shows the graphic tools on Microsoft Word version 6.0, which makes it a much more powerful and versatile system than simply being a word processor – it allows us to draw as well as enter text. A graphic design program displays a screen area for the design and several sets of tools which are the graphic components required to meet graphic design specifications. These tools include lines, shapes, brush and spray.

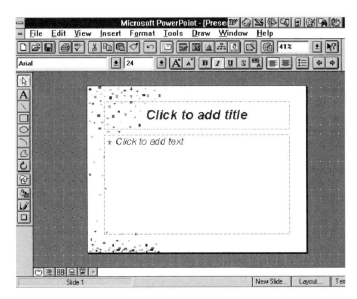

Figure 6.12 Microsoft Word graphic tools

Many different software packages which look and work in a similar way, such as Microsoft Publisher, are now available.

Although these are just two examples of the type of software you may use, we shall look at the components of the drawing menu board as they are very similar on all graphic design software packages.

Lines

Lines are easy to create by selecting the line tool icon. They are drawn by using the mouse and clicking at the point where the line has to start, holding down the mouse button until the line is drawn in full. It is possible to draw a line and later edit its length and width. Lines can be drawn in a variety of widths and formats.

It's also possible to draw arcs, curves and freehand lines – all using the same method as described for straight lines.

Shapes

Shapes include rectangles, circles and polygons. They are created using the same methods as lines by clicking on the shape tool icon from the toolbox and dragging the mouse along the desired path.

Colour

Modern computer screens can display up to 16 million different colours, and graphic design software allows the user to select the exact colour that is required at any time. Colours are indicated in the colour palette which is usually a separate menu option.

Did you know?

It is possible to buy CD-ROMs with pictures and Clipart that are free from copyright. This means you can use them professionally without having to buy a licence.

Shade

This feature can be useful if you wish to highlight a box or part of a diagram. It can give a three-dimensional feel to the picture. Figure 6.13 shows how simple it is to apply shading to a diagram – it is a case of selecting the area to be shaded and then specifying to the software the depth of shading you want to use in the appropriate menu option.

Shading is also a useful tool in graphic design software. It allows the user to include life-like colours in the graphic image – up to 16 million of them.

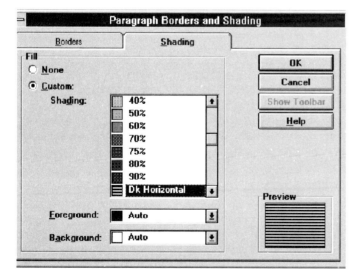

Figure 6.13 Screen for controlling the use of shading

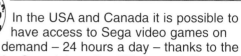

Did you know?

In the USA and Canada it is possible to have access to Sega video games on demand – 24 hours a day – thanks to the launch of the Sega interactive TV channel. Once set up on the system, it costs only $19.95 each month to access about $3,000 worth of games from a library.

Text

Text is placed into graphic images by inserting a *text box*. This is a small box that allows only text to enter it. It is placed and sized, again by dragging the mouse.

Once the text box has been created you can choose the font, style and size of text required. For presentation graphics such as PowerPoint for Windows, text is typed into template text boxes as shown in Figure 6.12.

Attributes

Style, thickness and *fill* are attributes. We have dealt with style and thickness already. Fill refers to the way drawn areas (such as rectangles and circles) are painted or filled on the inside. You can colour shapes with solid or shaded colours by using the fill icon. If there is no colour, the computer uses different shades to fill the shapes.

Brush

This is the computer equivalent of using a paint brush to achieve free-hand drawing effects. The attributes of the brush can be altered according to the software package being used. Try using the brush tool to create a range of different sized and shaped brush strokes. Just drag the mouse pointer to *paint*.

Spray

Spray is a technique used in many software packages that works in the same way as a can of spray paint. The user selects an *airbrush* icon with the mouse. The technique allows detailed and dramatic shading to be placed on diagrams by changing the width of the airbrush. Note how different shades can be mixed in together to achieved the effects, and the attributes the different shades have.

Producing presentational graphics

When producing presentational graphics you will have a set of design specifications to work from which will include some or all of the following:

- *Graphic type (bitmaps and vectors):* These have been dealt with in detail earlier in this chapter.
- *The purpose (of using graphic design software):* The purpose is to speed up designing. Rather than design using pencil and paper, graphic design software allows the user to use graphic types (with shapes already in the software that can be altered in size) and drawing lines and images that can be altered quickly and easily if they are not right.
- *Context and content:* The way information will be presented using technical drawings will depend on the context it is being used in. For example, publicity information on a poster will be set out in a different way from an architect setting out plans for buildings.
- *Dimensions:* It is important to include dimensions such as widths, sizes and heights when using graphic design software. Imagine the consequences of an architect designing a building, thinking he was working in metres, but because he hadn't put any dimensions on the plans the builders decided to work in centimetres!
- *Image:* If you ever use graphic design software it is important to think of the image the software will display at the end. You may want to think about the height, width and colours of it when it is printed. Will it show you everything you want? If not, the image will have to be altered.
- *Page attributes:* It is a good idea to set up the software before you start to work on it, so that the page attributes are known. By setting the margins, paper size and orientation, and getting them right from the start, you will not have to make changes later on and rework your design to accommodate the changes.

Producing technical drawings

Design specifications for technical drawings all include the following:

- *Graphic type (bitmaps and vectors):* It is easier to use vector graphics for technical drawings, if possible, as the file sizes are smaller than the bitmap equivalent.
- *Purpose (of using graphic design software):* It is worth taking the time to ensure technical drawings are

correct as they may well be reproduced thousands of times.
- *Context (such as publicity information, design layout and information presentation):* Do not put too much information around the drawing as this will make it difficult to understand.
- *Content:* Ensure only relevant information is used in the drawing.
- *Dimensions (size, units, tolerances).*
- *Image (width, height, colours and shades).*
- *Page attributes (size, orientation and margins).*

If you are uncertain about anything, go back and make sure you understand it as you must be aware of all the points covered in order to achieve the evidence standards.

Did you know?

Modern special effect graphics that we see on films are created by computers. The images that are filmed by the camera are *scanned* into a computer. Each single frame can take up 40 Mbytes of hard disk memory. Once scanned and saved, the technicians add the effects to create exciting, fantasy worlds.

Evidence indicator project

This project covers all the evidence indicators related to Chapter 6, Element 2.2. It has been designed to be carried out at the end of the element.

Performance criteria: 1–5

Key skills:		
	Communication	3.2, 3.3
	Application of number	3.1, 3.2, 3.3
	IT	3.1, 3.2, 3.3

Scenario

Dave's Designs of Wilmslow, Cheshire, have just commissioned you to create four graphics for them as you are regarded as being an expert in the use of technical drawing software. They require you to design a detailed layout of their new premises. The details you must include are as follows:

- There are four rooms – 4 × 8 metres, 8 × 12 metres, 5 × 5 metres and 12 × 9 metres.
- One room has to house eight design computers, chairs and equipment for eight people.
- One room is to house a sink, couch, four chairs,

a table and washing machine.

- The other two rooms are to be decorated and set out in whatever way you decide, the only stipulation is that one is to be a kitchen/dining area, and the other a recreational room.
- You must use both *bitmap* and *vector* drawings. Use bitmap for two rooms and vector for the other two.

1   Using presentational graphics, produce a picture of the rooms as *you* envisage them ready for a presentation to Dave's Designs. Remember to use shading and detail as well as basic artwork.

2   Dave's Designs have given you hand-drafted data that must be made up into a chart by computer. The data details the jobs completed by each employee over the past year. Using appropriate software, make sure the charts are included in your submission. Be sure the chart is well presented as it is to be framed and put on the wall for everyone to see:

Dave – 12 jobs completed	June – 7 jobs completed
Jamie – 8 jobs completed	Joan – 8 jobs completed
Bert – 10 jobs completed	Mark – 9 jobs completed

3   When you have the designs ready, Dave's Designs expect you to make a presentation using slide show software and the pictures and drawings you prepared. You will have to scan in your designs, or import them into the presentation software in their design software format. Print out copies of the material to be used in the presentation to complement your talk.

4   As part of your presentation, you should prepare notes describing all the graphic design software you have used to create the images and identify their components.

5   Keep a record of all your work on diskette as evidence. Make the presentation to your fellow students and video it.

For this presentation, you may like to consider the following:

- Using handouts which give a brief breakdown of the key points.
- A short period for questions from the audience.
- Feedback and comment sheets to be given to and filled in by the audience on how well the presentation was performed.
- Video the exercise so you can play it back later to see how well the presentation went.

It is also worth reminding yourself of a few key points when preparing a presentation:

- Find out how long your presentation is expected to last.
- Find out about your audience. Do they know quite a bit about your topic or do they know nothing at all?
- Write down everything that you want to say in your presentation. You can then either learn it off by heart – but still have your notes with you as a back-up – or be sufficiently rehearsed to remember all the facts in the correct order.
- You may want to write key phrases, or small cards as memory aids.
- Try to think of ways to illustrate your presentation, such as posters, charts, OHP transparencies.

Model data

If you mention the word 'model' many people think of plastic cars, planes and ships put together by children with glue. Fun as this type of activity may be, modelling does have a serious use.

Modelling data enables us to test situations, and answer possible 'what if' questions, such as: what happens to profits if we give staff a 3% pay increase? If we decrease the speed of delivery lorries, what happens a) to fuel consumption; b) time taken for deliveries...?

In the past modelling has been done on paper. It's easier now to model situations and relationships on computers.

After studying this chapter you should be able to:

1 explain the *purposes* of different *computer models*
2 specify *data parameters* and *rules of operation* of modelling problems
3 construct *computer models*
4 undertake 'what if' queries and produce *reports*
5 review the *effectiveness* of the model and *suggest improvements*.

Special Note

There is only one evidence indicator for this element. It is at the end of the element on page 106.

Did you know?

Computer modelling is used by companies all over the world as a cheap way of testing new theories and equipment. If you were to visit a company that designs and builds equipment for oil refineries, you would be shown plastic models of the proposed equipment. In fact, before any plastic model is constructed, a model of the plant will have been created on computer using CAD software. This would be done in three dimensions (3D). The designer would be able to use the computer model of the plant to provide views from many directions and to visualise walking through the plant. This is very similar to *virtual reality* video games that can be played in arcades.

Computer models

Below we look at four major types of computer models.

Simulation

Simulation is a software representation of a real situation or system that can be used for analysis or training. Airline companies use simulation to train pilots on the latest aircraft and in flying techniques. The advantages are as follows:

- It saves time – it's faster to train pilots on the ground than in the air.
- It's cheaper – training pilots in the air requires fuel. If the training is carried out in a simulator, no fuel is required. This not only saves on the cost but also helps keep the environment free from pollution.
- A simulation plane is less likely to fall out of the sky and crash than a real one! Therefore nobody can get injured.
- It's more convenient to train pilots on the ground than in the air – real planes have to fly taking up air space and occupying slots for take-off and landing. It also means that pilots can practise landing at Sydney airport in Australia without having to fly there to try it out.
- It's possible to test a hypothesis through flight simulation, such as: what happens if all engines fail at 30,000 feet? How will the pilot react? By simulating we can test the response without putting anyone in danger!

Did you know?

It is possible to book groups for half a day on a flight simulator at some of the larger airports in the country. If you decide to try this, the experience would be invaluable as evidence of a computer simulation – ask if you can take a video camera to record it all.

Simulators are being introduced on fairground rides in a bid to give customers the ultimate thrill. It's possible to sit in a simulator in Covent Garden, London, and experience the roller-coaster ride at Blackpool Pleasure Beach. It's not quite as good as riding the biggest and fastest roller-coaster in the world, but it comes close.

Prediction

A prediction is something Mystic Meg makes each week just before the National Lottery is drawn. In contrast, a computer prediction is the output from a particular process operating on carefully chosen data. Examples of computer prediction are as follows:

Weather forecasting Readings for temperatures, air pressures, wind speeds and precipitation are fed into the computer model from sampling points at regularly used locations and heights, and at synchronised times. The model processes all this data and make predictions that are important to airlines, mariners, farmers and holiday-makers. In extreme conditions weather forecasts can save lives by giving warning of, say, a hurricane or a flood.

Traffic forecasting Before large sums are committed to building a motorway, a major bridge or an airport extension, the traffic demand is predicted by running a computer model.

These two examples are on a big scale. There is no reason why predictions generated by computer models should not relate to more homely matters, such as the annual fuel consumption of your family car, or the number of spectators that might attend a football match.

WHAT WILL THE WEATHER BE LIKE TODAY?

Gaming

Computer games are all around us and easily recognised. An example of gaming might be a model of a forest where treasure is to be found. The attractions of gaming are as follows:

- Gaming is convenient and can compress time. It is not always easy to get hold of a Formula One car in Monaco and race it – even if you were to find one, it would take a long time to prepare it to race. By walking into an arcade it's possible to play a computer game to simulate the experience immediately.
- It's cheaper to play a game than to do the real thing – imagine having to pay for a replacement car each time you crashed one in an arcade game!
- 'I bet you'll crash on lap three' is a prediction that can be tested by playing a racing game and watching for the outcome.
- It's safer to play a game than the real thing. Would you rate your chances in a real-life *Mortal Combat?*

Computer games fascinate those playing them, partly because the players improve their performance as they gain familiarity with the interaction between player and game. Indeed, there is said to come a point after playing one game many times that the player identifies with the designer of the game, and starts thinking in the same way – and from then on does much better. Some games compensate for this tendency of players to improve with experience by making it harder to win after successive attempts.

As well as recreational games, there are computer-based games which serve serious purposes such as war games and business games. Business games allow participants representing rival companies to make decisions on questions of research, expenditure, recruitment, advertising expenditure, and product mix: after a number of rounds in which the players take turns to revise their decisions the model declares one the winner.

Activity

In a group of no more than four, hold a discussion entitled 'Modelling – how it affects our way of life'. Brainstorm as many different models as you know about. You may even wish to consider possessions that would not exist if it wasn't for modelling. For each example you list, what alternatives do you think there are and what were the costs involved in order to develop each model? You may have to do some research for this.

3D representation

If we draw a three-dimensional (3D) box on a computer, it's possible to view it from any angle we want. A practical example is looking at a model of a potential new building, to gauge the impact it would have on existing buildings and on the environment.

Designing and building a 3D computer model that is accurate enough to be useful needs care and skill, but once it exists it provides a powerful way of envisaging the item modelled. Models can, not only be rotated about any axis, but they can be expanded or shrunk (that is, zoomed in or out), given colour, made to show 'invisible' lines, and allowed to throw shadows and present highlights.

Just think, though – the Leaning Tower of Pisa would never have been built if it had been correctly modelled!

Purposes of computer models

Compress time

Compressing time refers to running a model as though it was the real thing, only in a much shorter period of time. It is unlikely that you will use a system like this in everyday life, but all our lives are affected by the technique! The weather bureau uses time compression computer models to forecast the weather on a daily basis. It takes the present state of the weather around the globe and speeds up its movement on a computer to forecast what it will be like near us each day. The Treasury economic model, used by government departments, agencies and consultants, allows the exploration of different assumptions on the performance of the national economy to predict, for example, levels of unemployment, interest rates and rates of inflation – well ahead of their actually occurring.

Cost saving

We saw earlier an example of modelling by an oil refinery manufacturer. This is done as it makes them more competitive and saves them money. If they make a mistake in their calculations, and a pipe is placed too low so that someone could hit his or her

head while walking past, this will be identified by the model. Changes can be made before any materials are ordered or work begun on the real site.

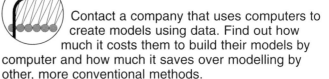

Activity

Contact a company that uses computers to create models using data. Find out how much it costs them to build their models by computer and how much it saves over modelling by other, more conventional methods.

Another example shows environmental rather than financial cost saving. It is possible to model the effects CFC gases have on the ozone layer. If we hadn't stopped using so many of them the problems would have been worse, but due to computer modelling, scientists were able to show the world how harmful to the environment CFCs are, and so their use has been stemmed.

Safety

A good example of safety planning is a structural test being performed by computer on a modelled building to see how it might stand up to an earthquake – very important in Japan and parts of California. One can see what stresses the building can sustain before it collapses, and then specify improvements to architectural practice, all on the computer. What's more, no one will ever get hurt, which certainly wouldn't be the case with a real building.

Convenience

If we think of any of these examples, it is obviously more convenient to model the effects by computer than travel to the site and run real tests there. The modelling method means we don't have to leave the office.

Hypothesis testing

This is something we can all do on a simple spreadsheet. It is all about using a computer model to test a hypothesis. For example, in Figure 7.1 a spreadsheet has been used to show the income and outgoings for a car sales company. The profit is shown in cell E4 and is calculated by taking the total outgoings, apart from the wholesale cost of the cars bought for sale by

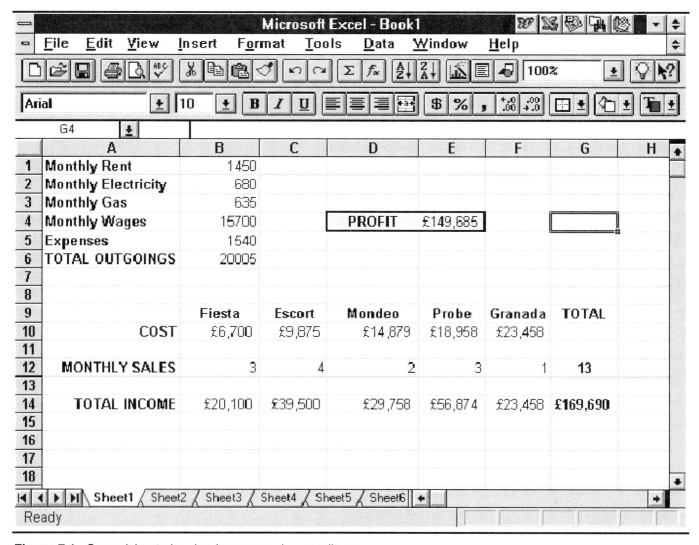

Figure 7.1 Spreadsheet showing income and expenditure

the business, away from the total income. Now that the spreadsheet is complete, 'what if' hypotheses can be run. For example, what would happen to the profit if wages were increased by 10%, or what would happen if there were an extra 10 Ford Fiestas sold in a month?

These *what if* questions are simple enough to answer without using a computer: the wage increase would lead to a reduction in profit of £1,570; and the extra Fiesta sales would increase profit by £67,000.

But simple changes on the spreadsheet would show the figures instantly, and correctly. If there was greater complexity in the model. The revision of the figures from the keyboard would still be immediate and correct. The bigger and more complex the

model, the more powerful the use of this software is seen to be.

Activity

Create a spreadsheet showing your income, outgoings and any savings you make. Now try answering the following:

1 How well off will you be in two months' time if these details remain the same?
2 Suppose you rip your jeans in three weeks and have to buy a new pair costing £35. What difference will this make to your savings?
3 Suppose McDonald's double their prices – what difference would this make to you?

4 What happens if the Office of Fair Trading halves the price of CDs?

Data parameters

When it comes to modelling data on computers, there are a number of areas we must recognise. Some have already been dealt with, such as the physical response time of the computer being used, the speed of the computer's processor and the cost of buying a faster machine. Others are new to us.

Input values

The data we use in computer systems, the input values, have to be accurate and within the boundaries and constraints of the system. If data is inaccurate, the model won't function correctly – if it works at all. If alphabetic data is entered when the software is expecting numeric data there will be a problem. Data can be entered on to a computer in the form of real numbers, integers or in specific formats set by software such as spreadsheets.

Constraints

A constraint is a maximum or minimum level at which a system can function. Everything has a constraint. *We* can walk and run – some of us faster than others, but even the fastest person in the world can't fly (without a plane) – this is a constraint that we accept as part of being human.

There are constraints imposed by individual software packages, such as the numbers of rows and columns a spreadsheet can handle; and there are constraints built into a model, perhaps a limit setting the greatest number of items that can be sold in one day.

If the performance of a 1300cc family saloon had been properly modelled, no matter how hard we tried, the car could never simulate driving at 250 mph – the system constraints wouldn't allow this to happen as the car simply can't reach this speed.

Did you know?

Many modern machines are designed and built with safety mechanisms so that the real constraints are never reached – even when the device is being used to its ultimate legal limit. This happens in lifts. Whatever the size, the maximum weight or number of people allowed in the lift, there are safety factors built in allowing the lift to carry up to several times the load allowed. The safety factors come in the shape of extra cabling to pull the lift up and lower it down, several braking mechanisms: should the lift fall it would immediately stop on its runners. Finally – if all else fails and the lift falls, there is a crumple cage at the bottom of the lift shaft to slow down the impact and reduce the damage done.

Variables

Variables are concerned with the relationships between pairs of values. This is best explained by two examples.

The shade temperature at a given place varies with the time of day. On a particular day, the record of temperatures might look like Figure 7.2.

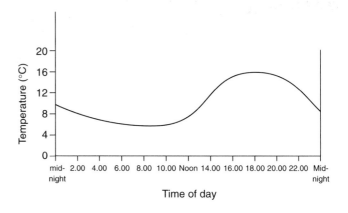

Figure 7.2 Temperature record for one day

The time of day is called the *independent variable*, and the temperature at any chosen time can be read from the graph of the relationship between time and temperature. The temperature value is called the *dependent variable*, because its value is determined by the choice of time in any instance.

Another example would be the relationship between the selling price of a book and the number of copies sold by a bookshop in a particular month. It might be illustrated as in Figure 7.3.

The value of the independent variable, picked by the publisher to be the selling price, would have an important bearing on the profitability of the book for the publisher and the bookseller, and on the royalty income of the author.

Figure 7.3 Relationship between the selling price of a book and the number of copies sold

Computer models can be used to find the dependent variable corresponding to a given value of an independent variable, provided that the relationship between them is programmed into the models, and that they use those independent variable values as inputs to processing.

Activity

Think of examples of relationships where the dependent variables are: response time; speed; cost; elapsed time; physical dimension; scale; position.

Calculations using operators

Operators are important for the design and use of computer models. They are of three types:

- **Arithmetic operators**
  These are the operators:

  + plus
  − minus
  × multiply
  ÷ divide

  with which you will have been familiar for many years. The modelling software may also accept '**'' to indicate exponentiation. For example, 27 squared, that is 27^2, could be entered as '27**2'.

- **Relational operators**
  These express the inequalities and equality:

  < less than
  ≤ less than or equal

  > greater than
  ≥ greater than or equal to
  = is equal to

  and also the conditional operator:

  IF

  These operators are useful in defining relationships for models. For example, if you wanted to say that a variable Q lies between 2 and 3, you could say '2 < Q < 3'.

- **Logical operators**
  Logical operators, sometimes called 'Boolean operators', have the role of making statements that have unique meanings. You may have come across statements like:

  To qualify for this allowance you must be over 18, resident in the UK, unemployed, and not already in receipt of the allowance or over 21 and not married.

  This example is a caricature, to make the point. There is, in this example, doubt about whether a married 19-year-old or a 22-year-old resident abroad would qualify. Boolean arithmetic uses Boolean operators, which include:

  AND
  OR
  NOT

  They provide tools for removing logical ambiguity. You might like to look in your library for a book on this subject; it can be of value in defining unique problems to be modelled.

Rules of operation

Whenever a model of any sort is created, there are certain rules of operation that must be observed.

Formulae

Formulae are widely accepted methods of representing calculations, generally in text or text/numerical form. They are widely used in computing and even basic computer programs rely on them to produce results. Probably the two most common formulae known to humankind are $E = MC^2$ and πr^2. Both require the user to insert values in the place of the characters. $E = MC^2$ is Einstein's famous equation which says that the energy of the system is equal to a constant proportional to the mass multiplied by the square of the speed of light. The second formula is the area of a circle whose radius is *r*.

We use formulae all the time in spreadsheets – one example is illustrated in Figure 7.4. Formulae are a sequence of values/cell references (e.g. A5) or operators that produce a new value from existing values. A formula always begins with an equals sign (=). The formula is asking the computer to add up all the amounts in the cell boxes A1–A11 and put the total in cell A12.

Activity

Ask a computer modeller to give a presentation to your tutor group on his or her area of expertise. During the question and answer session, find out how forecast models can help businesses with their profit and loss accounts and balance sheets. Are there any other types of modelling that can assist the running and management of business organisations?

Cell references

Relative cell reference

If we copy the formula from cell A12 in Figure 7.4 to cell C12, the formula itself would change from =sum(A1:A11) to =sum(C1:C11). This is a *relative* value as the arithmetic in the formula is the same: the only change is from column A to C.

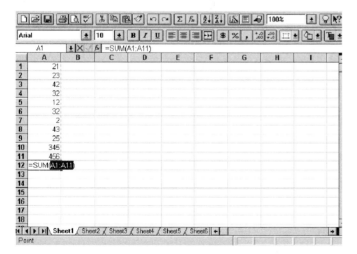

Figure 7.4 Using a formula to add a column of integers

Absolute cell reference

If the formula =sum(A1:A11) was copied into C15 and was still reading =sum(A1:A11), this is an *absolute* value – it hasn't changed at all. Most spreadsheets make values absolute by adding the $ sign before the grid reference that is to stay absolute – for example, =sum($A$1:$A$11).

Results of actions, relationships and the effect of variable changes

Let us look again at the spreadsheet in Figure 7.1. By making an alteration to the monthly wages bill, the spreadsheet shows the results of the action (Figure 7.5). However, the change here is showing more than just the results of an action. It is also highlighting the relationship between the cells and more importantly the monthly wages bill and the monthly profit. The change made to Figure 7.1 doesn't necessarily happen each month, as it could be a special bonus being paid, and therefore we would be unwise to base any assumptions on it. Naturally, more complicated data and changes could be involved, but the effects of the changes would still ripple through the data and modify the result.

Methods of operation and assumptions made

There is no set way that models have to be built or operated. It's a good idea, though, to be able to stipulate to anyone using the model how it should be used and any assumptions you may have made while it was being constructed. For example, if we look at the formula πr^2 we assume we know that *r* stands for the radius of a circle and π is the ratio of the circumference to the diameter, having the value, to five decimal places, of 3.14159. Someone using the formula without this knowledge is unlikely to be able to make sense of it.

Input and output methods

In Chapter 10 (Element 3.2) we shall be looking at the different methods of data input. In models, not only are these methods used, but in addition the software itself can provide part of the input and output process. This process is very similar to the *mail merge* facility, also covered in Unit 3, where the data from one software package is used as the input for another. This saves an enormous amount of time

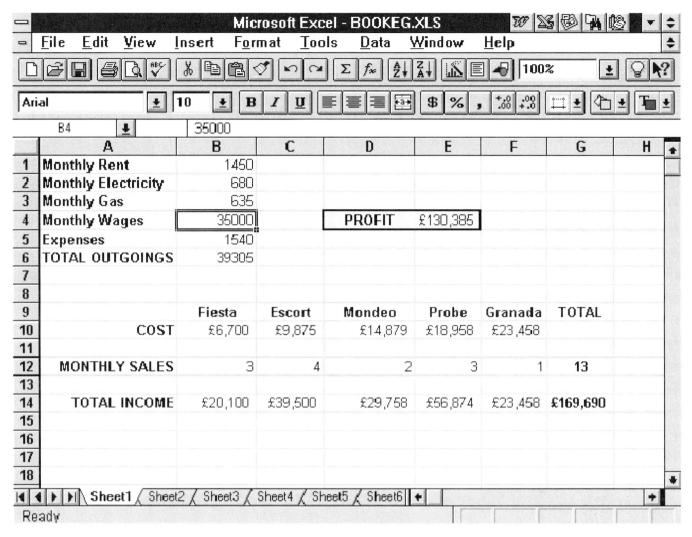

Figure 7.5 Modified spreadsheet

and effort. In examples such as this, the input for one software package is the output for another.

Constructing computer models

Before we actually construct a computer model, we should know that there are a number of ways in which this can be done. The most common way is through using a spreadsheet. Although this is perfectly acceptable for many purposes, it is not always so. If you want to be adventurous, try to find other ways of creating your models rather than on spreadsheets. Apart from the fact that it will look different, it will mean you learn more about

modelling and IT in general. This is helpful to your general understanding and knowledge.

Did you know?

During training, fighter pilots use a simulator to get used to extra gravitational pressures. Three or four G forces are not unusual; and it is claimed that up to eight or nine can be experienced. Rather than subject pilots to these exceptional forces in a plane, machines are used on land.

Astronauts suffer from space sickness during space travel. This is like very intense car sickness. To teach them to overcome the problem, scientists at NASA devised a space sickness simulator that induces the feelings of nausea without the astronauts leaving the ground. If they can't learn to overcome the problem then they can't explore the galaxy.

Simulation model

In Figure 7.6 we have created a simulation on a spreadsheet based around a bus service on a set route. The bus takes on passengers (shown in column C), has a travel time between each bus stop (column E) and has a loading time (column D). Column D is calculated by taking the number of passengers at each stop and multiplying them by the boarding time (D4). This is all added together to make the total time. (Note we have cut down on calculations for total time by making the sum a cumulative number – the totals are added up as we add to the column.)

If we wanted to simulate a change in boarding time (if the driver was asked to collect the fares, for example), we make the change in D4 and the spread sheet does the rest for us, as in Figure 7.7, though, as you will see, passengers would need to exercise considerable patience.

We put these calculations on a spreadsheet and have the software model it for us as it's obviously faster than working out all the mathematics by hand, and it also reduces the chance of us making mistakes.

You could build a computer simulation model of the operation of the National Lottery. You would need a random number generator, set to pick the first number from the range 1–49; then to modify itself so that the number of the first ball out is removed from the numbers still available; and to do so again for the second ball, and so on until all six are known. You could pick this week's numbers that way. You could

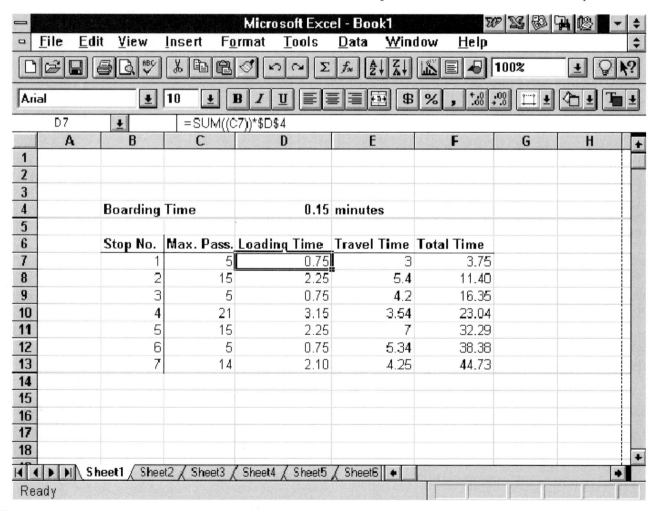

Figure 7.6 Spreadsheet simulating a bus schedule

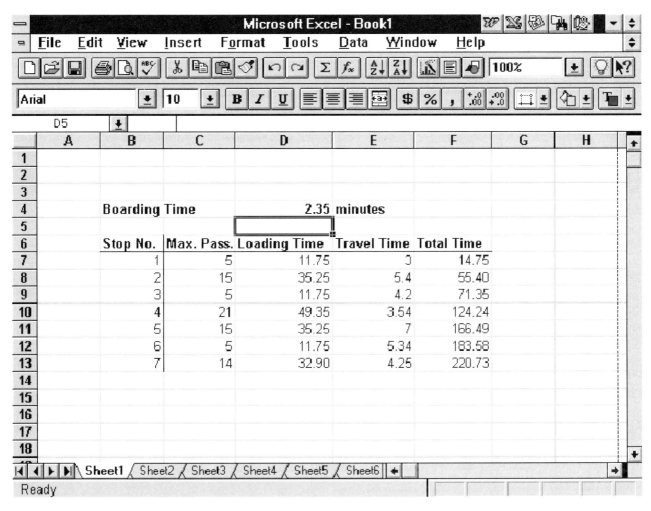

Figure 7.7 Modified spreadsheet

also change the rules so that you had, say, 40 balls and were to choose 7 numbers, and hence develop your own lottery game.

Did you know?

If on your 18th birthday you were to start playing the National Lottery and continued playing until your 60th birthday, your chance of winning the jackpot is said to be 1 in 5 – provided you bought 1,000 lottery tickets each week!

Prediction model

Long-term weather forecasting uses a predictive model. However, before you decide to create such a model as part of your evidence indicators, *don't!* The Meteorological Office uses one of the most powerful computers in the world to predict the weather and still they get it wrong from time to time, so we are unlikely to be able to do much good on a desk-top PC!

A more manageable prediction model can be written, say in Turbo Pascal, for predicting values for analysing break-even situations to help a small company. As you will see if you research the way that *break-even analysis* works, and the mathematics involved, it makes a complicated process easy as the computer predicts the answers rather than people working them out on paper with calculators. This type of model could, of course, be written on a spreadsheet or other modelling software.

Here is an example of prediction. A school, with a fixed number of pupils and an improving GCSE examination record, wants to predict the likely results for the next year. The assumptions are that the established teaching and coaching practices will continue to provide a rising standard of attainment. Figure 7.8 shows results in one subject.

GCSE grade	Number of pupils scoring grades			
	Year 1	Year 2	Year 3	Year 4
A*	1	2	3	
A	5	6	7	
B	8	9	10	
C	11	11	12	
D	14	14	13	
E	10	8	6	
Other	11	10	9	
TOTAL	60	60	60	60

Figure 7.8 Improving results for one subject

The predictions made for Year 4 will depend upon rules laid down for operating the model. Just looking at it, one could propose that A*s become 4, As become 8, and 'Other' becomes 8. That is called straight-line extrapolation. That would work for Bs which the application of that rule would make 11, and Es 4.

But this process does not work for the Cs and Ds. And there is a constraint, namely that the Year 4 total must come to 60.

Using the figures we have derived by straight-line interpolation, we have:

A*   4
A   8
B   11
E   4
Other   8

This makes a total of 35, leaving 25 to be distributed between the Cs and Ds.

Activity

Can you think of a set of rules for arriving at the prediction for all the grades? Obviously the figures must be whole numbers.

Case study

It was announced from Cape Kennedy in Florida that a planned Space Shuttle mission in 1995 was to include tests on Coca-Cola and Diet Coke in space. Three astronauts were to drink and evaluate the drinks three times over eight days – giving them marks for sweetness, fizziness and taste. The Coca-Cola company invested $750,000 to conduct the experiment to see how its products may perform in markets of the future.... in worlds we have yet to visit.

The most famous soft drink company in the world, if not the most famous company in the world, takes its marketing very seriously. Constant advertising and sponsorship deals with the likes of Elton John on a world tour are only part of how the company asserts its image. They intend to reinvent the drink for each new generation as it comes along. Figures show how successful they are. Coca-Cola is drunk in more than 195 countries, and consumed 773 million times every single day.

The company has more than a global strategy. It concentrates very much on local markets, ensuring the advertising is suited to the people in the locality. The Coca-Cola song *Always the Real Thing* may be played in the background on radio and TV, but the language and messages change depending upon where the tune is played.

Questions

1   What modelling methods may the Coca-Cola company use to assist its marketing of products?
2   How could modelling assist the company in the production of soft drinks?
3   Could modelling assist any competitors of Coca-Cola?

A game model

We see computer games everywhere – Sega and Nintendo are the biggest companies that specialise in the production of computer games, but there are others.

The model or rules a game follows are first developed in the mind of the game author. They are constructed in mathematical terms on paper to show the different options the player could take, and the conditions in which the game is to be played. Although this sounds simple, it is a complicated process. Consider how many options you have when it comes to crossing a road – do you walk or run, go straight across or veer to the left or right? Each choice you make can have an effect, adverse or otherwise, on the outcome of you making it safely to the other side.

Even a simple game like noughts-and-crosses has a large number of choices, and chess has such an enormous number that only recently have fast, modern computers been able to match world-class players.

We can illustrate the issues in creating and playing games by taking up a noughts-and-crosses game at the stage shown in Figure 7.9.

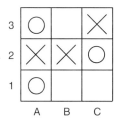

Figure 7.9 A game of noughts-and-crosses in progress

It is X's turn. The tree of decisions is shown in Figure 7.10.

The decisions at each stage, and there might in other games be very many more of them, can be set out as a decision tree. There is software for dealing with decision trees which help produce program code for tasks with many decisions.

If you decide you want to write a game that contains graphics, try something simple. Space Invaders is a good starting point: the player has to *zap* the invading space craft. There are plenty of good books available from libraries to help you write games. Some even include program code, and all *you* have to do is type it in, though you will not get the same satisfaction as you would if you had planned and written the whole thing.

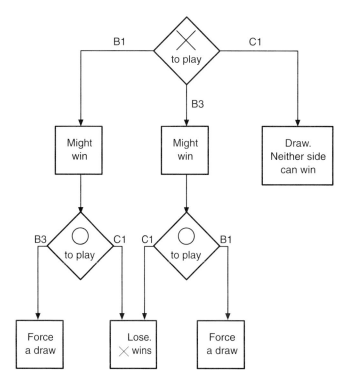

Figure 7.10 Decision tree for noughts-and-crosses

3D-representational model

CAD software such as Autocad is capable of creating models in 3D. The user draws the image or inputs numerical data into the CAD system and the software creates the image. We have looked at some of the uses of 3D software in industry earlier in this chapter. Some software is very easy to use to create 3D models such as kitchen designs, as the basic shapes and sizes are readily available.

Figure 7.11 gives four views of a computer 3D model. Once the model is held by the computer any view, from any direction at any size, can be put on the screen. If the 3D model was an ambitious subject, its model for the computer could not be created without the help of software features for handling e.g. cylindrical forms and extensive repetition.

It has often been said that 'a picture paints a thousand words'. Many believe CAD images are worth ten thousand words! How long would it take to describe the designs in Figure 7.11 in words?

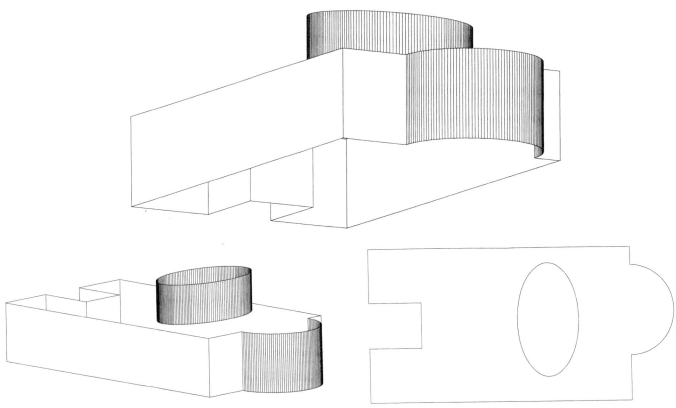

Figure 7.11 3D objects

Activity

If you can get suitable software, construct a very simple 3D model. A solid box measuring 3 × 4 × 5 would do.

Then you could try to elaborate on the model by boring tunnels through the box, adding flanges, shadows, and whatever ideas occur to you.

'What if'

Have you ever said or heard other people say 'What if we were to…'? It's possible to do a similar thing with computer models using 'what if' statements. Databases and spreadsheets are useful tools for this. In many ways, databases and spreadsheets perform similar functions. 'What if' queries are generally used in spreadsheets to refer to hypothesis testing. For example, we could set ourselves a hypothesis: there is a belief that there would be room for all the people in the world to stand on the Isle of Wight at the same time.

To test this hypothesis you would need to know the number of people in the world, perhaps ignoring those under three years old, and the surface area of the Isle of Wight. Then you could calculate how much of the area would be available to each individual, and make a judgement of whether or not that would be enough.

Your 'what if' exploration could cover the possibilities of the figures being wrong by some percentage, some people needing much more space than others and other variants.

Did you know?

Different people respond to the sun's rays in different ways – it's not easy to know when our bodies have had enough sun for the day. It would be ideal to be able to simulate how long each of us can be in the sun without running the risk of burning.

No personal simulator exists to do the job, but Creative Expressions from Leeds have developed a T-shirt that warns sun lovers when they are about to receive an overdose of ultraviolet light. The T-shirts are painted with photo-chromic ink which can't be seen until ultraviolet light reaches it. At that point the T-shirts start to change colour, letting the owners know when it's time to go indoors by the intensity of the colour change.

A simulation on your PC could relate your own vulnerability to that assumed by the T-shirt manufacturers. Repeated trials would let you refine the model.

Reports

Business reports usually rely on numerical data to support the statements made, and that data will often come from a computer model. Most reports follow a standard format – an introduction, a summary, the main body of the report where details are discussed, conclusion and recommendations and references of any books or other sources of information used to help write the report. It's the main body of the report we are interested in here – how we present modelled data in report format.

Numerical analysis sheet

Sometimes numerical data is provided, and it is felt best to show the actual figures rather than some other representation of them. Accountants tend to prefer figures to graphs and charts, because the latter can be drawn to emphasise a particular aspect of the figures which could possibly be misleading. For example, if there had been a small increase in a

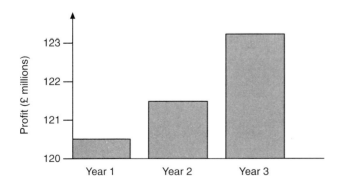

Figure 7.12 One way to show profit growth

company's profit over the past three years, it could be shown as in Figure 7.12. This on first glance would convey the impression that profit growth had been strong.

Sometimes reports show figures tabulated, or arranged in a special way, precisely because their significance is not obvious. This might be when a number of conflicting trend indications seems to be present, and there is to be discussion about the true significance of the figures.

Abstracts

Any report running to more than a page or two will have an abstract at the front. The abstract is sometimes called 'executive summary', or 'synopsis', or something else. The purpose of an abstract is to convey in compact form the essential issues and conclusions offered in the report. Frequently tables of modelled figures provide the pithiest way of conveying information. Such output from models might itself have to be compressed if it is to provide only what is needed for the abstract.

The essence of writing an abstract is to make it as clear and as brief as possible, consistent with covering the main points. Computer models can play an important part in this process.

Charts

Charts, if well chosen, can provide means of presenting quantities, ratios and trends that are quick to grasp and, possibly, easy to remember. Software may be able to draw charts which are immediately useful and attractive. You must always remember the needs of the reader and the importance of not misleading anyone. Always give a chart a title, make the scale and values on axes clear, and consider using colour. You should also state the source of the data on which your charts are based.

Use the range of types of chart available to you (Figures 7.13–7.17).

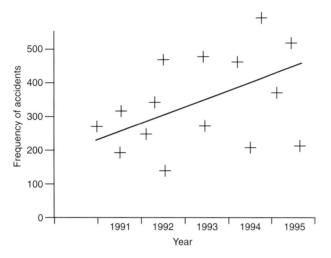

Figure 7.13 A scatter graph

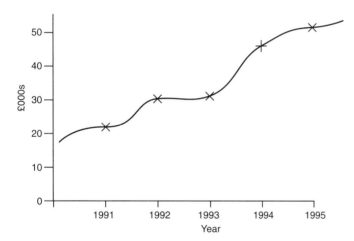

Figure 7.14 Historical records

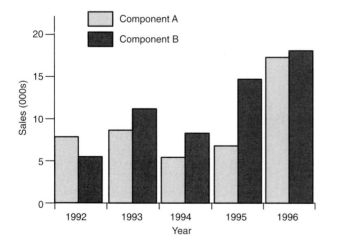

Figure 7.15 Histograms can be used to display figures relating to several different people, things or events

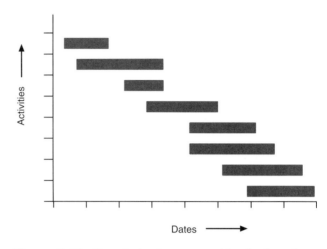

Figure 7.16 Gannt charts are used to display plans, and to record progress

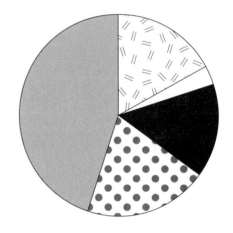

Figure 7.17 Pie charts show quantities, or percentages, or both

Pictorial reviews

In business reports, pictures tend not to be used. However, in the case of a data model, pictures may well help illustrate certain points. Again, they should be included only if they are relevant and help explain the situation further. They should also be clear and well presented. If a report has pictorial reviews and has to be copied, be sure that the pictures don't come out as black areas.

Colour pictures can have a role to play in, for example, a company's annual report.

The effectiveness of models and possible improvements

Effectiveness

Comparative cost

When a comparative cost model is run, we are trying to find out if there is another way of testing a model that is as good but cheaper or more cost effective. It may be that we have to ask *can we afford to run the model?* Although this question sounds funny, now we know all the benefits models have, it may be that actually creating a model is too expensive. If this is the case then it may be possible to have some other organisation run the model on our behalf. They may already have access to software that we would otherwise have to buy.

On the other hand, it may be that if it is simply too expensive to create a model, it may be too expensive to run the project as a whole. Consequently it may never be run. There have been examples of great ideas and inventions that never made it to the modelling stage because even if the models had been successful, the amount of money available to make the project work *after* the modelling was complete was too small. Always try to remember something simple when comparing costs. Ask yourself this: *is it cheaper to calculate profit with a calculator rather than with a PC and special-purpose software?*

Speed of response

In modern society, we expect responses to many of our queries immediately. Twenty years ago, if we wanted a book from a library we would have had to look up the title on an index card. This process might have taken up to five minutes. Nowadays we simply type the title of the book into a computer and it tells us where it is in a matter of seconds. In fact, if we wait for more than one second we become agitated and impatient, such are our expectations. We tend to be the same with computer models. We expect immediate results as soon as we have created the model foundations. In reality, models cannot always perform as quickly as we would like. The technology simply isn't good enough yet to satisfy our high demands. If it takes longer to create a model than it does to build and test the real artefact then, on the surface of it, the model is of little use. This may not be fair, though. All the other benefits of computer modelling that we have been looking at

probably still apply. *If it takes longer to run the model than it does to run the project, is it worth modelling?*

Accuracy

Is there any point at all in modelling if it's not accurate? Logic and our first instincts would tend to answer *no*. This is not always the case, though. Prior to a mission into space, models are created to simulate how the craft will respond to everything that will come its way during the mission. There is no way that it can be perfect – after all, nobody really knows what is out in space, so how can a model be built 100% accurate? Without modelling in such instances, however, the task would be far more dangerous, and would depend on the quick thinking of those in control as they respond to what happens during the mission. There are always occasions when an imperfect model is much more valuable than no model at all.

Comparison with alternatives

There may be several ways of using computers to model data and provide desired types of result. There are different approaches, such as using spreadsheet packages or writing programs for a particular task. And within these approaches there are sure to be many possible ways of doing the job. There are many spreadsheet packages for PCs, and a number of different ways of using each.

There are both standard, multi-purpose programming languages; and there are languages devised to help with modelling. These languages themselves can be used in a number of ways.

Before settling on a technique for modelling, for whatever purpose, be sure to review the possible approaches.

Efficiency

It would be nice if all models worked well and had beneficial results – they don't. Some model types are better than others at the tasks they perform, just as a Harrier Jump Jet is better at taking off vertically than a Boeing 747 jumbo jet: they all have limitations. If a model is inefficient, a number of fundamental arguments for modelling may be reduced or even eradicated – it won't be cheap, it could be dangerous, it could make mistakes and it could cost more to use than expected. Whilst modelling, we should also be aware that it is not just the model itself that has to be considered. The environment it works in is important too – a computer model employing more people every week is not necessarily efficient.

Improvements

Modifications to rules of operation

If we are using a flight simulation model and find that even the most experienced pilots crash and that their accidents are attributable to shortcomings of the simulator, it may be necessary to change the rules of operation. This means that the program instructions running the model should be changed to make the simulator more realistic, and easier to use.

Changes in data parameters

There may be data parameters built into the model that are wrong and therefore need changing. For example, in a flight simulator model during a test flight, the model of the plane may have been deliberately set up with the wrong flight co-ordinates, testing the pilot to see if he or she discovers the problem in time. To change the co-ordinates would mean going back to the machine program instructions and making alterations.

Models should always be subjected to critical appraisal to see if ways of improving them and their operations can be found.

Evidence indicator project

This project covers all the evidence indicators related to Chapter 7, (Element 2.3). It has been designed to be carried out at the end of the element.

Performance criteria: 1–5

Key skills:	Communication	3.2, 3.4
	Application of number	3.1, 3.2, 3.3
	IT	3.1, 3.3

With a group of friends, *brainstorm* the different types of models you can think of. You need to select two models from this brainstorming session that you are happy to model on a computer. One of your choices **must** be a *predictive* model.

With your selected models, use information from books, CD-ROMs, the Internet, tutors and libraries:

- to access information about them and explain their purposes (cost saving, convenience, time compression, hypothesis testing and safety)
- to specify three data parameters (input values, constraints, variables and calculations using operators).

Specify four rules of operation for your models (formulae, cell references, results of actions, relationships, the effect of variable changes).

Specify their methods of operation, any assumptions made, and the methods of input and output your models utilise.

Build your models on computer – most students use spreadsheets or databases, but if you feel adventurous you can use another system. As well as building the models, you have to produce outputs relating to your models to show you have

1 undertaken at least three 'what if' queries
2 tested the system for effectiveness, covering the *comparative cost* of your models, the *speed of response* of your models, a *comparison with alternatives* to your models and the *efficiency* of your models (don't forget to suggest any improvements you can think of)
3 given suggestions for improvement such as modifications to rules of operation and changes in data parameters.

Develop a control system

The role played by control systems in industry and in the home, is now vast. Control systems do more than make operations of various kinds more efficient and more convenient – they also affect employment, competitiveness and the environment.

Until we stop to think about it, we are probably unaware of how much a part of everyday life control systems are. Their use in controlling processes and devices, by detecting when it is necessary to vary output, tends to mask our appreciation of just how much impact they have had on our lives and the changes they have brought both at home and in work.

This element is partly practical. You will build a control system and satisfy yourself that it is working as intended. First, however, you will need to gain an understanding of control systems and their uses.

After studying this chapter you should be able to:

1 explain and give examples of *control systems*;
2 select *components* suited to a given *specification*;
3 produce a *schematic diagram* of the system;
4 create a *control procedure*;
5 construct a *control system* according to the given *specification*;
6 test the system for *effectiveness* and *suggest improvements* to the system.

Special note

There is only one evidence indicator project for this element. It is at the end of the element, on page 121.

Control systems

Before looking at the application areas where control systems are used we will first look at the principles that underlie all control systems. To help in focusing on these principles, we will consider two commonplace examples: supermarket doors which open automatically as you approach them, and thermostatically controlled domestic ovens.

In these two examples, sensors detect either a change in status or the crossing of a threshold value. The sensor at the supermarket door detects the proximity of a customer who was previously not there; the oven thermostat detects that the temperature has risen above, or fallen below, some previously set value.

By introducing a computer into the control process a more complicated or subtle set of decisions can be made, or many separate control functions can be handled from a single centre. However, a general-purpose computer is not a requirement in a typical control system.

The essence of a control system is:

■ a method of detection, or sensing;
■ a means of conveying sensing information;
■ a means of comparing that information with some set value;
■ a device to decide, on the basis of that comparison, whether or not action is required;
■ a procedure which decides what action to take, if any action is required;
■ a means of conveying that decision to equipment capable of giving effect to the decision; and
■ equipment to carry out the action required.

This sounds very complicated, but it need not be. Think of security lights outside a building. There is a detector to sense the presence of heat or movement, wiring to a control panel which has access to a source of electric power, wiring to the floodlights and the lights themselves. In this particular case, the control system will embody a timing device which will turn the lights off after, say, 90 seconds, if there is not at that time an indication from the sensor that they should be on. In this example both the input and the output at the control system are binary: the sensor indicates that a change has occurred, or has not occurred; and the lights are either on or off. Many control systems deal with variable quantities, such as rate of flow or temperature.

What is common to all examples of control systems is the concept of 'feedback'. The feedback is some quantity related to the output which is used to modify the input: that input may be on/off, as with the security lighting; or it may be variable, perhaps related to input sensor readings.

Feedback in the control arrangements allows one to think of the process of control as a loop, and this is a convenient way to picture any control system (Figure 8.1). As we work through the pages on control systems the concept of feedback and feedback loops will keep appearing.

Let us now look at six examples of control systems applications.

Environmental control

The control of the temperature in a greenhouse is an example of environmental control. One crucial characteristic of this type of control system is that on setting the desired temperature level the gardener is actually giving the system two levels. If control is exercised by opening some of the glass to reduce the internal temperature, and closing it to allow the temperature to rise, these operations will occur when the thermostat detects and reports slightly different temperatures.

When the temperature rises to some level, say T_1°C, the glass will be opened. When it falls to some lower temperature, say T_2°C, it will be closed again. You should note that if these temperatures T_1 and T_2 were not different the glass would be continually in motion opening and closing – a state of affairs known as 'hunting'. The difference between the two temperatures, that is $T_1 - T_2$, will be set when the system is installed. It will be set to match an acceptable range of temperature in the greenhouse with a sensible frequency of movement of the glass panels which can open and close.

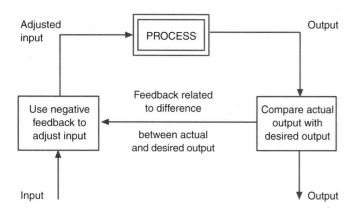

Figure 8.1 Schematic diagram of a control system with negative feedback

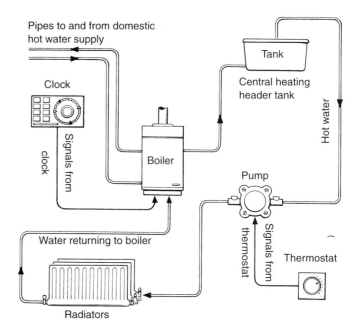

Figure 8.2 Central heating system controlled by thermostat

Another example is the control of central heating in a house. Usually a thermostat is fixed to a wall in a part of the house where an even, equable temperature is required. The signals from the thermostat start or stop the flow of hot water through the radiators (see Figure 8.2).

The house is warmed by the radiators through which hot water flows, driven by a pump. The thermostat is set to maintain the temperature at the place where it is fixed, at a given level. The thermostat exercises control over the temperature by sending signals to the pump, turning it on or off.

In the boiler there is also a thermostat. Its job is to ensure that hot water at a chosen temperature is supplied to the central heating header tank. As the pump draws off water from the tank it is replaced from the boiler. In addition to this system there is also a clock that can turn the boiler on and off. The boiler could, for example, be turned off overnight to save fuel.

You should note that even this relatively straightforward central heating system embodies three control systems:

1   The clock turns the boiler on or off at times set at the clock.
2   The boiler thermostat turns the heating within

the boiler on or off according to the temperature of the water sent to the header tank.

3   The thermostat turns the pump on or off according to the temperature registered at the thermostat itself.

If there are no radiators close to the thermostat their effect on the thermostat will be delayed. If the thermostat is immediately over a radiator, in cold weather the rest of the house is likely to be colder than desired because the thermostat will be especially well heated and will turn the supply to radiators off according to its setting. In some central heating systems the hot water for the radiators is not pumped, but circulated by convection. In such cases the only thermostatic control is on the boiler.

The consideration of domestic thermostatically controlled heating becomes complicated if some radiators have their own thermostats, and if internal doors are closed. The problem also gets worse if some windows are opened.

Process production control

Classic examples of process production control, or 'process control' as it is usually called, are oil refineries, paper mills and water purifying plants; chocolate-blending installations could be added to the list. In these instances there are many variables to be sensed and controlled. For example, temperature, viscosity, specific gravity, acidity and others have to be measured by sensors and, where they are found to have varied from the required band, adjusted.

The variables may not be completely independent of each other, and the model of the relationships may require comprehensive computer software to represent it accurately and in detail, and to judge the timing and extent of the required actions.

There is another class of production process control in which a human being is in the feedback loop. On a production line an operator who sees, or hears, or even smells something that is not as it should be may feel impelled to press the 'panic button', and so stop the line. Here the sensor is one or more of the operator's senses. The operator's brain gauges the seriousness of the malfunction and decides if action is required and, if it is, a hand is used to carry out the action by pushing the button.

There are many straightforward examples of this kind, but there are others where there is a combination of automatic sensing and human decision-making in the control system. Let us look at car assembly at BMW.

At the start of a car's production a small transmitting device is attached to its chassis. This communicates with the controlling computer, allowing the state of production to be determined at any point in the production process. As the computer knows the exact stage of production of the car, it knows what parts it will need next. This is particularly important as each car is made to order and is not a standard model; it therefore needs its own set of parts to be delivered to the right section of the assembly line at the right time. This is achieved by *computer integrated manufacture (CIM)* software, which decides the components required next arranges for equipment, take them out of stock automatically and delivers them in time for assembly.

Quality control

Quality control is the process of ensuring products reaching customers have been made to their correct specifications. In recent years, much greater emphasis has been placed on this. No customer wants to buy goods that are faulty and expensive to replace, and no manufacturer wants to waste money and materials, and lose customers due to lapses in product quality.

Any loss of quality could easily result in sales being diverted to a foreign product. For example, customers in the UK will quickly stop buying cars made by a manufacturer in Britain if they know people who have found them to be unreliable and of poor quality. Instead, they may decide to purchase a Japanese vehicle with guarantees of higher standards and reliability. With this knowledge in mind, UK companies have taken effective steps to ensure their goods are as well made and as faultless as possible. Quality control is exercised in every sector of the economy, and in every size of enterprise, but lends itself most conspicuously to automatic treatment in manufacturing.

Marketing executives are likely to tell production staff what quality standards the market demands. Inspection machines can be designed and built to examine completed products and to detect whether or not they breach the permitted tolerances. These machines will then accept or reject products as they go past an inspection point. They will probably also record the amount by which a product departed from the standard so that action can be taken to correct errors in manufacturing.

For high-volume production the inspection may be conducted on a sampling basis. A factory making thousands of bolts, say, each day might feel that

109

close enough control was provided by inspection of output once for every 100 bolts, or perhaps every 10 minutes. Needless to say, the inspection machines themselves have to be inspected from time to time to check that they are performing their task accurately.

Statistical process control (SPC) is a statistical approach to the control of quality often adopted for high-volume production. Records of measurements are kept and examined automatically.

If a trend is detected showing, for example, that the length of a machined part is approaching the maximum permitted, there will be an opportunity to intervene and adjust the manufacturing process before items are rejected, and thus wasted.

Did you know?

Statistical process control systems were first developed by the Ford Motor Company to improve the way they built cars. Not only was the system used in each of the Ford factories but it was also required of all companies that supplied components to Ford. If a supplier didn't work with statistical process control then Ford wouldn't buy their parts. This safeguarded the quality of the parts Ford were buying.

Security

The aim of security is to protect assets, property or information-based knowledge systems against accidental or malicious damage, or theft. Due to

worldwide increases in crime there are now more security systems coming into use each day, some being more evident than others. Have you ever been to a bank now at night to get money from the ATM? Some banks now have their machines inside their premises. To gain access to them at night you have to swipe your bank card through a magnetic reading device to unlock the door. This is an example of physical access control – only authorised people can get through. It is also useful reference for the banks too; should any damage be done to the premises, the ATM will have a record of the customers who used the equipment and the time they visited.

Modern house alarm security systems use sensors to detect movement in a room or interference with an external door or window. The sensors are connected to a control panel which monitors each of the sensors in the system. If it decides that any sensor calls for a response, it sounds the alarm. Car alarm systems are very similar; each sensor is monitored by the alarm control system. When it decides a sensor has been triggered, the alarm is sounded.

Automated video camera systems are further examples. Cameras can be moved from side to side and up and down by an operator in a control room. This allows a wide area to be covered as one person can operate a number of cameras to survey many locations at the same time. Cameras may be activated at regular intervals creating 'time-lapse' shots; or they may be activated by indications that a sensor has detected an unusual situation.

Some hotels use electronic security systems as a benefit to their customers by issuing guests with special electronic (swipe card) keys, or punched plastic cards acting as keys, to open their room doors rather than using a conventional key. The information stored on the card is read and relayed back to the central hotel computer that checks the key is for the correct room. If it is, then the door is unlocked. To improve room security further, each time a room is vacated, a new key is issued with a new code on it. At the same time, the hotel computer is updated with this code so that the new key is valid and the previous key will no longer open the door. To save hotel staff carrying hundreds of electronic keys they are issued with master keys.

Transport systems

If you have travelled on the M25 you may have noticed cameras placed at intervals allowing vehicle speed and density to be noted. They are linked to a

computer, at police headquarters, which calculates the speed that will keep the traffic flowing evenly. When this speed has been worked out, the computer relays information to traffic signals above the motorway, telling motorists the speed at which they should travel.

Incidentally, a motorway's optimum for achieving speed vehicle 'throughput' is said to be a maximum

of about 25 mph. But there would be an outcry if that speed were to be shown on the overhead gantries!

Similar systems are used elsewhere. In parts of London, the French company SLE is installing a system in which bus stops have light emitting diodes (LEDs), informing passengers when the next bus will arrive and where it is heading. This is achieved by a system of radio signals from each bus to a central computer. The information is used to estimate a time of arrival of each bus at its next stop on the route. These details are sent from the computer to each bus stop where they are displayed on the LED. This is illustrated in Figure 8.3.

Robotic production systems

As we saw in Chapter 1 (Element 1.1), robots are computer-controlled machines, very often used for jobs either too heavy, too difficult or too dangerous for human beings to perform. There are more robots used for car assembly than for any other type of task. Almost every job on a production line can be handed over to a robot, suitably programmed. Robots are also used for the inspection of components and finished vehicles.

Robots can be seen in the paint-spray sheds of car manufacturers. In the past, cars were hand spray-painted on the production line. This was found to be potentially harmful as paint can probably cause lung

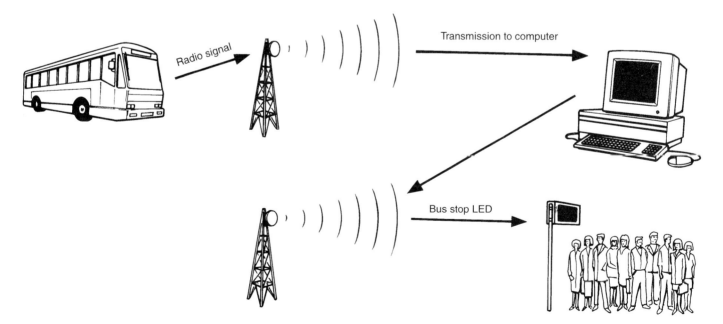

Figure 8.3 London Transport bus information system

111

diseases and problems such as asthma. Robots now do the job without any ill effects.

Robots are more efficient and economical than us too, as they don't tire, and they don't require breaks, food or wages, and can work 24 hours a day, with just routine maintenance. What is more important, the robots can do the task as part of an integrated manufacturing control system. Predetermined standards can be set and programmed. Any failure to meet them will be soon detected and corrective action easily taken. Where there are a number of robots in one plant their operation can be overseen by a master computer which compiles statistics on reliability, speed of operation and types of tasks.

Activity

Contact a number of manufacturing companies, and at least one transportation business, to find out what control systems they use and what their definitions of control systems are. Ideally, the manufacturing companies should include one undertaking mass production, one making batches of items and one a job-shop making to order.

1 How do control systems improve their manufacturing performance?
2 Have control systems made the companies more profitable?
3 Do the control systems make the companies easier to manage?
4 Are the companies more or less security conscious now they use control systems?

Components suited to a specification

Let us return to the domestic central heating system we discussed above, and as shown in Figure 8.2, to consider how such a system might be specified. Taking the components of the system one by one we can see what characteristics would have to be laid down:

- *Boiler* Type of fuel, and fuel consumption. Capacity for water, and temperatures limits. Control though internal thermostat, external clock, and external regulator and switch.
- *Header tank* Capacity and location.
- *Room thermostat* Temperature range. Nature of signals sent to pump.
- *Pump* Flow rating and power consumption. Signals from thermostat.

- *Radiators* Surface areas, locations, limits on water temperature.
- *Fuel and power supplies* Ratings of boiler and pump.
- *Water and pipes* Restrictions on hardness of water and diameters of pipes.

Sensors

A sensor is an appliance used to detect when a discrete change has occurred, or the value of a continuous variable such as pressure or temperature. In the example of the central heating system, the thermostat is the system sensor, detecting changes in temperature within set limits. If the temperature goes beyond these limits, the pump is turned either on or off.

Heat

Many applications require sensors to detect temperatures, usually to indicate when a threshold has been crossed. Sometimes the sensor is used directly, to operate as a switch. An example is based on a bi-metallic strip (Figure 8.4).

Different metals have different thermal coefficients of expansion. Use can be made of this difference by fastening together straight strips of different metals when both are at the same, convenient temperature. When the temperature rises one strip expands more than the other, and the composite strip adopts a

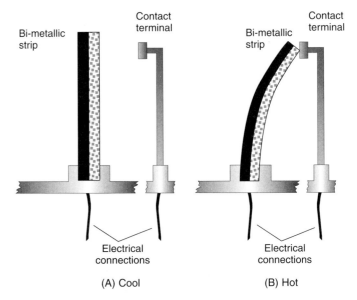

Figure 8.4 The use of a bi-metallic strip to close an electric circuit when heated

curved shape. This movement can be used to activate a switch.

Light

A common light sensor is a solar cell, used to harness rays of light to power calculators and digital watches. Silicon is used in solar cells to sense changes in light. Any light shone on to the silicon reacts with its atomic structure, changing light energy into electrical energy. To make effective use of the electrical energy, electrodes transfer it from the silicon to a control system.

Rather than change light energy into electrical energy, some light sensors detect changes in device resistance when light hits them. The resistance change varies the electrical current in the detecting circuit and this change can be quantified with a meter. A photo-electric cell or photodiode works in this way. As light levels increase, the photodiode's resistance falls, allowing more electricity to flow through the diode.

Video

Video sensors work in a similar way to photodiodes. A grid of photodiode sensors is put together to detect light coming from and around objects in front of them. When an object is placed before the sensors, the photodiodes react to the light coming from and around it. Electronic devices scan the photodiode grid to make use of all the information and to create an electronic copy. This type of system is used in video cameras such as those made by Canon and Casio.

Activity

In what commercial ways could video sensors be used other than in video cameras? What advantages would they hold over alternatives? How do the alternatives compare with video sensors in terms of cost and efficiency?

Sound

The detection or sensing of sound is crucial in modern life. Without sound sensors, telephones, tape recorders, radio stations and microphones would not work. Microphones detect sound and convert it into electrical energy, very often for transmission lines.

Let's look at the sensing devices within a microphone. The fundamental requirement for a microphone is a magnet. Around this is a metal coil or spring. Connected to the top of the coil is a diaphragm, very similar to the diaphragm in the human ear. As sound hits the diaphragm, it vibrates and the coil moves up and down around the magnet, intercepting the magnetic field lines and generating a current. The changes in voltage constitute an electrical transcript of the sound wave that hit the diaphragm. This voltage can be sent to an amplifier so it can be recorded.

Proximity

Proximity sensors detect the presence of an object without touching it. They are used in many locations such as lift doors, car park barriers and intruder alarm systems. They work by emitting a light, ultrasonic or infra-red signal that hits objects which reflect the signal back.

More elaborate proximity sensors can detect the delay between transmitting its pulses and receiving the echo. The length of delay is proportional to the distance between them. Correctly calibrated, the sensor can report to the processor what that distance is.

An electric buggy with a proximity sensor on the front can manoeuvre its way around a room without hitting anything. The proximity sensor emits signals which are reflected back from objects around the room to a receiving device on the buggy. The buggy control system constantly monitors the length of time it takes for the signal to be returned. Its program makes it aware that a signal returned in less than a predetermined time means the buggy is too close to an object and must change direction in order to avoid a collision. The control system makes the buggy rotate. When signals return at or after more than the predetermined time, the control system stops the buggy rotating and the cycle begins again

Contact

In contrast to proximity sensors, contact sensors respond only to force or pressure. Examples are:

■ Sensors laid below the playing surface (alongside such lines as the service line) on some tennis courts. Connected to a sound source and loudspeaker, they can make known whether a ball was in or out.

- Pressure pads fitted under carpets as part of an intruder alarm system in a house or office.
- Probes on some machine tools to detect a cutting head advancing too far and, by intervening, preventing damage to the workpiece.
- Sensors on robots to provide 'force feedback' to inform the control system of the degree of resistance the arm is encountering.

Activity

Find at least two examples of:

- a sound sensor
- a proximity sensor
- a contact sensor.

For each example, discuss the job being done by the sensor. Could the task be accomplished by other means? What similarities and differences are there between each of the sensors you have chosen?

Processors

A processor is the decision-making component of a control system. It can range in scope between a single special-purpose chip such as might be used to control the cycle selected on a dish-washer, to a powerful general-purpose computer programmed to control the processes of a nuclear power station.

The processor in a process control application is usually dedictaed to that role. Source data is derived from monitoring the process by suitable sensing arrangements, and computations making use of that data define the control signals to be sent to the process.

There are two forms of process control: *discrete* and *continuous*. Discrete process control is exercised over the manufacture of individual items such as, for example, castings. Continuous process control monitors physical properties such as temperature, viscosity, density and colour, and seeks to maintain consistency.

In discrete process control the processor is prompted by the occurrence of an event such as the arrival of a component at the inspection station. In continuous process control the monitoring is carried out regularly at appropriate time intervals. In the former information about quality is made available by the system; in the latter the system can directly control the outputs from the process.

Activity

Find two examples of applications where electronic processors are used: one should be in a domestic piece of equipment in which the processor chip is programmed during manufacture to keep doing the same job; and one should be industrial or commercial, where the processor can be reprogrammed by the user, as required. What advantages do they hold over alternative methods? How do the alternatives compare with processors in terms of cost and efficiency?

Process control procedure

The logic within a process control procedure reflects how a system should work under normal conditions. Developing a control procedure requires us to know exactly how the process should perform so it can be compared with the way the process is performing. Any difference between the actual and required results highlights an error which must be corrected.

The examples given at the beginning of this chapter hint at the wide range of possible process control applications.

Output devices

Heater

Portable warm-air heaters provide an effective means of controlling the temperature of a room. They contain metal elements that become hot when electricity is passed through them. The air surrounding the element warms up due to radiation and conduction, and rises and circulates, thus warming the room. A thermostat attached to the heater, set to a predetermined level, senses when the room temperature is as desired. It then turns off the electricity supply to the heating element. When the room temperature falls below the predetermined level, it turns the electricity supply on again, allowing the element to warm up and the cycle to continue.

Light

Lights are often used as security system output devices. Using a controlling device that allows electricity to flow at predetermined times, or when it becomes dark or light outside, lights can be turned on and off. By building proximity or heat sensors into the system, it is possible to turn lights on and off as part of a more sophisticated security system.

Sound

Sound is an effective warning signal when used in control systems. By building proximity or pressure sensors into a system, a controlling device can set off an alarm siren. Sound generated automatically is also used to alert people to dangerous areas, should they approach them, in factories.

Fan

Fans are used to help maintain temperatures. They work in PCs, for instance. Warm air driven out by the fan is replaced by cooler air from the room. Just as in the heater, a thermostat, set to a predetermined level, senses when the temperature has been sufficiently reduced to switch off the electricity supply to the fan. When the temperature rises above the predetermined thermostat level, it turns the electricity supply on again, causing the fan to restart.

Some fans have extra control built in to them. As well as sensing the temperature of the surrounding atmosphere, they detect when their own motor becomes too warm. At this point the electricity supply to the motor is cut until it is again sufficiently cool.

Actuator

An actuator is any item of equipment that conveys a signal or a movement to another item of equipment. Actuators are required in control systems to convert a signal into the desired action. For example, in the central heating system the signals from the room thermostat are fed to an actuator in the pump to make it go on and off in the way needed by the system.

Interconnecting devices

It is common to want to connect devices together – computers and printers, video recorders and televisions, and control systems and sensors. This is not always easy as they may respond to different types of data signal. Computer devices use digital signals (1s and 0s) and most other devices use analogue signals. To make devices that use different signals work together, interconnecting devices are needed. Typically, an incoming signal which provided a controlling processor with continuously sensed information in analogue form would be fed through an analogue-to-digital converter to provide binary input to the processor. And binary output from the processor would be passed through a digital-to-analogue converter to provide usable instructions for an external device.

Computers use interconnecting devices when they interface with a microphone. An output port will contain a digital-to-analogue converter if it is to change computer-generated signals from a device such as a CD-ROM into sound.

Activity

Find four control systems in your home that require interconnecting devices to make them work correctly. What I/O devices are used, and in what ways are they similar to a computer I/O port?

Specification

Specifications are detailed requirements of how a control system should perform and what components must be used to make it meet the performance criteria. Without specifications, nobody accurately knows how to build systems or what the jobs they are supposed to do are once complete. We looked at aspects of a control system specification for the domestic central heating system. We now think about specifications more generally.

Input

What system inputs are to be included? Some are manual, such as a computer keyboard, and some automated, such as a scanner using a sheet-feeding device. In the example of the central heating system, both manual and automated inputs exist – the user manually selects the required temperature, and the system feeds back data to alter the water temperature. At the same time, the central heating draws the gas and electricity it needs automatically.

Tolerances

All systems must be given tolerances in their specification. This applies to physical dimensions and to variables such as temperature. Earlier in this element we saw how statistical process control utilises tolerances to ensure products meet their required standards and specifications. In a similar way, as long as systems operate within an agreed margin, they are effective and acceptable.

Responses

All systems must respond to their inputs once they pass some planned threshold value. That is their purpose. A control system must have a specification for the responses it is to make.

Costs

Budgets have to be set so that the commercial viability of products can be assessed before manufacture. A computer-based control system for an oil refinery represents a minute proportion of the total cost, so this issue may not be crucial. But gauging correctly the cost of the controller in a domestic washing machine, where tens of thousands may be sold and the market is extremely competitive, is absolutely vital.

Output

The form of the output required from a control system is normally central to the reason that the system was chosen and installed. The greenhouse described earlier had a control system so that it could be maintained at a desired temperature. An output that opened and closed ventilation panels appropriately was needed.

An intruder alarm system is useful only if it turns on lights, sounds a siren, or telephones the police. The outputs demanded dictate the nature of the system.

Type of feedback

Feedback is a necessary part of any effective system. Without it the system cannot regulate itself. Feedback can be positive or negative. Negative feedback modifies output in the opposite direction from the change detected on the input.

For example, if a thermostat detects that a room has too high a temperature the effect of the signal it sends is to reduce the flow of heat into the area. That is negative feedback.

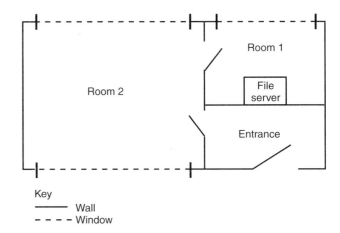

Figure 8.5 Example specification

Positive feedback occurs when change to the input increases the difference in output when the desired output value are added together. This has no role in control systems as it causes run-away instability.

We need to select components to fulfil the specifications. An example of a specification for the security of a small business suite is shown overleaf:

Overall system feedback, other than temperature control, comes from collating the printed system reports and deciding a plan of action to take in future. What appears at first sight to be a formidable specification becomes much more manageable when it is broken down in this way.

Selected component	Specification
Heat/temperature sensor Heater, fan	Temperature control Time limit on restoring temperature to correct value, within tolerance
Light sensor and outside lights	Outside lighting
Proximity sensor – PIR detectors	Outside lighting
Contact sensors	Windows, floor of entrance
Video cameras and recording	Inside entrance Outside around the building
Interconnecting telephone device to police	Police alert
Audible alarm – 200 decibels	Audible outside alarm
Computer control	Process control system

Table 8.1 Component specifications

Security system specification for the Computer Company Ltd

A plan of the area to be secured is shown in Figure 8.5. All entrances (doors and windows) are illustrated. Any disturbance to the internal environment must be brought to attention through alarm signals. The system must be monitored 24 hours a day – any alarm must be checked. The following rooms have special system specifications that must be met:

General Interconnecting device to alert Police of any disturbance.

Room 1 Temperature control set at 20°C, plus or minus 2°C, at all times. If this tolerance is exceeded the control system should take steps to correct it.

The response time for temperature correction is 5 minutes.

Output is to take the form of both immediate temperature correction and a computer printout of the situation.

Prevent window access. Any window movement is to trigger the system. If the system is too sensitive to wind or rain on the window, system sensitivity to be altered by decreasing the sensitivity by 5% and reset. Output to take the form of sounding the alarm and a computer printout of time and actions the system took.

Room 2 Prevent window access. Detect motion during silent hours. Tolerances not to be so rigid that insects can trigger the system. Response time is 0.5 seconds.

Feedback to be a computer printout at the time of the incident.

Entrance Detect entry. Detect movement on floor. Tolerances not to be so rigid that insects can trigger the system. Response time is 0.5 seconds. Feedback in detailed printout of the incident and video footage – inside and out.

Outside Lighting to come on at dusk and go off at dawn. Floodlights to come on upon entry to car park. Response time is 0.5 seconds. A computer printout should report any disturbance. Audible alarm – loud enough to be heard half a mile away.

Did you know?

Human beings have their own feedback systems built in – and we don't even have to think about using them either as our brains do all the hard work for us subconsciously. If, for example, a bit of dust lands in our eye, the eye senses the presence of the dust and informs the brain. This in turn tells the eye lid to blink to remove the dust and lubricate the eye with a tear. If the dust is not removed, more tears are released into the eye until the dust is washed away and removed altogether.

Creating a control system

We shall consider a device which needs a control system, and use it as the basis for:

- producing a schematic diagram;
- creating a control procedure; and
- planning the construction of a control system.

The device is an automated vacuum cleaner that finds its way around a room and cleans the floor without running into furniture.

The first requirement is to produce a schematic diagram of the system. Figure 8.6 gives a simple version of the diagram that would be needed for the device to be designed and built. Lower-level diagrams giving greater detail would also be necessary. In addition, a description of the proposed system covering the following aspects of it would be essential for the designer to understand what was wanted:

- *Environment definition* In this example, the size of the room, the nature of the floor covering and something about the obstructions.
- *Sensors* The number, type, and location of the sensors; and the signals required from them.
- *Processor* The power, nature of processing, frequency of inputs and outputs, and location.
- *Output devices* In this case, there are two motors, one for suction and one for propulsion, and mechanisms for steering the cleaner
- *Feedback* The feedback from the sensors has to be prompt enough, and accurate enough, to prevent collisions.

From all the information provided you would be able to create the control procedure needed for the vacuum cleaner. You would consider the following:

- *Input* Apart from the power supply, the input would come from the sensors and be fed through analogue-to-digital convertors.
- *Decision* This is programmed into the processor.
- *Process* The program running in the processor will give effect to the decisions it has made.
- *Output* Through the digital-to-analogue converters the processor outputs activate the motors and steering gear.
- *Feedback loops* The purposes of the feedback loops shown on the schematic diagram are to make the cleaner perform to specification. They are essential, as without them the processor would not have up-to-the-minute data on which to work.

The next task is to construct the vacuum cleaner. That calls for a full design, and the selection of all

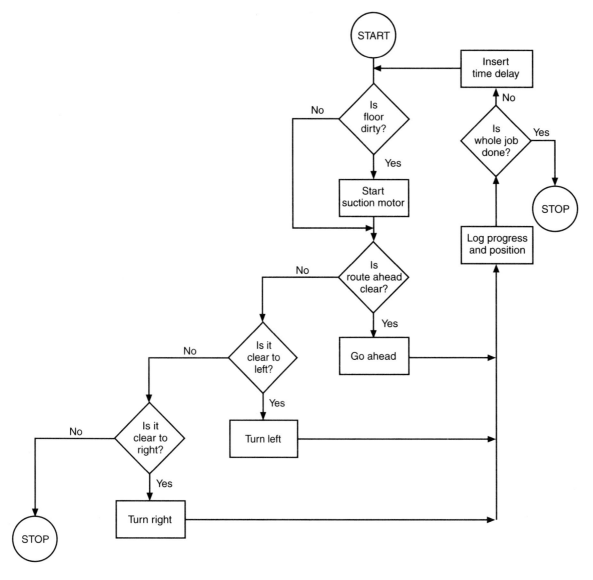

Figure 8.6 Schematic diagram for automated vacuum cleaners

the components necessary for fulfilling the specification. This is an ambitious project, but you will learn from thinking about it.

Did you know?

A control system for pet quarantine using a computerised tagging system has been introduced to Parliament by Tony Banks MP. His system will involve all pets that are properly vaccinated being electronically tagged (by having a computerised identification chip implanted into them). The tiny microprocessors have their own power source, and radio transmitters built in to allow computers around the world to read them and check the animal's medical history. The system will be kept up to date by vets who treat the animals, thus providing constant monitoring of the welfare of the pets with the possibility of providing feedback to the quarantine authorities. The aim of the system is to end six months of misery for animals and owners when the animals have to stay in quarantine in order to enter the country.

Testing the system

The need to test systems under safe conditions before they go to their customers is of paramount importance. Releasing them untested could result in increased costs and, possibly, danger. There are a number of important areas that must be considered during a test.

Effectiveness

Before we can say how effective a system is, we need to know it's working to specification properly. We have to test it. *How?*

Look at the control procedures in your system (such as the sensing rates, the range limits and the rate of output). If they work, is it possible to make alterations for improvement? What about the sensors in the system? Can their sensitivity be increased to make the system better? Or would that make it worse?

Let's use the example of the alarm system again to make comparisons and to check system effectiveness.

Comparative cost

Does the cost of designing and building the system justify the job it is doing, in this case acting as a security device on a building, or does the cost of the system make it uneconomic?

Its job is to provide peace of mind for the owner. It is difficult to stipulate a value for this – as long as the owner believes the system to be worth the cost that is all that is wanted. It may be possible to buy a similar system for less. Again, though, peace of mind for the owner makes one system better than the other.

Speed of response

How long does it take for the system to react when you test it? Is it within the limits allowed in the specification? An alarm system should give an immediate response if activated.

Accuracy

Are system devices such as the temperature control and lighting control accurate enough, or do they come on and go off unexpectedly?

Comparison with alternatives

Could you use different components in any area of the system? Would it make it more cost effective if you did? Comparison could cover maintenance costs, expected operational life, ease of use, convenience and size.

Efficiency

Does your system support efficiency or does it cause annoyance and make more work? Efficiency can concern itself with reliability, suitability of alarm warnings and ease of training people to use the system.

Did you know?

Wouter Couzijn, an undergraduate at the Technical University at Delft, has used Lego to build a robot to pick up and transport equipment in a warehouse. The robot could be easily adapted to fit in a wheel chair, and comply with instructions from a disabled person to move from one named place to another – for example, from the sitting room to the kitchen.

Mr Couzijn believes that such as robot could incorporate an infra-red detector and could be used to find and fight fires.

Improvements

Now you have tested and looked at the effectiveness of a system, can you make any suggestions for improvement? The following areas ought to be addressed.

Use of different devices

To help make suggestions, it's sometimes a good idea to develop a table showing the suggestions next to components and elements of the system. An example is shown in Table 8.2, which is based on the building security system discussed above and shown in Figure 8.5.

Change in feedback

What about going back to the drawing board and changing the feedback system you devised? Can it be improved? Most systems can, though there is not

Table 8.2 Specification improvements

Selected component	Suggested improvements
Heat/temperature sensor Heater, fan	Ultrasonic movement detectors that sense any motion. Solar cells could be used to power the heater and fan saving money and electricity
Light sensor and outside lights	Pressure pads that turn lights on when touched
Proximity sensor – PIR detector	'Trip wire' laser beams that activate the system when the beam is broken. They are particularly accurate, but effective only over a limited area.
Contact sensors	They could be sited on cupboards and doors.
Video cameras and recording	Rather than leaving this equipment running constantly, ensure it is turned on only when a detector or proximity sensor is activated
Interconnecting telephone device to police	Also connect this device to the owner at home or on a mobile telephone or paging device
Audible alarm – 200 decibels	Have lights started flashing when alarm is activated

always a perfect way of devising a system. If you develop the Apollo vehicle (in your evidence assignment below) you may find the wires connecting Apollo with the PC to be cumbersome. It may help to use a radio transmitter in Apollo and a receiver in the PC. You may have found that the feedback was too slow. Apollo may have left its curved line. Therefore it may be an idea to alter the information feedback in the system – possibly by changing the computer program in charge of Apollo.

Alterations to sensitivity

In the case of a temperature-controlled greenhouse, for example, the equipment may be constantly changing for minor variations in temperature. If this is the case, the tolerances need to be altered so that the equipment makes alterations only when the tolerance levels are opened out by a further degree or two.

In the office security example, did you achieve an even level of sensitivity or were some aspects of the system much more sensitive than others?

Modifications to software

Can the software you devised be altered or improved? No two people would ever write a program exactly in the same way, so one version is generally going to be better than another. If you can make your program shorter but still do the same job

then that's an improvement – it will take the computer less time to process the information, and the program will be easier to maintain.

Modifications to situation or object

Would it be helpful to alter any of the situations or objects in your system? For example, in Figure 8.5, it may be helpful to brick up the window in Room 1 as the room holds only the file server. What is the point in having a window that is never used but needs security devices working on it all the time? Surely it's a waste of money?

The best way to make improvement suggestions is to have a friend or colleague study your system while you study his or hers. Highlight anything that you feel could be improved or altered, and state why. Once complete, discuss the details with each other and incorporate anything you feel worthy.

Did you know?

Although many companies can see the benefits of using mobile IT control systems, most of them have not yet invested in the equipment to take advantage of the possibility. It has been highlighted by the national press that in a 300-firm survey carried out in June 1996 by Mori, only 12% of companies currently plan to use the technology. It does make one wonder if companies around the world will take advantage of this fact.

Evidence indicator project

This project covers all the evidence indicators related to Element 2.4 (Chapter 8). It has been designed to be carried out at the end of the element.

Performance criteria: 1–6

Key skills:		
	Communication	3.1, 3.2, 3.4
	Application of number	3.1
	IT	3.1, 3.2, 3.3, 3.4

Scenario

You have to design, build, operate and test a special-purpose vehicle which we shall call Apollo. Apollo has to be able to move forwards, and to steer, under its own power on a level area. It has to be able to follow a strong black line on a white, well-lit surface, following the bends and curves. It is to have four wheels, none of which is to touch or cross the line once the vehicle has started.

You have to

- make a schematic drawing of the system which must include two types of sensor and two types of output device;
- construct Apollo to operate acording to the specification in the scenario; and
- write notes to show that you have
  - tested Apollo, convering the range (alterations to control procedure, change of sensitivity of the sensors, and the use of different sensors);
  - explained this and other uses of process control systems covered in this chapter;
  - selected the components used in Apollo; and
  - suggested improvements in Apollo.

Using information technology: Unit test 2

1 Details such as page numbering at the top of a page are known as
  a The header
  b The footer
  c Page details
  d Standard document information

2 Details such as page numbering at the bottom of a page are known as
  a Base information
  b The footer
  c Page details
  d Standard document information

3 Which of the following is an example of graphic design software?
  a Lines
  b Chart
  c Attributes
  d Image

4 Which of the following is *not* an example of presentational graphics?
  a Bit map
  b Lines
  c Shade
  d Text

5 The thickness of a line is
  a Set up in the layout of a design
  b An attribute of a component of graphic design software
  c Part of a picture
  d Built in to the page attributes

6 Which of the following is *not* a component of graphic design software?
  a A polygon
  b A slide show
  c A circle
  d Text

7 The design specification for a slide show will include
  a A block schematic
  b Shapes
  c Attributes
  d Content

8 Which of the following is *not* part of a design specification for a technical drawing?
  a Layout
  b Product design
  c Bit map
  d Block schematic

9 Which of the following is a purpose of computer models?
  a Simulation
  b Cost saving
  c Prediction
  d Gaming

10 Which of the following is *not* a purpose of computer modelling?
  a Safety
  b Convenience
  c Hypothesis testing
  d Gaming

11 How can computer models save money?
  a PCs are cheap
  b By applying constraints to systems
  c By compressing time and eliminating the need to test in the real world
  d They are convenient

12 In a CAD system, which of the following data parameters is of interest?
  a Simulation
  b Scale
  c Cost saving
  d Convenience

13 Which of the following is *not* used in calculations with operators?
 a Relational
 b Logical
 c Scale
 d Arithmetic

14 A calculation set out in a spread sheet is known as a
 a Cell reference
 b Method of operation
 c A formula
 d A mathematical calculation

15 Which of the following is *not* used as a rule of operation in computer simulation?
 a Scale
 b Effect of variable changes
 c Method of operation
 d Relationships

16 What can be generated by using a *what* if query?
 a An operational report
 b A search routine report
 c A numerical analysis report
 d A new database

17 An automatically opening/closing window in a greenhouse is an example of
 a A sensor
 b Response
 c Output device
 d Environmental control

18 A manufacturing organisation such as Pepsi-Cola places great emphasis on
 a Heat
 b Quality control
 c Sensors
 d Feedback

19 A level of noise with a tolerance of 4 dB will be picked up by
 a A sound sensor
 b A light sensor
 c A contact sensor
 d A proximity sensor

20 In a process control procedure which of these provides the control?
 a Output
 b Input
 c Responses
 d Feedback

21 The process of taking information from the end of a system and placing it back at the start is known as
 a Output
 b A feedback loop
 c Environmental control
 d A sensor

22 A schematic diagram is likely to hold all but which of the following?
 a Sensors
 b Processors
 c Environmental definition
 d Environmental control

23 The decision-making element shown in a schematic diagram is illustrated by a
 a Sensor
 b Processor
 c Output device
 d Environment definition

24 In order to test how effective a transportation system is, one may measure
 a Inputs
 b Outputs
 c The speed of operation
 d Accuracy

25 If we are comparing one control system with another we are checking its
 a Effectiveness
 b Efficiency
 c Accuracy
 d Speed of response

26 Output devices include
 a Sources of light
 b Sensors
 c Transport systems
 d Tolerances

27 Testing the effectiveness of a new computer system will include
 a Use of sensors
 b Environments definition
 c Type of output used
 d Speed of response

28 A house security alarm includes all but which of the following?
    a Sensors
    b Processors
    c Block schematic
    d Process control

29 Which of the following is an operation of process control?
    a Sensing
    b Tolerance
    c Accuracy
    d Schematic diagram

30 A feedback loop
    a Makes decisions
    b Processes information
    c Introduces control into a system
    d Allows inputs to enter a system

Organisations are able to function only if they make use of the information available to them: to flourish, they must obtain all the information they need economically and they must process and store it efficiently.

This unit, which builds on much of the material you will have covered in Units 1 and 2, first points out in Chapter 9 the wide range of types of organisation that exist in a developed economy such as ours. It goes on to show how information is generated within organisations, and how it flows between their functions. This part of the unit will be of greatest value to you if you think of as many types of organisation as you can, and if you arrange to visit a few to see how their information moves around.

Next, in Chapter 10, you will be looking at information processing needs, methods of processing, and types of data handling systems. You will then be making comparisons between the needs for information handling in at least two organisations.

Chapter 11 teaches the importance to all organisations of information stored in files and databases. You will be creating three database reports to show different aspects of database operation and management.

Finally, Chapter 12 focuses on the importance of protecting data on both individuals and organisations, the health and safety issues in data handling systems, and the obligations of systems users for installing appropriate security arrangements for the data for which they are responsible.

An external test forms part of this unit.

Chapter 9

Investigate the flow of information in organisations

We have progressed through the examination of computers and IT systems, what they do and how they work. This knowledge is vital, but there is little point in it unless we can put it to practical use. IT is widely used in every industry sector, in public services and in enterprises of all sizes. The effective use of IT is increasingly important in the running of all of them. In this element we examine the flow of information in these organisations. To complete this element successfully, and to give you practical insights into the use of information, you should try to undertake visits to local organisations. You may find it helpful to work on this element alongside Element 3.2 (Chapter 10) where you have to study an actual data handling system.

After studying this chapter you should be able to:

1 describe and give examples of *types of organisation*
2 explain the *forms* and *types of information* generated and used by *functions* in organisations
3 produce diagrams showing the flow of information between *functions* in organisations
4 compare the flow of information in different organisations.

Describe and give examples of types of organisations

Two or more people working together in a structured way to accomplish specific tasks are entitled to call themselves an organisation. Indeed, a sole trader may well be considered to be an organisation. We are surrounded by organisations, and it should come as no surprise that most of us are members of them, even if this simply involves being a member of a school or college, a brass band, sports team or fan club.

All organisations must have a purpose in order to exist. They may provide goods or services designed to meet the requirements of consumers, or they may exist to help others. There are a number of different types of organisations.

Organisations

Commercial

The term *commercial organisation* can be applied to any establishment that aims to make a profit for its owner or shareholders. Normally their main role is the purchase, manufacture and sale of goods, or the provision of services. This is in contrast to a non-commercial organisation such as a charity that does not make profits but exists to distribute contributions to worthwhile causes. Examples of commercial organisations include hairdressers, opticians, dentists, accountants and solicitors, as well as enterprises of all sizes in manufacturing, distribution, retail, financial services, agriculture and other sectors.

Industrial

Industrial organisations use human skill, components and raw materials to assemble or manufacture goods. You will see from the previous paragraph that industrial organisations are a particular group within commercial organisations. In addition, there are some industrial organisations, such as government plants and laboratories, that are not commercial.

Case study – Coca-Cola

Coca-Cola is the most successful product in the history of commercial organisations. The syrup for the drink was first produced by a pharmacist, Dr John Styth Pemberton, who took it to a local pharmacy where it sold for 5 cents a glass. The syrup was one day mixed with soda and found to be better than before. Advertising for the new soda began and its popularity grew. In 1916 the now distinctive contoured bottle was developed and it soon began selling strongly, even beating soda fountain sales.

By 1929, 64 Coca-Cola bottling operations were operating in 28 countries. The fundamental principle behind the product was control of quality. No matter where the drink was to be bought from, the Coca-Cola company insisted it tasted the same. Advertising continued throughout the twentieth century, as did Coca-Cola packaging, with the company introducing different-sized bottles in 1955.

Never happy to rest on its laurels, the Coca-Cola company introduced new soft drinks including Fanta, Sprite and TAB (its first low-calorie drink). In the 1960s Coca-Cola merged with the Minute Maid Corporation, adding citrus drinks to the company's range of offerings.

In 1988, a worldwide survey confirmed that Coca-Cola was the best-known and most admired trademark in the world. A US national business magazine stated 'Coca-Cola is so powerful it's practically off the charts'.

A simple soft drink developed in Atlanta in 1886 created a commercial empire with a place confirmed in the history books, selling nearly half the soft drinks consumed in the world.

Public service

Public service organisations exist for the benefit of the nation, or areas or groups within it. They are not owned by any one individual or organisation. In the past more public service organisations existed than today, as in recent years many have been privatised – that is sold by the government in a bid to make them more efficient and effective. Examples of public service organisations are government departments and agencies, the armed forces, the courts and Parliament, at a national level.

Local government has different structures in England, Wales, Scotland and Northern Ireland, and the structures themselves change. There are regions, counties, districts, parishes and community councils. These local authorities share between themselves local responsibilities for housing, education, police, roads, planning and many services provided to people within their boundaries.

Central government is directly responsible for health care, social security, defence, education policy, overseas representation through embassies and consulates, foreign policy and many other areas of policy and operation. The departments of central government are staffed by civil servants. Local authorities employ local government officials, some of whom may be part-time employees.

Organisation structures

The structure of an organisation refers to the way in which activities are grouped or arranged. Organisational structures affect the way information flows around an organisation.

All organisations require a chain of command or structure, specifying the responsibilities of each job and who reports to whom. The result of these chains is a pattern of multiple levels called a hierarchy. At the top is the board, director or manager, responsible to the organisation's owners for operation of the entire organisation. It is important to select a suitable organisational structure for any organisation, for two reasons. First, working relationships in the organisation can be affected by the type of hierarchy. If it's too wide, managers can be over-stretched and employees may not receive enough guidance. Secondly, the hierarchy can affect the decision-making process.

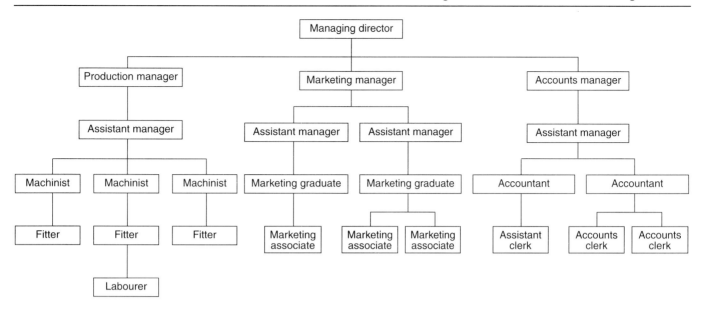

Figure 9.1 Typical organisational structure for a small manufacturing company

Hierarchical

Every organisation needs a structure, as people must know the limits of their responsibilities. A hierarchy has many levels or grades of staff, a tree-like management structure and strong patterns of vertical communication. Let's look at a hierarchy in diagrammatic form. A typical example of a company structure can be seen in Figure 9.1.

Case study – Marks & Spencer

Marks & Spencer is a company started by one man, a Russian refugee called Michael Marks. He sold goods from a tray around his neck in villages close to Leeds. As he couldn't write English, he had a friend create a sign indicating everything was a penny. Things have changed somewhat since then! By 1930 the company had over 200 branches throughout the UK, and in 1991 first recorded sales of over £1 billion.

The company believes that people are their most important resource. Each store has a manager, a deputy manager, a personnel manager and other senior management. Other staff are recruited locally, and all staff understand the way the company operates, being kept informed by newsletters and staff magazines.

1 Why do you think the company operates in a hierarchical manner?

2 Find out about the company principles. Are they affected by the company structure?

Did you know?

The Ford motor company employs many thousands of people around the world – there are 20,000 engineers alone. As they don't all work in the same place, a communication system is needed to ensure all work is co-ordinated. This is achieved by a Worldwide Engineering Release System (WERS) that took the company five years to develop and cost $77 million. The system gathers engineering data from Ford sites around the world and distributes it to the sites where it is needed, through the use of ground and satellite communication networks.

To communicate more effectively with company employees, Ford developed a television network with TV screens installed in Ford plants and offices. Details about the company are broadcast daily. A similar system is being installed in Ford's British car dealer network to communicate directly with employees selling vehicles. It will also be possible to use telephone links to communicate from the showrooms back to studios to give instant and live feedback and coverage of events taking place around the world.

Flat

In a flat organisation, there are fewer levels or grades of staff. Sometimes an organisational structure is

127

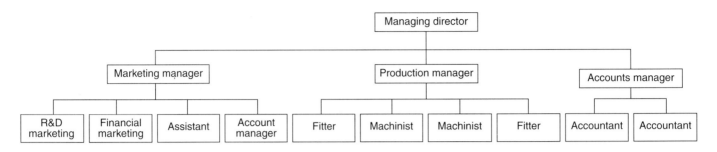

Figure 9.2 Example of a flat organisational structure

considered to be 'flat' if a manager or supervisor has more than five subordinates reporting. The emphasis is placed more on co-operation and teamworking across the organisation as a whole rather than giving authority to individuals on a 'ladder' system. This is illustrated in Figure 9.2, where below the managing director are three managers (accounts, production and marketing) – everyone else in the organisation has the same level of authority.

Did you know?

An example of a flat organisation is Virgin. Although there are managers in charge at different levels, employees work towards common goals and make their own decisions along the way – the top management do not make *all* the decisions.

Case study – Hanson PLC

Hanson PLC is a multinational organisation owning businesses in a number of different fields. The company runs tobacco firms St Bruno, Castella, Embassy and John Player Special. Several building companies also come under the company's wing, as do industrial products such as Switchmaster and SLD Pumps.

1 Hanson is organised by product. How do you think this affects the organisation structure of the company?
2 Hanson's business interests span the globe. What are the advantages and disadvantages of this?

Case study – The Rogers Corporation

Bob Rogers started The Rogers Corporation in 1972. He had intended the company to

employ only himself and his family, but the company took on a life of its own – it is very successful!

Bob employs his two daughters (Joanne and Lindy), his son (Steve) and 120 other 'locals'. Although Joanne, Lindy and Steve hold management positions, Bob has always been keen to keep the company working as effectively as possible without a heavy management hand. Bob employed people as the need arose, but didn't take on extra managers or supervisors.

The Rogers Corporation makes computer keyboards – very important in recent years. The functional departments are:

■ Marketing
■ Sales
■ Manufacturing
■ Accounts
■ Research & Development.

Although people are employed to be in a functional area, Bob is keen to stress the importance of keeping information flowing – 'just because you work in marketing doesn't mean you shouldn't know what's going on in accounts,' he's often heard saying.

The employees appreciate this. Rather than just working in their own functions all the time, they freely and happily move around, offering thoughts of their own to the way the company could improve. Because people like the atmosphere they often work overtime without asking for extra pay, and take work home with them to make sure it is ready on time. Bob is convinced his flat structured company is effective for this very reason.

1 Why do you think a flat organisation structure is successful in this company?
2 Find examples of companies that work in a hierarchical structure and flat structure, and compare the different approaches.
3 What are the main differences in the day-to-day running of the different approaches to the companies' structures?

Why are we concerned with the way organisations are structured? Surely that's for people studying business studies? Organisation structure *is* very important to anyone in the world of IT – we need to know how information flows around an organisation – that's what this element is all about. If we don't know how information flows in an organisation then information technology can't work – after all, IT is all about the flow of information. It's a good idea for your tutor group to contact a few local firms and find out how they are structured, just so you can see how any differences work.

The table below lists possible advantages and disadvantages of the two types of organisational structure. Remember, though, that most enterprises adopt a structure that falls between the extremes of hierarchical and flat organisation. Also, recognise that the most appropriate, and most effective, structure for an enterprise may depend on its maturity, its market characteristics and its size.

Type of organisation	Advantages	Disadvantages
Hierarchical	More frequent opportunities for promotion	May impede decision-making
	Greater scope for developing expertise	Likely to encourage set ways of behaviour
	Easier definition of roles and responsibilities	May hamper the assembly of special-purpose teams for intermittent tasks
Flat	May encourage development and exercise of initiative	Consequences of an individual leaving at short notice may be serious
	Opportunity for corporate responsiveness to unforeseen events	Risk of failure to let centres of competence emerge

Figure 9.3 Hierarchial and flat organisations compared

Evidence collection point

At this point your tutor may wish you to start work on the project which will prove to your tutor and assessor that you understand this section of the element. If so, turn to page 142 and do

Section 1 of the project. This covers the first evidence indicator for this element.

Explain the forms and types of information generated and used by functions in organisations

Forms of information

No matter what type of organisation you belong to, there are only three forms that the information you use in it can take.

Verbal or oral

Verbal or oral information arises from people talking to one another. In a business environment, it can be used to communicate ideas, decisions, instructions, questions, requests and news. It is often quick, but is not always as it seems. For example, some people are sarcastic. The *actual* words being spoken are not meant in their true way – there is an unspoken message that is coming across. People do not just talk to each other through words. They also talk through their body language. If you are praised by a tutor for a piece of work you did, but the tutor glowers at you at the same time, you are unlikely to believe the praise – the glower will affect the words that are spoken.

There are a number of different occasions for verbal or oral communication which include the following:

- *Group meetings* where large numbers of people meet together to discuss matters of importance. It's unlikely that any detailed matters will be dealt with as there will be too many people to make this possible.
- *Specialist meetings* where detailed matters in which all those present have an interest are discussed and where decisions may be taken.
- *Departmental meetings* take place to tell everyone in the department what is going on. It's quite common to have one departmental meeting a week in many companies.
- *Project meetings* in which those working on a common endeavour can review progress, and plan.
- *One-to-one meetings* – when your manager asks you if both of you can have a talk, then this counts as a *one-to-one meeting*. It's quite reasonable to say that an interview or a yearly job evaluation come under this heading.
- *Briefing groups* are not meetings as such, but more a session where one person informs everyone else what is going to happen. At the end there may be a question-and-answer session.
- *The 'grapevine'* where rumours start. It's a very powerful management tool if used correctly, as information can be passed around quickly and efficiently without the need for managers to spend time or effort telling everyone.
- *Lectures, formal presentations* – You no doubt know about lectures already! They can be very formal, with the lecturer talking to the group as a whole, taking any questions at the end.
- *'Open door' policies* where employees can go to talk to their manager any time they are at work. They are effective, as the manager gets to know about problems as they occur and doesn't have to wait until later to be told.

Documents

How often have you thought you told someone something only to be informed by them that you hadn't? If you had a record of what you said you could refer back to it to find out precisely what words you used. Without the record it's a problem. The way around this is to make a record on paper. It's not practical to do this for *everything*, but if important information is documented and signed by the parties concerned then it is unlikely to be disputed. In law, anything not documented is more

difficult to prove – if a witness claims to have heard someone else say something then it is classed as hearsay, and will not stand up to the same degree of scrutiny as written evidence. One of the problems with documented information is that it is bulky.

The process of documenting information varies from simple to complex. The process might be used to convey information needed by several people in different places. Complex information may call for extensive detail, often when information has to be looked at over a period of time. There are several different methods of documentation. They include the following:

- *Letters* can include all the different forms of letters, notes and memos requesting or providing information. They generally need a response within a short time.
- *Orders* stipulate the goods or services a client requires.
- *Invoices* are bills sent out to customers once the goods or services have been despatched or, perhaps, received. They generally ask the customer to pay within a specified period.
- *Delivery notes* – when goods are delivered, they are usually accompanied by a delivery note giving details of the day, date and time of despatch or delivery, and any other details the supplier wishes to include.
- *Information bulletins* – these may be on a notice board or an electronic bulletin board. They are less likely to need responding to than paperwork, but give staff information on events and changes in the company. Some organisations may use regular *newsletters* as information bulletins.
- *Newsletters* – Large organisations tend to produce newsletters to send to staff rather than put information on notice boards. This is particularly useful when the organisation employs large numbers of people spread out over a large site or number of sites.
- *Company reports* provide a more formal way of informing people. They are often prestige publications to give confidence to shareholders and the financial markets. They tend to be used also to let people on jobs or projects know how well the work is going. They also act as records for future use.
- *Employee appraisals* – appraisal reports are written by a manager about an employee's performance during the last 12 months. The employee reads the report, and if he or she agrees with the contents, signs it and keeps a copy. Another copy is kept by Personnel in the employee's file for

reference should the information ever be needed in the future.

- *Notice boards* – if you want to inform a lot of people about something without talking to them, then a notice board is convenient. However, notice board documents are generally very informal and cannot be confidential or aimed at one particular person as everyone in the organisation can read them.
- *Operations and training manuals* – if you've ever tried to read any of these you'll probably be aware that they can be boring and impenetrable. Why? Because they have to be complete and entirely specific to make sure that all the necessary details are covered. If they are anything other than wholly specific then the information in them could be misinterpreted.
- *Employee suggestion schemes and questionnaires* – invite employees either to make suggestions for improvements at work or, when they are given questionnaires to fill in, give their views on different aspects of work.

Did you know?

To make your documents stand out more, a company called Paper Direct in Leicester has developed a range of business paper and presentation sets. They are user friendly, allowing Windows-based software to help make document designs. Printing is simply a process of feeding the paper into popular printer models – the software (that Paper Direct can supply if necessary) does the rest.

Electronic

Electronic information overcomes the problem of space. By using the computerised equipment discussed in earlier chapters, such as hard disk drives, volumes of information can be stored in small spaces. Electronic information is also easier to transport than documents – think about email and the Internet. The type of information which can be sent by email is the same as that listed for documents. The difference is that the information can be conveyed around the world in fractions of a second, or perhaps a few seconds. Imagine how much longer it would take to carry the information to its destination. Electronic communications can be established along cables of many kinds, or through the use of satellite or terrestrial broadcast channels. Unit 4 addresses these techniques. The systems of electronic communication include in some physical

form fax, email, the Internet, telex, teletext, mobile phones, electronic pagers, television, radio and others.

Figure 9.4 Fax machine

So what are the advantages and disadvantages of electronic communication? As with other modes of sending information, the details of how it is sent to a customer electronically and what is included will depend on its purpose. For example, a travel firm may give you information on the date of your holiday, the time and place of the flight, the destination and maps of the area. A company making pipes will be able to give information only on *their* products – the lengths, material, weights, diameters, delivery time and the cost.

Activity

Find out what methods of electronic communication are used in your school or college. Make a list of the types of information used and its urgency, volume and confidentiality, and the advantages of using these systems over verbal or oral communication or documentation.

Types of information

The type of information that is generated in an organisation depends very much on the organisation itself, and also on the function of the department generating or using the information.

131

Sales and purchases:

Whether you're buying or selling in an organisation you will be involved with orders and invoices.

Orders When a company receives an order for goods or services, the customer details are noted with the requirements of the order. This has traditionally been done using pen and paper, but to speed everything up it is common practice now for the person taking the order to key details into a computer. This makes the job of creating invoices far quicker and more efficient. The detail that may be taken could include:

- the name, address and telephone number of the person placing the order
- the address the order is to be sent to (if it's different from the previous address taken)
- the goods required in the order
- the time and date.

These details can then be transferred into an invoice.

Preferred Hi-Fi Ltd
10 Katherine Street
Reading
RG1 7PA

Tel: 0132 444 7000

PURCHASE ORDER

VAT Reg No 414/62731/77

To: Video Manufacture plc
Bridge Trading Estate
Bridge Lane
BR1 TTA

Date: 17 December 199-

Order No: 8365192

Please supply

QUANTITY	DESCRIPTION	REF. NO.	UNIT PRICE
10	Two-head video	VM2SP	205.00
10	Four-head video	VM4SP	239.00
5	NICAM video	VM4NV	313.00

Yellow copy: file

Figure 9.5 Example of a purchase order

The *invoice* shows all details of the sale:

- The names and addresses of the buyer and seller – if the order is lost then anyone finding it can send it back to one or the other.
- The delivery address – so the Post Office or delivery company knows where to send the order to.
- An invoice reference number – this is for tracking the order. If there are any problems once the goods are received, the buyer can ring up the seller and quote the reference number. This way both parties know exactly which goods are being dealt with.
- Details of the products being sold (the cost, quantity, date of sale) – this is generally a very short description of the product. It may include a product code or reference number. For example, if a publishing company sends a book to someone, the invoice will include the book title, the author and the ISBN (the international reference number the book holds).
- The quantity and cost of items being sold – so both parties know exactly how many items are being paid for, how much each of them costs and the total cost.
- The date and time of the sale – this simply gives more details regarding the sale, should anyone need them.
- Payment instructions – whether payment may be made by credit card or cheque, for example.
- Discount rate – whether there is a discount for bulk orders.
- VAT – presently set at 17.5%. VAT is Value Added Tax that must be paid on most goods.

Case study – Radio Works Ltd

Radio Works Ltd is a company in Coventry making radios. They have recently extended their range to include car radios and hand-portable television sets. They specialise in high-quality products, and have a reputation to match – many of the major high-street stores buy radios from them and put their own name on the products – House of Spencer being the biggest.

Last week, Julia Montgomery was in her local branch of House of Spencer near the Metro Centre in Gateshead looking at radio sets. She found the radio set she was after, but wanted it in red – the one colour not in stock. Julia made her way to the inquiry desk and asked about ordering a red model. She said she would order one if it were available.

Simon on the enquiry desk took down Julia's customer information and typed it into a computer. He waited a few seconds while the computer phoned through to Radio Works Ltd's computer. He asked their computer if any red radios were in stock, and when this was confirmed he ordered one. After waiting a few more seconds, Simon's screen flashed and a notice appeared saying the radio would be delivered in two days' time. Simon told Julia when her radio would be ready for her to pick up, and gave her a customer information sheet with details of the time and date of its delivery.

Meanwhile, a sales order and invoice were being prepared at Radio Works Ltd to be sent with the red radio to House of Spencer.

Two days later, the radio arrived at House of Spencer with a purchase order and invoice. The purchase order was signed immediately upon receipt and sent back to Radio Works Ltd. The invoice was sent to the accounts department at House of Spencer for payment.

When Julia returned to pick up her radio, she was presented with a copy of the sales order (made out to House of Spencer, but with her details on as well, being the final customer) and her radio, and promptly paid for it. House of Spencer had sold the radio to Julia before they had even paid Radio Works Ltd for it themselves! This is positive cash flow for a business.

Market information

Market information comes from market research – how well an organisation knows its market, and how much information an organisation has about the market it works in. Organisations obtain market information by

- working in the same market for a long time and developing an understanding of how the market reacts to change
- market research questionnaires and interviews;
- reports from sales representatives
- items in trade journals
- purchasing the information from outside agencies
- employing other companies to carry out market research for them.

Many organisations are now collecting market information that wouldn't have done so in the past. For example, hospitals are now interested in the average length of time each patient stays, and how many operations take place each day. Hospital A finds that the average length of stay of patients having operation X is Y days, whereas for hospital B it is Y + 3 days for the same operation. Hospital A may advertise this, as it can tell people they will be

out of hospital and back at home three days faster than they would if they go to hospital B for the same operation. Another example: educational publishers keep records of the number of students studying different subjects so they can predict how many books can be sold in each subject area.

When we think about supply and demand in marketing, we consider the different ways companies and customers work with each other. Every company wants as many customers as it can cope with. However, not all customers want the products companies sell, and so we have to find ways to bridge the gap. Knowing this, companies find as much information as they can about their customers' preferences. It's not always easy – companies have to look at their own stocks and trading records to work out how successful they have been. They are concerned with the following:

- *How many items from each product line were sold*: Companies are always interested in this so they know how well they are doing. If there are any lines that are not selling then they have wasted the money invested in stock. This may mean that they can't afford to make new products and, if the worst comes to the worst, they can't afford to pay wages! At this point, the company becomes bankrupt and closes.
- *Stock*: Companies not only need to know how many products they have sold but also how many products they had and have in stock. In an ideal world, a company has a bare minimum of stock – just enough to meet demand.
- *Size of market*: There's an old saying that everything has a price. What this means is that anything can be sold at a price – exactly what that price is depends on many things. For example, it is theoretically possible to sell a car that has been in a crash. The owner is unlikely to get much for it! Whenever we deal with products we have to know how many people will be willing to buy them. Even the greatest product in the world won't necessarily sell in big quantities if its price is very high. Think about some of the supercars made by Jaguar, Lamborghini, Ferrari and McLaren. They cost from £60,000 and go up to £600,000. Although there will probably be millions of people that would dearly love to own one of these supercars, very few of us ever actually do. Why? Because the price is too high for us. The market the companies are working in is very small and the products have to be priced accordingly to make up for the fact that they won't be able to make or sell them in large quantities. In a similar way, Toyota, Ford, Nissan, Rover and Renault aim

Figure 10.6 Car assembly line

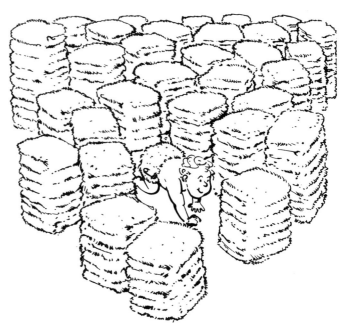

for mass-produced cars at relatively low prices. Why? Because that's the market that most people can afford to buy cars in. If they priced their cars much higher, nobody would buy them.

■ *Value of market*: You may be thinking that this is related to the size of the market and to some degree you are right. However, some small markets are incredibly valuable to some companies. Next time you go into a department store, pay a visit to the perfume counter. You will probably find the most expensive perfumes don't sell as often as the cheaper brands. They still make a lot of money, though. Why? It's generally the case that one brand of perfume costs as much as another to produce. The prices are different because they are aimed at different markets. The cheaper brands are happy to sell more bottles for less money. The more expensive brands sell fewer bottles, but want more money for each one they sell. Even though they sell fewer, they make a bigger margin on each bottle they sell.

■ *What makes people buy?*: There is no perfect answer to this question. If there was then no company would ever go bankrupt. Advertising encourages people to buy products by letting them know what's available on the market. The most important factor is to find a product that people need. For example, new-born babies need nappies. It is common to use disposable nappies as they are more convenient. They also need replacing constantly (or at least as long as the baby needs them), and there seems to be a never-ending supply of babies! Therefore, any company

making nappies has found a market need. In itself, this doesn't guarantee that people will buy their products. They want goods that are reliable and that have a reputation for quality. People also want value for money – they need to feel that the goods they buy are worth the money they pay for them. Walt Disney was aware of this when he first opened Disneyland in California. He told all his employees that if a ride was meant to last for a minute then they should make it last one minute and five seconds. If it lasted only 55 seconds, customers would feel they were being cheated. By making it last just that little bit longer, customers would think they were getting more than their money's worth – almost as though they were getting something for nothing.

■ *What competitors sell*: This makes a big difference to the way companies work. The last time you saw a new product launched, were there any similar products on the market soon afterwards? There generally are, because if one company sells a product that is successful, competitors try their best to do the same – they just make their own version of the product. A good example of this is in the early days of the PC industry. Apple Corporation in America was selling computers quickly. IBM wanted to sell computers too so they created their own version of the PC. IBM sold more PCs than Apple, but IBM didn't think that they would have competitors in the market place. Other companies were starting to build their own versions of the IBM PC which were

134

100% compatible but far cheaper. The world market loved it and bought the cheaper machines in preference to the IBM PC.

- *Price and quality*: This has been discussed in the light of some other examples so far. Let's just think about these two factors alone, though. If a product is of a high enough quality, does the price matter? If the price is right, does the quality matter? It all depends on who is buying the products. Normally, anyone buying goods is balancing the price and the quality of the different products on the market. They find what is best for them. A rule of thumb is to say that people buy the best-quality product they can at the price that is right for them.

Did you know?

At the beginning of the twentieth century, the Eastman Kodak company had remarkable success with its Brownie camera. It was loaded with a 100-exposure film and, once used, returned to Kodak for developing. The camera was then reloaded and resold. In 1987, Kodak decided to release a similar product – this time a single-use camera already loaded with film that had to be returned to a processor for developing. Some 100 million were sold until 1993, when environmental pressure groups highlighted the volume of waste the product was generating.

However, in 1990 Kodak had developed a system whereby the cameras could be recycled. The processors get paid for each camera they return to Kodak, where the film is reloaded. This can happen up to six times for a single camera and, by 1994, 33 million cameras had been recycled – the recycling rate had hit 50%.

This case study illustrates how a company can alter its products if customer demand is great enough. Do you believe this could happen to all companies?

Design specification

A design specification is a document giving details of every aspect of a product. It's required so that designers can produce drawings and technical data to have the product made. It's also important that the production, management, sales and marketing departments are aware of all aspects of design so they can start costing, promoting and selling the product. The type of information needed to produce a design specification may include the following:

- what the customer requires (this information comes from the marketing department)
- the materials to be used in production (machine operators need this information, along with sales teams so they can tell clients about the product, and purchasing so they can buy the raw materials required)
- thickness of materials to be used (the production department need to know this so they can ensure they have the necessary machines to do the job)
- technical details of the product – height, width, weight (again, the production department need to know this information to make sure their machines can cope. The purchasing department also need to know so they can find a supplier that can supply the goods at the right specifications)
- how robust it has to be. For example, a passenger lift has to be more sturdy than a chair for safety reasons. (Sales personnel need to know this when they are telling customers how the product will perform. So too will the purchasing department as they must know the materials they are buying will be capable of doing the job)
- costs of materials they have to work with so they don't go over budget (the purchasing department needs to know this, as well as accounts and any project manager who is involved)
- details of competitive products
- training requirements for proper use of the product
- health and safety considerations.

Sample design specification

Climbing boots

- **Outline requirement:** Range of sizes of good quality boots for mountaineers and hill-walkers.
- **Materials:** Sole, vulcanised rubber with conventional tread. Uppers to be double-skin leather, with metal hooks and eyelets.
- **Thickeners:** Sole, 8 mm, uppers, 3 mm each layer.
- **Technical details:** Sizes 4 to 13. Weight for a pair to be between 1.0 kg and 1.4 kg. Two width fittings. Reinforced heels and toe caps. Plastic insole, porous. Nylon laces. Colour brown.
- **Robustness:** Must be rugged enough to match competitive products.
- **Price guideline:** Less than £80 retail.
- **Target availability date:** 30 Aug XX.
- **Marketing support:** Advertising programme to be announced.

Figure 9.7 Specification for a product

Operational information

This information relates to the way an organisation works. Typical examples are work instructions, quality standards, decisions, responsibilities, holiday dates and hours of work. Some organisations will have more operational information and others less. This type of information may be set out in a firm's staff handbook.

Additional entries may cover copyright in inventions, sickness, discipline procedures and union membership.

Customer information

Companies keep records about customers so they can contact them in the future or so the information can be used to help the company do the job for the customer more effectively. This information will generally include the following:

- name
- address
- telephone number
- payment record
- credit limit (Customers very often don't pay for goods when they take them – they are invoiced and pay at a later date. The customer is using credit to buy the goods. If they always pay on time then they have a good credit record and the amount of credit they can have is increased. If they don't pay bills on time then the credit limit may be reduced or even removed)
- the addresses of all branches of a corporate customer.

Depending on the business, other information may be kept. A hairdresser, for example, may keep details such as the colour of hair dye used on different customers' hair. Dressmakers keep detailed measurements of clients, and dentists keep records of all work done on people's teeth. A salesperson may be interested in keeping personal records about clients such as the names of their children or where they go for their holidays. This way they create a bond that may help in future sales.

Did you know?

Sainsbury's thought that the customer loyalty cards offered by rival company Tesco were not a threat to them as Sainsbury's was the market leader in supermarket shopping. Tesco's loyalty card system was so successful that Sainsbury now offer their own reward card to customers!

Supplier information

The more an organisation knows about its suppliers, the stronger its bargaining position will be when it comes to buying new supplies. What type of information should they know?

- a contact name and address
- the products they make
- prices of products
- names and addresses of alternative suppliers
- lead times (how long it takes for delivery of goods).

Functions in organisations

We now turn our attention to organisational functions – what they are and what they do. We shall look at *internal* functions first.

Purchasing

In their simplest form, purchasing departments buy materials and virtually anything else that is needed in organisations. It's not always as straightforward as this appears. As organisations are constantly trying to buy everything for the best price they possibly can, part of the role the purchasing department has is to *find* the products needed at the best possible price. This doesn't mean they find the cheapest – they must buy quality products – but the products they *do* buy have to be the best they can get for the money they are spending. They also have to strike the right balance, often between lower price and smaller quantities bought.

Marketing

It is commonly thought that *marketing* is the same as *selling*. This isn't the case. A marketing department is concerned with finding out what people want to buy, passing this information on to the other departments in the organisation, who in turn will make the products. They concentrate their efforts (generally) around the Four Ps – *product, price, place* and *promotion*.

Product

This is the product that is to be sold. It has to be able to do the right job, be the right size, shape, colour. If a company is not willing to alter its products in line with what the customer wants, it will probably go out of business. Henry Ford (who started the Ford motor company) sold the first mass-produced car. He told *his* customers 'You can have any colour you want – as long as it's black.' Ford could afford to say that – there were no alternatives to his car in the early days of the twentieth century. It's not the same now – if the customers don't get what they ask for then the company goes out of business.

Price

How much will the product cost? If it's too expensive then nobody will buy it. If a product is too cheap people may not buy it because they think it's no good. It is a case of setting the right price for every product.

Place

Where is the product to be sold? You may find that it's possible to sell a product in one country but not another, owing to local laws or cultures. For example, Cadbury's Roses chocolates sell in huge quantities in the UK. When Cadbury's decided to try to sell them in the Arab states, they had to change part of the recipe as it clashed with the local culture. If they hadn't done this, the product simply wouldn't have sold.

Promotion

How is the product to be advertised or promoted? Should television advertising be paid for, or would it be better to use magazines or direct mail, as it's cheaper? It all depends on the volumes you intend to sell. It also depends on *where* the product is to be sold. Is it to be sold locally, or on a national basis? It may be an idea to test the market by giving away free samples and asking people what they think of them. There are very many ways of promoting products.

Design

The design department in an organisation is responsible for making sure that the product design meets any legal requirements and the specifications

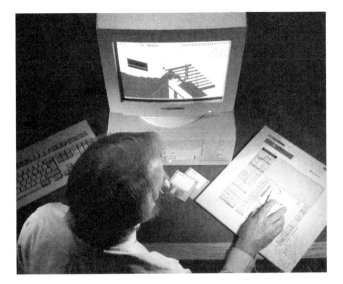

Figure 9.8 Designer using CAD

of the customer (from the information the marketing department issued). They take into consideration the materials the product will be made of, the conditions it will have to function in, the people that will be the end users of the product and any other needs that are special to each individual product. The main tools of a design department are now IT-based computer-aided design (CAD). Modern CAD systems allow designers to make alterations to drawing designs quickly and easily, and through linking CAD with computer-aided manufacturing (CAM), the product manufacturing time can be greatly reduced.

Operations

In contrast to the 'operational information' looked at earlier, we are here concerned with the operational management of the business itself. The operations function in an organisation is responsible for making sure that all work relating to production is carried out. They make the decisions as to how the products or services are made, and which members of the team will make them. The operations function obviously changes from one organisation to another, depending on the type of product or service the organisation provides.

Sales

The sales team are responsible for selling whatever the organisation makes. They spend a good deal of time travelling to clients, trying to match their needs with the products the organisation is selling. This sounds easier than it is. As there is so much competition in the market today, customers have a greater choice of products than ever before. They can therefore pick and choose what they buy. Sales teams very often have quotas they have to meet. This means that they have to make a certain number of sales each month or else they are below their targets. This is very important – if the products don't sell, the rest of the workforce will end up without jobs.

Once a salesperson has sold something to a customer, they are keen to keep that customer happy. This is because it's far harder to get new customers than it is to keep old ones.

Finance

This area is the responsibility of the accounts department, normally answering to the finance director, or controller, who has to have regard for the overall financial health of the enterprise. This executive must ensure that budgets are set and met, and that the flow of funds is in line with the business's needs.

The accounts department ensure that all completed work is paid for, and that bills and invoices coming in to the organisation are paid. All personnel employed by the organisation are paid by this department, very often directly through bank accounts. Earlier in this chapter *credit* was discussed. It's the finance department that arranges credit facilities for customers.

Personnel

The personnel department is responsible for employing staff throughout an organisation. They are also responsible for making sure that staff are looked after while at work. Any training staff need, any legal obligations the company has to work to, any matters relating to the well-being of staff are also the responsibility of personnel. They essentially look after staff and make sure their needs are met.

Now that the internal functions have been discussed, we need to look at the *external* functions that organisations perform.

Suppliers

Almost every business needs suppliers to provide components, parts, information or intangible services. There are also suppliers of money, who help organisations to run efficiently. Companies often have more than one supplier for any product or service to provide competition and back-up.

Customers

Every commercial undertaking needs customers. The flow of money from customers is likely to be the principal source of funds.

Legal and statutory bodies

In most countries there are legal and statutory bodies that exist to look after the interests of the consumer and to protect the interests of the country. In the UK, legal bodies include the Inland Revenue, which collects taxes on behalf of the government. Statutory bodies include OFWAT who supervise the companies that run the water industry. The Monopolies and Mergers Commission ensures that no one company becomes too big and powerful. In the USA, the equivalent of the Monopolies and Mergers Commission is the US Justice Department Anti-Trust department. Recently, they were investigating Microsoft, believing that the company was becoming too powerful worldwide.

Did you know?

Many companies operate strict rules of practice stipulating whom they can trade with – over and above any restrictions owing to legislation that exists. The Body Shop as an organisation is keen to support natural products that come from third-world countries. Levi Strauss & Co. have strict guidelines stating they will not trade with countries where their brand image may be harmed, in countries where the health and safety of workers is not of paramount importance or where human rights are ignored, and where political problems exist.

Evidence collection point

At this point your tutor may wish you to start work on the project which will prove to your tutor and assessor that you understand this section of the element. If so, turn to page 142. If you have already started the project you may be ready to do Section 2. This covers the second evidence indicator for this element.

Produce diagrams showing the flow of information between functions in organisations

Internal functions

There are no two organisations that work in exactly the same way. The information flow inside organisations depends on what the organisation does and the type of structure it has. So, although we can't be sure that they apply to *every* organisation, we can make some generalised assumptions as to how information flows between functions. You should visit several organisations to research their information flow.

At first sight the pattern of information flow between internal functions looks very complex. The possible links look like Figure 9.9. However, it is not so daunting in real life, partly because not every link has much information to carry.

In any one business, top management identifies the functions that need to be recognised individually. These are the functions needed to provide efficient operation of the enterprise as a whole. Thereafter the nature of the information that has to flow will define itself.

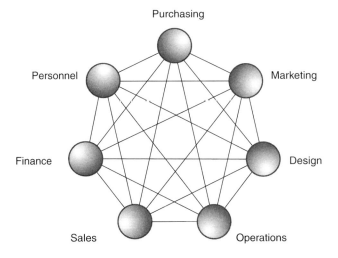

Figure 9.9 Theoretical, fully multiplexed information flow between functions

Also, the actual arrangement of the links, or channels, used for conveying the information may well be in the form of a spoked wheel, with all information flow being sent to and from the centre of the wheel like this:

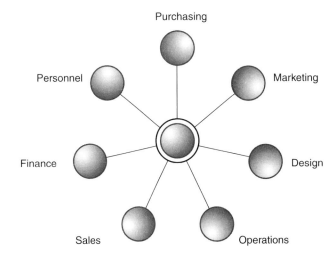

Figure 9.10 Centralised management of information flow between functions

On reaching the centre the information would be directed to the function intended to receive it. Chapters 14 and 15 (elements 4.2 and 4.3) enlarge on this subject.

Examples of the types of information flowing between functions within a medium-sized manufacturing company are discussed below.

Finance to all other functions

All functions and departments need to know their financial targets and performance history including:

■ budgets, and budget changes
■ financial performance reports
■ approval of expenditure requests.

Operations to personnel

Personnel have to respond to the operational needs of a business. To fulfil their role properly they need complete information in good time:

■ recruitment goals for engineers, production workers and graduate trainees
■ sickness and injury statistics
■ applications for early retirement.

Sales to marketing

Marketing needs as much information as possible from the sales force about the market:

■ reports on competitive activity
■ resistance to sale of particular products
■ opportunities identified in the market.

Operations to design

Design needs to know the outline specification of products that are to be developed so that manufacture can begin at the chosen moment:

■ maintenance problems
■ reliability problems
■ manufacturing suggestions.

Information from marketing

The other spokes of our wheel will likewise carry other information as it is needed. As an example, suppose that marketing had identified the opportunity to sell a new kind of product, and wanted to tell finance (who would have to approve whatever expenditure would be needed to bring the prospective new product to the market), design (to give early warning of a possible design requirement) and purchasing (so they could start looking for sources of supply for the materials that would be needed). The flow of information would look like Figure 9.11.

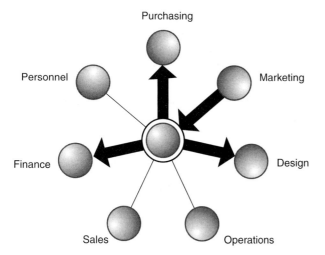

Figure 9.11 The distribution of marketing information

External functions

Now that we've looked at the flow of information between the internal functions, let's consider the external functions. They are

■ suppliers
■ customers
■ legal and statutory bodies.

Customers and suppliers

The categories of information flowing between businesses and their customers and suppliers are similar, but go in opposite directions:

From customers, to suppliers
■ requests for prices
■ purchase orders
■ payments
■ fault reports.

To customers, from suppliers
■ price quotations
■ catalogues
■ delivery notes
■ invoices
■ statements
■ promotional material.

Legal and statutory bodies

The information flow will be to and from all these bodies for a large company, but possibly only to and from some of them for a small business:

■ The Inland Revenue collects tax under 'Pay As You Earn' (PAYE) from employees, and directly on business profits.
■ Departments of Health and Social Security receive National Insurance contributions, and deal with statutory sick pay, medical cover at work and other matters.
■ The Health and Safety Executive administer the law in their field, and distribute guidelines on good industrial practice.
■ Customs and Excise handle VAT payments and refunds.
■ The Office of Fair Trading takes a keen interest in commercial conduct.
■ The Data Protection Registrar monitors the operation of the Data Protection Act, and follows up complaints and abuses.

- If the company is quoted on the Stock Exchange there are procedures and financial ratios that have to be observed.
- The Ministry of Agriculture, Fisheries and Food arranges supervision of businesses operating in these fields.
- Local authorities have interaction with businesses over planning, roads, the business rate and many other topics.

There are other legal and statutory bodies with which certain businesses will need to exchange information.

Evidence collection point

At this point your tutor may wish you to start work on the project which will prove to your tutor and assessor that you understand this part of the element. If so, turn to page 142. If you have already started the project you may be ready to do Section 3. This covers the third evidence indicator for this element.

Comparing the flow of information in different organisations

You will get far more out of this performance criterion if you arrange to visit a few organisations of different sizes and with different functions and organisational structures. Don't just leave it to your tutor – organise it with a group of friends. This way *you* benefit from the experience of organising visits. The bosses of the organisations will be far more responsive to you if *you* arrange it yourself rather than leaving it to your tutor.

If you can't get out to visit a few organisations, use the case studies that follow as a start for comparing information flow through organisations. Read through the case studies and work out the differences between the organisations. When you have completed this task, either phone or write to a number of organisations requesting relevant information.

Many people don't believe that companies reply to this type of request. You will be surprised just how many want students to be aware of how they work – after all, they want the best students to work for them in the future. If you show you are keen, you could be the one! Companies also see students as potential customers. Proof of how interested companies are to help students is here in this book.

Case study

The Headline Mail Order firm works from a large warehouse in York. Telephone operators take orders by telephone for clothes and household items and input the data into the company computer system. Customer details are taken, along with credit card details.

The computer checks with the credit card companies to make sure the cards have not been reported lost or stolen. Provided everything is OK, the transaction is approved. The computer checks the warehouse to see if the items the customer wants are in stock. If they are, an order is placed.

The warehouse employees receive the order and take the required item out of stock. They scan the bar code to update the company computer system. An invoice is automatically generated by the computer. Both the invoice and the order are sent to the *despatch division* for posting out to the customer. The whole process from telephone order to despatch can take as little as twenty minutes!

This operation shows one way of passing information around departments in an organisation so jobs can be done quickly and effectively.

Let us now think about two completely different kinds of organisation, and note the similarities and differences in the characteristics of their internal information flows.

A multinational manufacturing company

At the top level the company may need a flat organisational structure because the board will have to direct all the operations through the manager responsible in each country. We can suppose that below that level the structure is steeply hierarchical.

The effects of this arrangement will be that within each country the business will reflect the culture discussed earlier. There will be the risk of inflexibility and a tendency towards bureaucracy. There will, however, be the opportunity for top management to insist on standard procedures throughout the whole enterprise, and also to ensure that there is uniformity in business practice and the products made and sold, in so far as local conditions make that sensible.

The nature of the flows of information will be along the lines explored in this chapter, but we want to consider the particular problems at the top level of the business where differences in national laws, languages, accounting practices and business customs have to be taken into account. All these considerations will lead to a much richer interchange of information than would otherwise have been necessary.

One has only to consider the successful activities of Japanese and Korean companies with factories in the UK to focus on the issues.

A small publishing business

Suppose this business is a partnership with just one office. Its main concerns are:

- identifying markets for its books
- securing authors to write books for them
- producing books ready to sell
- selling and distributing books
- controlling the finances of the business, and planning.

The information flow to support this business will be informal, in all probability because of the compact form of the operation. It will include:

- reports on sales, by title and by customer (normally book shops)
- promotional mailings to customers and prospective customers
- correspondence with authors and prospective authors
- receiving manuscripts from authors;
- payment of royalties to authors
- billing customers, and receiving payment
- purchasing printing capacity externally
- distributing financial performance figures, budgets and business plans.

By thinking about these two examples of businesses you will be preparing yourself for tackling Section 4 of the evidence indicator project which follows.

Evidence collection point

At this point your tutor may wish you to start work on the project which will prove to your tutor and assessor that you understand this section of the element. If so, turn to page 142. If you have already started the project you may be ready to do Section 4. This covers the fourth evidence indicator for this element.

Evidence indicator project

This project has been designed to cover all the evidence indicators related to Chapter 9 (Element 3.1). It is divided into four sections. Tutors may wish students to complete the sections at the appropriate points marked in the text. Alternatively, tutors may prefer their students to do the entire project at the end of the element.

Performance criteria: 1–4

Key skills:	Communication	3.1, 3.2, 3.3
	Application of number	–
	IT	–

Scenario: Sunrise Radio – 101.9 FM
A new radio station is being set up in your town. It is to be known as Sunrise Radio – 101.9 FM. The marketing department have a problem. Before Sunrise Radio begins broadcasting, it need clients to buy advertising time. The management must make local companies aware of how advertisements can help them boost sales. However, the marketing department is concerned that they are not attracting the right companies to advertise.

You (as a consultant) have been asked to write a report informing the marketing department of the types of organisations that exist and explaining the flow of information between departments in them, so they are more aware of whom to target.

Section 1
Your report should include a description of all types of organisations: commercial, industrial, public service; and organisational structures: hierarchical and flat. Give two examples of each type of organisation.

You can find out about different types of organisations by visiting some and studying their procedures. You may also be able to find out about organisations by conducting research in the library or by choosing a company as an example, and finding out more information by looking up their description on the Internet.

Section 2
The managing director of Sunrise Radio was very impressed with the results of your report. She now has advertising booked for the first two months of broadcasting.

She has realised that her own organisation structure at the station is not yet right for meeting the internal information-handling needs of the radio station – and if it doesn't start right then it will only get worse as time goes by. You have been commissioned to research and write a report detailing the forms and types of information that exist, and which is of particular use and importance to the radio station. This should include all forms of information, at least four types of information and at least three internal and two external functions.

To help with this, it may be of benefit to visit a local radio station and discuss with employees what information *they* have to deal with in their working lives.

Section 3
The managing director found your last report particularly useful. She has to convince the board of directors that the details you submitted would be useful to Sunrise. Rather than have them read your report, she is keen to know if you can generate some diagrams to illustrate the flow of information between the functions in the radio station. They should be clear and of a high quality as they need to be presented to the Board.

Section 4
Further to their meeting with the managing director, the board of directors is interested in the ideas you helped her put forward. They are not all convinced though, and need to know if the information flow is the same in all organisations, or if it differs.

Write a final report, using any diagrams, tables or information you want, to compare the flow of information in a radio station with that in at least one other organisation, illustrating the same range of types of information that is described in Section 2.

Chapter 10

Investigate data handling systems

So far in this unit we've looked at the ways in which information flows throughout organisations. It's all very well knowing that there is information there, but it has to be *handled,* used or manipulated correctly to be of any benefit. It's quite possible for people to handle data. The only problem is that people are relatively slow and are liable to make mistakes. It's here that we turn to computers to work for us as *data handling systems.* If time is spent setting them up accurately in the first place, then the savings can be immense.

After studying this chapter you should be able to:

1 explain *methods of processing* and *types of data handling systems*
2 compare *objectives* of selected data handling systems
3 compare *methods of data capture* in the selected data handling systems
4 examine *data handling processes* used in systems
5 review performance of systems against their respective *objectives* and make recommendations for improvement.

 Did you know?

In November 1994, Virgin launched its own brand of vodka. It was only a test launch, within the M25, to see how successful the new brand would be.

Cadbury's carried out a similar project before the launch of its Whispa bar. They developed new technology capable of making the chocolate bars after they became aware there was a market for aerated chocolate products. Newcastle was chosen as a test site.

It is only through regional tests such as these that companies can collect data and collate it to predict how successful products will be if launched nationally. Both companies will have used data handling systems to help analyse all the information collected, and help their decision-making.

Consider for a moment the meaning of the phrase *data handling.* It is the process of accepting, holding, manipulating, and presenting data, for a reason. The *reason* may be different for every example we look at. Some people use a Filofax to keep track of their friends' telephone numbers. Others use them as diaries.

A system is a set of rules that have to be applied to the way data or information is manipulated. For simplicity we use computers to do all the hard work for us – we tell them what to do by programming them with the rules.

Methods of processing and types of data handling systems

Computers process all the time – that's one of their main benefits – they are quick, cheap and reliable – and they don't get tired! But do they always process in the same way? For that matter, do we process information in the same way computers do?

It's a good idea every now and again to remind ourselves that *people* design and build computers and, of course, program them. Computers are capable of doing only jobs we tell them to do, so the processes they perform are usually based around a *human* process – if not exactly, then probably close to it.

So what methods of processing are used, by computers or people? Let's see.

Batch processing

This refers to the type of processing that involves the collection of jobs or material to be processed over a period of time. A schedule is created for the jobs that have been collected, followed by one processing session to complete the task. This process has very little contact or interaction with the user. Collect notes until you have 100 pages, then sort and file them – that's batch processing!

Computers batch process information, very often to update the contents of databases. An example is a database holding information about electronic components for several large projects. The user inputs a code number for each component, all specifications and names. When all information is input for the entire *batch,* the computer is instructed to take this information and insert it into the database in the correct order, within the area for each project.

One benefit in using this method is to allow the user to check information when it's typed in to the computer, but *before* it's entered into the database. Any changes that need to be made can be carried out quickly and easily, without having to check the entire database. Batch processing may not be particularly fast as a lot of files are perhaps being processed at a time. Often batch processing is run overnight when computers are not doing other things – they can be used during office hours for other jobs.

The Post Office uses batch processing techniques to sort mail. The sorting machines are not in operation until there is a batch of letters to be sorted. The letters are loaded into the machines that optically read post codes; and each letter in turn is put in a bag for delivery to its particular post code area.

Case study: record charts

Have you ever listened to a chart show on the radio and wondered exactly how they know which record got to Number One? It's all done by computers and batch processing. Every time a customer buys a record in a record shop, it's logged

on the store computer – generally through a bar code reader. The night before the show is to go out, a computer at the radio station contacts the store computer and has it send all its information relating to records sales over the past week. It does this to perhaps several hundred record shops and once they are all finished, adds all the sales together for each record.

All the information is sent to the radio station in batches – generally overnight when telephone calls are cheap and the lines are less likely to be busy or needed for other purposes. If information was sent to the radio station's computer every time a sale was made, the telephone lines would be jammed!

Transaction processing

Whereas batch processing takes a quantity of data and puts it into the system for processing as a single task, transaction processing works in 'real time', or 'immediately'. The computer handles one transaction at a time. Transaction processing systems make sure that other entries to the records in use are impossible and locks other users out while updating is taking place. This is vital if data clashes are to be avoided, and the risk of uncertainty over the contents of a record is to be prevented.

The speed of the computer system will need to be gauged so that individuals wanting to enter transactions are not kept waiting for unacceptably long periods.

Case study

You may have seen credit cards being used in stores. In the past the stores needed the numbers on the front of each card to make an imprint on to carbon-copy paper. This was sent away to the credit card company and the transaction took place. It's not the case now – the details on the *front* of the card are semi-irrelevant as the black strip on the *back* of the card holds all the information needed.

When the customer hands over a credit card to the shop assistant, it is scanned by a special electronic reading device. The machine that does this rings through to the credit card company and runs a check on the card to make sure it's not stolen, and that the person using it has enough credit left to make the transaction.

This is an example of transaction processing – only one transaction is taking place at a time, unlike batch processing where possibly thousands of different items

Figure 10.1 A credit card

of information are presented to the system for processing in a single run.

Single-user processing

If you are using a computer by yourself then you are single-user processing. It's simply a case of one person on one machine doing the job.

For example, you may be given the task of keying names, addresses and telephone numbers into a computer database. This is single-user processing as you're doing it yourself.

Multi-user processing

If you had the task of typing in 1,000 names and addresses into a computer, you would be grateful for any assistance you could get. This is impossible in single-user processing. Multi-user systems link PCs in to a network that is generally controlled by one computer called a *server*. This central computer stores all the software and data files. When one of the PCs in the network has data entered into it, it contacts the central computer and accesses its storage files, ensuring its latest data is saved. As well as having a computer network with a file server, it's possible to use a *mainframe* computer.

A mainframe computer network consists of **one** computer (i.e. one CPU) only, and terminals linked in to this machine. PCs can be used instead of 'dumb' terminals by loading the PCs with software which makes them emulate terminals. Each user of the system has a separate user area (and user file area

to store data in) that nobody else can access. As far as each user is concerned he or she is the only person using the machine, as each terminal responds to all commands in much the same way that a PC does. The CPU is shared among all users, all printers, scanners and any other peripheral equipment.

Why do we have multi-user systems? Multi-user processing systems are appropriate when there are large amounts of data to be entered on to the same computer system. They also have a role when users need to undertake different tasks which all need software or data held centrally. Multi-user systems also allow peripheral devices such as printers to be shared between users.

An example of this arises when telephone directories are put on to a database. Rather than have lots of people enter the data on different PCs and then downloading all the information into one computer at the end of the job, many operators input it on a multi-user mainframe system to save time. This is illustrated in Figure 10.2.

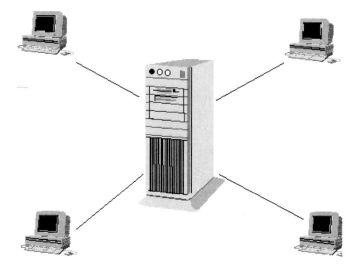

Figure 10.2 Mainframe network system with terminals or PCs.

As computer networking has become more widely adopted companies have taken advantage of the possibility of integrating procedures and data across departments. This has created a need for structures to be standardised throughout an enterprise.

One example of this is the definition of the date of a sale. To generate reliable statistics there must be a common understanding of the term: is it the day a customer signs an order, the date the invoice is prepared, the date the availability of the item is confirmed – or what?

Did you know?

Mainframe computers were once the dominant product in the world of computing. The industry leader was IBM. IBM believed PCs being sold by Apple were no great threat to their position in the world market and decided not to develop their own. It was a different story a year later when IBM realised the PC would largely take over from the mainframe computer. Reacting quickly, IBM designed its own PC, which is still the basis for most modern PCs.

As PCs have become more user friendly, flexible and networked, mainframe computers have been needed for fewer and fewer applications. Those that are used are capable of being connected to PCs in a network – the mainframes too have had to become more user friendly and flexible simply to keep up with what the market wants.

Centralised systems

A centralised system uses computer processing based in one building or area. All computer terminals in the system are connected to the same computer at a focal point, in contrast to having networks spread out over a distance.

A mainframe computer system is a centralised system if the mainframe computer and all terminals from it are on one site, with all the terminals being connected to the central computer. This arrangement is convenient for maintenance as the processing for the entire system is contained in one small area and not widely spread.

Distributed systems

Distributed systems are multi-user systems. They provide a number of co-operating computer systems and communication links to allow dispensed users to derive a flexible service from the system as a whole.

Distributed systems can take many forms:

- Data files may be distributed, or duplicated if required.
- Software may be held locally for certain users, or made available for all users.

- Coverage may be local, national or international.
- Responsibility for statistics, budgets, maintenance and development may be shared if required.
- A wide variety of types of terminals, PCs and bigger computers may be incorporated.
- A wide variety of types of communication channels can be used.
- Security requirements may vary over different facilities of the network, and over different user groups.

A practical example for the use of a distributed system can be seen in the insurance industry. Typically, one computer system holds the data and information about customers, while another holds the information about the insurance policies. Together the system provides facilities for combining this data. When the two systems are brought together to give a customer a quote, the information is gathered and the quote is based on both the insurance policy and the customer details, such as age, profession, income and nationality.

Activity

Compare two examples of processing taken from the methods we have just looked at.

Data handling systems

We have so far looked at methods of processing, but we also need to know about the types of jobs that can be done by data handling systems. There are no absolute rules as to what a computer does when handling data, although there are standards. Try to find out how local firms operate their data handling systems. In the meantime, we shall look closely at some types of data handling systems that exist.

Bookings

Booking systems, also known as reservations systems, are encountered in many aspects of day-to-day life. Examples are

- booking an airline seat
- booking a hotel or B&B room
- booking a place on a package holiday
- reserving a theatre or concert seat
- reserving a book at the library
- making a hospital appointment.

Some of the systems allowing you to make such bookings will be computer-based; others will be run clerically. Either way the requirement is to allocate a limited resource in a way that is governed by a set of rules and that is convenient for the person wishing to make the booking.

Large reservations systems, such as those used by major airlines, involve international data traffic, very high transaction rates and a need for rigorous security.

Payroll

We have already seen how money transactions can take place without actually handling cash. Wages are now generally processed by a computer. If employees are paid according to the number of hours they work, the clocking-on computer may be linked to the wages computer. Not only does this make the task of information transfer faster, but the wages computer also automatically calculates and deducts tax, National Insurance and pension payments, as well as calculating the wages for the week. Any changes in tax rates are easily updated when the Inland Revenue

sends a new disk of details to companies for loading on their payroll system. The payroll system also prints cheques and pay slips, and may arrange for salary payments to be made through the Bankers Automated Clearing Service (BACS).

The main events the payroll performs are shown in Figure 10.3.

Ordering

Ordering systems may handle large quantities of data. Car manufacturers make exceptional use of them with all the subcomponents they require. All components in stock have bar codes attached. When removed from stock the bar codes are scanned and the stock computer takes the item off its database. A predetermined reorder level is set. When this point is reached new stock is ordered. This way the company never runs out of raw materials, or parts.

Sales order processing systems link orders placed on suppliers to reductions in stock levels caused by sales. This kind of system is important in a fast-moving goods operation.

Event and frequency	Action
Introduction of a Finance Act which gives effect to the Chancellor's Budget proposals, usually once a year	Any changes in tax are brought into effect
Annually	■ Employee total tax records for the past year are reset ■ P9, P60 and tax records are printed – P60 sent to employee ■ Any employee who has left the company has records removed ■ Tax details printed and sent to the Inland Revenue
Monthly	■ Any sick leave entered on to the system ■ Pre-payroll is prepared with any alterations taken into account such as unpaid leave taken off wages ■ Salary slips printed and sent to employees ■ A giro credit disk with the above details is prepared so the bank can make salary payments
Weekly	■ Employee time sheets are prepared and entered on to the company computer showing the hours worked ■ Weekly pre-payroll is prepared ■ Weekly exceptions details (reasons for non-payment) are printed ■ Payslips are printed ■ A giro credit disk with the above details is prepared so the bank can make wages payments ■ Company allowances are printed – the Inland Revenue may wish to see this as employees sometimes have to pay extra tax if they receive perks with their job – such as a company car
Daily	■ Changes in employees' status must be accepted and filed. Examples include changes to address, rates of pay or salary, tax codes and any changes in marital status (part of everyone's wages is exempt from tax and how much depends or whether you are married or single)

Figure 10.3 A payroll system

Invoicing

An invoice is a bill. By issuing it a supplier or retailer asserts that a contract exists between buyer and seller for the particular transaction described. The concept of this is in some ways similar to the way the ordering system works. When goods are ordered (perhaps by a company or an individual over a telephone – a catalogue company is a good example of this), invoices are *generally* printed at the same time.

When the order is typed into the data handling system, the computer issues an invoice to the customer. The computer uses the information given with the order and puts it on the invoice – the name, address, cost, and invoice number, as well as details of the goods being bought. At the same time, the data handling system can create a database record showing the details of the invoice.

Normally, before an invoice is printed the system will examine the customer file to check the credit-worthiness of the customer; and also to identify the level of discount to which the customer is entitled, and to apply any discount earned by the products or quantities of products being supplied.

One of the greatest assets an invoicing system has is that it can be set once to do tasks and then it just gets on and does them. For example, you may have seen invoices with VAT (Value Added Tax) added on to the bottom. The rate of VAT is set by the government. It is currently 17.5%, and *most* products and services have this added on. On an invoicing system, once the rate of VAT is set, it automatically calculates and adds the value of VAT that must go on the invoice. If the government changes the rate of VAT then the system is altered and it automatically calculates everything at the new rate.

Stock control

Every item of stock held by a computer will have a stock number. Very often this will be accompanied by a bar code, as we have already seen. When an item is taken out of stock it's logged on the computer. The software recalculates the stock level. In the same way, whenever any new stock is input to the computer the stock level is recalculated.

This is a good example of a data handling system. As far as the computer is concerned, stock is nothing more than a set of numbers, but as long as all stock physically coming in and going out is correctly entered into the data handling system, the computer simply handles the information and keeps accurate records.

Have you ever thought how many different products a supermarket such as Tesco, Sainsbury's or Safeway has on display? There will be more than 25,000 product lines. Without the help of a computer stock control system it would be almost impossible for each store to maintain accurate records of stock. Not only does the computer make it possible, but it also makes it very accurate – it can tell how many items are bought each second of the day.

A good stock control system will have reorder levels set, so that once the stocks on the shelves go below a set limit, new stocks are automatically ordered from the suppliers. This type of efficiency has meant that supermarkets and other companies can work on a 'just in time' (JIT) system. They build up confidence in the reliability of the delivery arrangements, and then order goods only when they are needed. If they don't need them, they aren't ordered. This saves them money, as they don't own stock when it's not selling.

Did you know?

EDI stands for Electronic Document Interchange. Use of the scheme allows suppliers and customers to send commercial documents from computer to computer automatically, thereby saving time, reducing costs, improving record-keeping and increasing accuracy. The retailing company Marks & Spencer plc uses EDI to link its shops and suppliers.

EDI links Marks & Spencer stores to their suppliers by telephone line, allowing individual stores to make orders with very short lead times. For example, if it is a particularly hot summer, it's possible to reorder summer clothes rather than any other stock if it is known they will sell. EDI also makes stock control an automatic procedure, keeps production running and allows staff to check if items are available for customers in other stores throughout the country.

Personal records

Personal records are held by a number of organisations including:

- registrars of births, marriages and deaths
- Department of Social Security
- Department for Education and Employment
- driving licence authorities
- police, perhaps
- credit reference agencies
- medical practicioners and hospitals
- employers
- census offices.

The threat to the liberty and privacy of individuals posed by the possibility of amalgamating the information held by a number of these agencies was largely responsible for the introduction of the Data Protection Act 1984. There are also less formal personal records held for members of clubs and local groups.

In the past all information was stored on paper files. Although it's not always the case, the information is often held on computer nowadays. If we move from one part of the country to another, for example, and need to change doctors, it's possible for our old doctor's surgery to send the information to the new one – quickly and efficiently by computer. For example, you could be discussing a problem with your doctor when he asks you a question about an illness two years ago. Without you having to think, he could key in the required date in your computer records, and the system would produce the information. Information may be stored about us in one format in our personal records, but it can be handled by the computer system to give us the answers to questions in another format. This is done by a database management system that we shall be looking at later.

There are other benefits to the doctor's surgery too. If certain groups have to be contacted for regular screening, or children need to have vaccinations just before their fourth birthday, rather than looking through each record on paper, the computer system can work through its files and find anyone matching

the requirements keyed in to the system. It's also possible for records to be called up from a distant place using a computer – if, for example, a doctor is called out at night, patients' notes can be accessed from the network without having to go to the surgery.

Activity

Contact a number of local companies and find out if they use data handling systems to assist them in their day-to-day business. If they *do* use them, find out what the advantages are for:

- the employees
- the managers
- the customers.

Case study

The car manufacturer Daewoo have car sales points in many of the larger Halfords stores throughout the UK. Rather than have sales people and cars to view on hand, Halfords sales points have a touch-screen computer system where customers can insert the exact specifications of the Daewoo car they want, and the computer displays a picture of it on the screen.

If the customer wishes, a test drive can be ordered, or a car can be bought directly through the computer console, without ever talking to anyone. These last two features require the computer to be connected through a modem to a central booking computer for the entire country.

Levi's introduced a similar system in their Regent Street store. Called the Interactive Fit Guide, it explains the differences between styles of jeans and, armed with the customer's details, fits the customer with the most appropriate pair.

1 Explain the methods of processing each of these systems uses or could use.
2 What type of data handling system would each system use for best results?
3 Could any alternative data handling system be used?

Evidence collection point

At this point your tutor may wish you to start work on the project which will prove to your tutor and assessor that you understand this section of the element. If so, turn to page 157 and do Section 1 of the project. This covers the first evidence indicator for this element.

Objectives of selected data handling systems

Speed

Speed is relative – 30 seconds is no time to wait for a bus, but a very long time if you are holding on to a precipice by your finger-tips. Once, shoppers were prepared to wait 10 to 15 minutes to go through a supermarket checkout. Then the stores, seeking a competitive advantage, thought people would choose to shop with them if they didn't have to queue for so long, so bar code readers were introduced at checkouts. This brought other advantages too, such as easier pricing and stock control.

In an ideal world, the best data handling system will give the user results within a fraction of a second after pressing the Return ↵ key – no detectable waiting at all. This is not always practical though, as the more data the data handling system holds the longer it will take to do the job.

Activity

As a group, think of three situations where computer data has speeded up an operation making it better and more effective – for the business, the customer or both.

Accuracy

There is no point in having a data handling system that gives results that are wrong! If, for example, a student selected information from a library computer on the book *IT – Today and Tomorrow* and was told there were ten copies of it on the shelves, but found they were all out on loan – the data handling system is useless – and *very* frustrating to use. The chances are the student won't bother to use it again. The data handling system is therefore only as good as its accuracy.

Cost

When buying anything, most people look at the cost and see if they are getting good value for money –

'will we get our money's worth out of it?' We do this all the time – when you next buy a can of Coca-Cola, check the price. If it's 25 pence you'll buy it without hesitating. If it's 45 then you'll think about it. If it's £1 then unless you are so thirsty you'll collapse if you don't have a drink, you'll probably walk out of the shop.

In the way we check the price of a can of Coca-Cola, we check the cost of a data handling system. If you employed a workforce of ten thousand, it would be worth computerising the payroll system. If you employed only one other person then it would hardly be worth it! Running costs can be measured by headcount, time spent doing a job, materials used in a job, wastage and spoilage.

There is always a trade-off between cost and performance, but extra cost may not yield extra performance that you need or that is helpful to you. In some cases there may not be any trade-off between cost and accuracy, as all modern systems have accuracy checks and fail-safe mechanisms built in to them.

Support decision-making

Businesses use decision-making support systems all the time. The Ford car manufacturing company uses them to help assess if a new business venture is worth while, or to see if it's too expensive to risk. Similar systems are used to help make forecasts for the weather.

Did you know?

For many years, Canon, the company that makes photocopiers and cameras, has used computers in their products to make them light and versatile. They developed a camera that is capable of focusing on whatever the user looks at through the eyepiece. You might expect equipment as clever as this to cost several thousand pounds and be available only in specialist shops. It's actually available through most high-street camera retailers – and the price is very reasonable too – thanks to manufacturing technology advances, and the economies of scale.

Activity

Imagine that these three types of organisation have computer-based data handling systems:

- a charity employing ten people, working from one office
- an airline based in the UK and flying from Gatwick and Manchester. Seat reservations can be handled through any travel agent
- a corner shop open long hours, seven days a week, that does not use bar codes.

Try to visualise what the main objectives of the data handling system would be in each case. Rank speed, accuracy, cost and decision-making capability in order for each type of business.

Methods of data capture

There are many types of equipment available for capturing data for input to computer systems. Some are specialised, but the following nine are widely used. We first look at the main characteristics of each, then you can try to match the most appropriate device to each of two applications.

Keyboard

This is the most universal of all input devices. It captures data by the user keying it in. It would not need to be bought for a particular task because it will already be part of the system. Further, a keyboard can be used to issue commands to the system, or control a range of functions. Its speed is that of the person operating it.

Mouse

The two-button mouse which forms part of most PC configurations is a low-cost pointing device which is almost essential for working with graphical user interface (GUI) screens and some software products. Some manufacturers offer mice with three buttons and other control features to meet the needs of particular applications.

Keypad

This equipment provides a means of entering numeric data, using just one hand. It is similar to the block of keys on the right-hand end of a standard keyboard.

Bar code reader

This reader is familiar in supermarkets, libraries, and warehouses. Its purpose is to decode the data held in a bar code by noting the black and white spaces making up the bar code panel. The equipment may be built into, say, a desk, or hand held.

OMR

This stands for optical mark reader. It is a device for reading marks that have been made clearly on a card or form in precise places. An application is the form used to enter your choice of numbers for playing the National Lottery; another is for scoring marks earned by candidates in multiple-choice questions such as those that make up your GNVQ unit tests. OMRs allow the results to become available earlier than would otherwise be possible.

MICR

This stands for magnetic ink character recognition, so an MICR reader is the equipment for making use of the technique. These readers are used for a narrow range of applications which call for the capture of data from very large volumes of documents. The characters that can be read by MICR are limited to a set of 13 which includes the digits 0 to 9. You will see these slightly stylised characters running along the bottom edge of a cheque. MICR machines control the sorting of many millions of cheques every day by magnetising the characters and then reading them. This is the largest and best known use of MICR.

Magnetic strip reader

This device has become prolific. Filling stations, shops and many other commercial locations can accept plastic credit, debit, and bank guarantee cards, and capture the data recorded on the magnetic strip by 'swiping' the cards through this kind of reader.

Voice

Voice input has not become widespread because of the difficulty of interpreting what is said without ambiguity. Experiments looking at using a person's voice to recognise an individual, making use of ways of speaking that are said to be as distinctive as finger-prints, have not yet led to the introduction of such measures. There are, however, two sorts of applications which are successfully in operation. One is for workers whose hands are not free to use a keyboard, either because they are disabled or because they need to use both hands for what they are doing. These people can create a voice input on a limited range of topics, such as progress with a given task. The other involves using a telephone to record responses to a range of questions.

Touch-tone telephone

The keys on a touch-tone telephone can be used to enter data to a system which provides for input in that form. An example is the directory inquiry service in which the recorded operator voice says to the caller 'To return the call, press 3.'

Evidence collection point

At this point your tutor may wish you to start work on the project which will prove to your tutor and assessor that you understand this section of the element. If so, turn to page 157. If you have already started the project you may be ready to do Section 2. This covers the second evidence indicator for this element.

Examine data handling processes

Calculating

All calculations are based around the four mathematical functions of addition, subtraction, division and multiplication. It is also fair to say that the making of comparisons is part of the calculating process. By seeing if some quantity is larger than, equal to, or smaller than some other quantity, the program can direct the flow of processing to take the chosen route.

Using Microsoft's Excel spreadsheet package, the following formulas are used for the mathematical functions mentioned.

Addition (+)	e.g. = sum (B2 + B3 + B4 + B5 + B6 + B7)
Subtraction (−)	e.g. = sum (B3 − B2)
Division (/)	e.g. = sum (B3/B5)
Multiplication (*)	e.g. = sum (B3*B5)

See Figure 10.4 which illustrates these examples.

It is also possible for spreadsheet packages to take information from one file (or part of a file) and use it for a calculation in another.

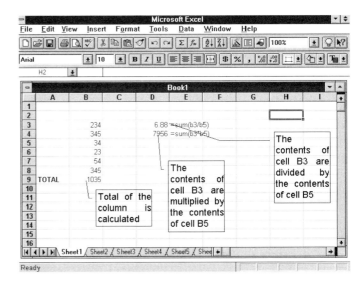

Figure 10.4 Calculations on an Excel spreadsheet package

Converting

The word 'converting' has four distinct meanings when considering the handling of data:. The first meaning is the conversion of file formats from one software product to another. For example, the text file held ready for printing in Microsoft Word can be

153

converted, by software, into a form that can be read and printed by WordPerfect. The same can be done between Lotus and Excel.

This is common now with software, as companies are keen to sell it to people that have traditionally used other makes. By including file conversion filters, new users can take files of work from other packages and use it in new systems. Microsoft's Word 6.0 word processor not only allows the user to convert files created in WordPerfect, but it also has special Help features to assist in getting used to the new software, (Figure 10.5). Some experimental systems also translate text from one language to another, or interpret spoken commands.

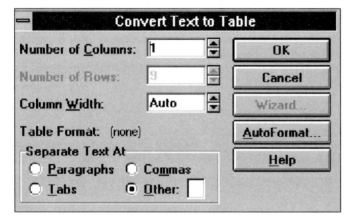

Figure 10.5 The Windows 'Convert' screen

The three remaining meanings of the word 'converting' are as follows:

- the conversion of file data from one arrangement into another: perhaps from rows to columns
- the conversion of data representation from binary to decimal, for example bar codes, or the reverse
- the conversion of page layout from 'portrait' to 'landscape', and effecting changes in presentation of a printed or graphics page.

Sorting

Sorting is a useful procedure in any data handling system. It allows the user to input data in any order and sort it either alphabetically (a to z or z to a), numerically (1, 2, 3 or 3, 2, 1), by column, or by row.

Sorting was a much more formidable task before the development of direct access devices. In the 1960s, sorting very large files held on magnetic tape customarily took many hours.

Sorting is used by schools all the time for putting the names of students into alphabetical order. The names are simply typed into the computer in any order at first, but once the job is done, the computer is told to sort them into alphabetical order. This makes it easier for staff to find details relating to students, such as their names, addresses and telephone numbers.

Sorting could be performed so that the names were arranged alphabetically within the class, or within year groups or so that name and address records were in postcode order.

Activity

Using word processing software, enter a list of 20 names and addresses. Have the software sort them into alphabetical order. Copy the list to the clipboard and paste it on to a spreadsheet.

Searching

If a data handling system holds a million records and we need the information on just one of them, we don't want to have to work through each record until we find the correct one. It's far easier to have the data handling system search for what we want. We can even do this on a word processor – we ask the software to search for a word and it works its way throughout the text until it finds it. If you look at Figure 10.6 you can see that there are other options available in this Windows facility that can narrow down the search to make it more specific.

This screen allows the user to do more than look for the occurrence of a specified word. The user can narrow the search in various ways. For example, if the word 'soft' was wanted, but not 'software', that can be prescribed. Patterns of words or, indeed,

Figure 10.6 Setting up a search for a particular name record

numbers or letters, can be specified – say in a search for a reference to a vehicle registration. The possibility of finding words that sound alike but are differently spelt, like, say, 'rows' and 'rose', can be requested.

Companies search through information held on database all the time. You may have received letters just before your birthday offering you special discounts on merchandise, or you may know someone who received a letter on his or her 18th birthday from his or her local MP. Impressive as it may seem that these people have spent time and trouble checking when *your* birthday is, it's all done by a computer. They go to a database and tell it to search through to find anyone with an 18th birthday over the next month. Anyone that comes up on the list is then sent a letter.

Selecting

In selecting data, we generally use a mouse to point to a menu entry identifying the type of information we want. There may be a nested set of menus, so that several pointing and selecting steps are needed.

In a college database with details of students on it, it's possible to find the name of the student and select it. The database works through its records until it finds all the information relating to that student. This information may include a photograph, exam results, address, schools attended and anything else the college feels is important.

Merging

Data handling systems can merge data from one file into another. They take two sets of information and put them together in a new file – in order. The two files are put together as one.

This is a very useful procedure in IT. Let's suppose we have two databases of information. If we need some information from one database and some from the other, we would have to keep on *opening* and *closing* the files to look at the two of them. If we *merge* the two files together, it makes life far easier – the information is placed in one file only and is easier to see. It also saves a lot of time going between the two files.

For example, if you had two files of names and addresses for mailing prospective customers, both in alphabetical order, they could readily be merged to create a single new file.

Grouping

A data handling system holds a lot of information. It may be that a school data handling system holds information on each pupil – name, age, date of birth, hair colour and sex. It's possible to have the system work out groupings of this information. For example, we may need the information about all pupils who are female, 12 years old and live within 1 mile of school. Rather than working through each pupil's record, we tell the data handling system our requirements and it finds the file of every pupil who meets our specification. This saves hours of work.

Insurance companies use grouping when they deal with cars. For example, when they come to review the costs of insurance each year, the companies may look at each make and model of car to see how many claims there were against it the year before, who claimed, where they live, what sex they are and how old they are. Rather than working through paper files to find this information, they simply tell the computer database to search and find groups of people owning the make of car in question.

Computer operating systems, which we shall be considering in Element 6.1, need knowledge of groups of registered users who are to be granted access to various levels of privileged system information.

Activity

Contact five local companies that use computer systems. Find out how each system works and what it does. Make a comparison of the data handling processes that are used in the systems. What similarities are there and how do they differ? In your view, could any of the data handling processes be improved for any of the companies you contacted?

Evidence collection point

At this point your tutor may wish you to start work on the project which will prove to your tutor and asssessor that you understand this section of the element. If so, turn to page 157. If you have already started the project you may be ready to do Section 3. This covers the third evidence indicator for this element.

Review performance objectives and make recommendations for improvement

Have you ever wanted to go to a new club or disco? Possibly one your friend told you about? Finally, to celebrate the end of term you go along. Did it measure up to your expectations? Was it as good as your friend said? Was it the same, better or worse than your usual disco? Was it worth the money and the extra travelling time to get there? Did you meet interesting people you would never normally get the chance to meet? You are reviewing the performance of the club against certain objectives.

Normally a new computer-based data handling system is specified by the intending user, and developed by an IT contractor or internal IT department. The resulting performance of a data handling system may be reviewed against its objectives.

User satisfaction

User satisfaction should be guaranteed if the system fulfils its specification in terms of:

- processing functions and documentation
- speed of operation
- cost of development
- time taken to develop.

In addition, the user will be looking for robustness and ease of maintenance, and also the simplicity with which individual users can be taught to use the system. The alternative methods that might give the required results will usually have been evaluated in a feasibility study before construction of the system began.

However, if there is doubt about the choice of method expressed *after* the system has been commissioned and accepted by the user, then there is no reason why the feasibility study should not be revisited and an appraisal of methods and the choice made carried out.

Problems

Every user of a data handling system experiences different problems. Common problems are the loss of data, loss of electricity supply, inadequately trained users, lack of speed and inaccurate data that has been entered on to the system.

One problem that arises frequently is that the user's requirements change during the period when the system is being built. There are IT risks in changing the specifications during building and testing; and there are, presumably, commercial risks in delaying the introduction of what has been decided as being the system that is actually wanted. These commercial risks grow if the delivery of the completed system falls behind schedule.

Case study – Moss Print

Moss Print in Ryton have been in operation for 18 years. The company is owned by two brothers – David and Mat Moss. They are both experienced printers and keen to see the company expand. Sadly, some of the skills and techniques they have acquired over the years are being superseded by new technology. Ten months ago, David realised that to remain competitive Moss Print would have to invest in computer equipment. As nobody in the company knew anything about computers, they would also have to employ someone who did.

David and Mat decided upon an Apple computer system that would enable fast setup and creation of printed materials. When the system was finally installed they

Advantages	Disadvantages
Short turn-around periods for setting out printed work on the page. Far faster for correcting mistakes, and allowed error checking (e.g. spelling check) to take place assisted by the computer	The new system took time to find and implement. This cost the company money
Allows pictures to be scanned in to the computer quickly and cheaply	The cost of the new system is a major investment for the company
Will increase the volume of work the company can complete in the future	The computer can be operated only by one employee as nobody else has the expertise – if she is off then no computer work gets done
Software help facility assists non-expert users	Slow training of staff is expensive and means we have to allow them to go to college on day-release courses
Makes the company more competitive in the printing market	The company has to pay the bank back money each month for the loan for the new equipment

Figure 10.7 Installing a computer system: advantages and disadvantages

wanted to know how it worked. On one of the software packages they decided to create a table showing the advantages and disadvantages of the exercise they had just gone through (see Figure 10.7).

You probably think that Moss Print had to adopt IT in order for the business to survive, but look at these questions:

- Do you think the two brothers would be competent to define the objectives of their new computer project?
- What do *you* think the objectives should have been?
- In view of their lack of IT expertise would it have been better to obtain all the computer-based services they needed from an external service?
- If the installation is to be in-house, how can the business protect itself from absence of the key individual, or from system failure?

Security

There are security considerations for the company that owns the data handling system. The system must be looked after so that no unauthorised person may gain access to the system and use the information on it. Passwords and user identification numbers are put in the software. Some organisations also use *physical* security measures to look after their systems. Swipe cards are used to identify the individual user as well as passwords and user identification numbers.

In general, computer installations need to protect themselves against

- theft of data and software
- malicious damage to data and software
- unauthorised copying of data and software
- deliberate damage to equipment or machine-readable material
- accidents of all kinds, of which fire is the most common.

Hackers

Hackers are people who constitute a risk to the confidentiality and security of computer systems. They try to gain access illegally, and don't have passwords to enter the systems. How do they manage to enter the systems without passwords? They use their own software to break password codes. It takes hours and sometimes days to break a code, but *some* people can do it. However, this is the easy part! Gaining access to a computer system is one thing – doing anything once you are in there is a different

matter. There are so many security codes on large computer systems that it may be all but impossible to use any data. There are stories of hackers gaining access to credit card companies and banks and transferring money to their own accounts. This has been done, but companies are now aware of it, and are making it ever more difficult for anyone to hack into their computers. The Computer Misuse Act is directed at penalising hackers, and hacking is now a criminal offence.

Evidence collection point

At this point your tutor may wish you to start work on the project which will prove to your tutor and assessor that you understand this section of the element. If so, turn to page 157. If you have already started the project you may be ready to do Section 4. This covers the fourth evidence indicator for this element.

Evidence indicator project

This project has been designed to cover the evidence indicator related to Chapter 10 (Element 3.2). It is divided into four sections. Tutors may wish students to complete the sections at the appropriate points marked in the text. Alternatively, tutors may prefer their students to do all the entire project at the end of the element.

Performance criteria: 1–5

Key skills:	Communication	3.1, 3.2, 3.3, 3.4
	Application of number	–
	IT	3.4

Scenario
Exotic Paintings is an exclusive commercial picture gallery selling a few high-value paintings each week. The gallery maintains a mailing list of 2,500 names and addresses of contacts to be invited to exhibitions: those expecting to attend each return a tear-off slip. Every week the gallery also scans the catalogues of all relevant picture dealers and records items of interest.

Humdrum Books is a large, busy high-street book shop with eight staff and daily sales of about 200 books. The shop also handles a range of magazines and periodicals.

Section 1
First think about the businesses and visualise the computer operations that will be going on in each.

For each, do you expect to see batch processing and transaction processing? Single-user and multi-user processing? Do you see any role for centralised or distributed systems? List the main data files and outputs that Exotic Paintings and Humdrum Books will need.

Section 2

In carrying out their day-to-day business activities explain which data collection methods would be most suitable. Now consider the objectives of both systems in terms of speed, accuracy, cost and support for business decision-making.

Section 3

Assuming the systems do meet their objectives, but being the first systems introduced to the firms in each case, those objectives are fairly modest. Think about ways in which they could be extended so that in future years IT can confer greater benefits to the two businesses.

Section 4

Finally, write a report on the processes, performance, objectives and scope for improvement for both user organisations.

Use information technology for a data handling activity

It's all very well knowing the theory behind an IT system, but actually using one and getting it to do what we want is more important. It's now time to put your learning to good use and undertake handling activities. Do try to follow all instructions your tutor gives, and undertake practical activities on a data handling system with an established database. We shall look at the criteria you have to work with, but it's up to *you* to find and use appropriate data handling systems and data handling processes to satisfy the criteria.

After studying this chapter you should be able to:

1 Undertake *file maintenance* activities on an established database;
2 use *data handling processes* to produce required *database reports*;
3 apply appropriate *accuracy* and *security checks*;
4 *evaluate the effectiveness* of the data processing activity against its specification.

We are using Microsoft Access as the software in this chapter because it is commonly used throughout the world of IT and effectively illustrates the points we need to highlight.

Did you know?

Radio stations now use databases to select the music they play. All the details of records and compact disks, with every song on them, are entered into a database. When the programme producer is ready to prepare for a new show, the time, date and *type* (for example, rock music, house music) of the show are entered into the computer. Taking this information into account, the database selects the records based on what hasn't been played recently, or on some other criterion.

File maintenance activities on an established database

In order to undertake file maintenance activities on an established database, you need a database that is substantial enough to give you worthwhile experience. A relational database of 100 records would be suitable. The significance of the word

relational is explained in Chapter 23 (Element 7.1). This gives you the opportunity to undertake file maintenance and create realistic database reports.

An example of such a database is presented in Figure 11.2. H. Coogan, in record 10, is shown as FEMALE in capitals as we shall be changing it later. Here, details relating to members of a sports club have been entered on to a database. *You* must ensure that each record in any database you use for the practical work of this element contains at least five fields. Each field is an attribute, and is presented in a column with a heading. In Figure 11.2 the fields are: ID, *Member's Name, Sex, Age, Full Member, Annual Subs* and *Subs Paid?* (the counter at the bottom of the record is simply the means by which Microsoft Access numbers each record as it is entered – in this case, each entry is being ordered sequentially). Member no. 7, Shelley Hill, is a junior member aged 10 whose annual subscription is £50.

If you can't find a suitable database you will have to build one. Although it sounds like an enormous job, it's good practice for you and will help you understand better how databases work. If *you* are in this position of having to create a database but don't know what one even looks like, look at the following explanation of a simple database set-up in Microsoft Access. Your database may not be exactly the same but it gives you a good idea of the steps that are required.

Figure 11.1 Microsoft Access File menu

ID	Member's Name	Sex	Age	Full Member	Annual Subs	Subs Paid?
1	S Almond	Male	49	Yes	120	Yes
2	Joanne Jones	Female	20	Yes	120	Yes
3	Noelle Roberts	Female	27	Yes	120	Yes
4	Ron Bozern	Male	30	Yes	120	Yes
5	Melanie Sinclair	Female	30	Yes	120	Yes
6	Lianne Brown	Female	25	Yes	120	Yes
7	Shelley Hill	Female	10	Yes	50	Yes
8	Jaime Roberts	Female	20	Yes	120	No
9	Lindy Hall	Female	20	Yes	120	Yes
10	H Coogan	FEMALE	20	Yes	120	Yes
11	Simon Man	Male	25	No	75	No
12	Margery Man	Female	26	Yes	120	Yes
13	Pauline Archer	Female	50	Yes	120	Yes
14	Noel Filter	Male	40	Yes	120	No
15	Wal Seymour	Male	30	No	75	No
16	Hil Seymour	Female	30	Yes	120	Yes
17	Jona McClean	Male	25	Yes	120	Yes
18	Peter Whewell	Male	40	Yes	120	No
19	Maria Ireland	Female	30	No	75	Yes
20	Victoria Clerk	Female	45	Yes	120	Yes
21	Mike Baron	Male	34	Yes	120	Yes
22	S. Pate	Male	35	Yes	120	Yes
(Counter)			0		0	

Record: 23

Datasheet View

Figure 11.2 Sample database built for this chapter

Database set-up

When the Microsoft Access applications software is loaded on a PC, we are in a position to create a new database, so we go into the File menu and choose New Database. This is shown in Figure 11.1.

As with all new databases, we must assign a *file name* to this database before any data is entered. This informs the software that there is an area put aside for the database. In this case we've called the new database 'SPORT' (see Figure 11.3).

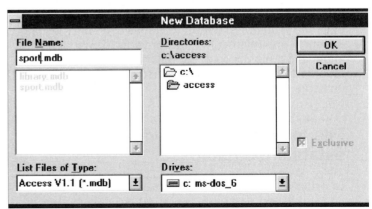

Figure 11.3 Screen used to assign a file name

160

We have now created a new database, but at the moment it stands empty without any records or other details. To load it with data we have to tell the software that we wish to develop a new set of *records* in the database called 'SPORT'.

Did you know?

Oracle and Ceefax that can be accessed on television screens are examples of online databases. Databases of information are stored and transmitted by television companies. The information can be decoded by television sets containing decoding devices. Keying in the required database page number through a keypad (that transmits this information to the decoder by infra-red signals) informs the decoder to search through the transmitted signals until it finds the correct one. The decoder then displays the pages on the screen.

These are not interactive databases; though – the Prestel database is and it allows users to transmit as well as receive information. Rather than having a signal constantly broadcast with all the information available on a database, the Prestel database stores larger volumes of data and transmits only *requested* data. Any data not requested by the user is not accessed and therefore not seen.

You are given a Field Name prompt. This is the part of the software that allows us to insert our own column headings. At the same time we can insert a Description of the *field* and can set parameters for the Data Type such as whether the field is to be a number, character or Yes/No answer.

Did you know?

It's now possible to have a computerised map installed in your car that can even speak to you. All you need is a portable PC and the software. If this isn't good enough, you could add a Global Positioning Satellite (GPS) receiving antenna. This has the added advantage of being able to track your car anywhere in the UK. If you are lost and need directions, the system tracks *your* car and works out the best route to get you where you are going. It even allows you to scan in local maps and use the system simply by talking to it! However, you would need a fairly powerful notebook computer to run it – the full system software takes up 11 CD-ROMs.

We have seen how easily a database can be created, but once it exists, can it be altered? Certainly – if it were not possible to alter it there would be little point in having an IT-based database.

File maintenance includes data entry (both manual and automated), the amending of records, deletion of records and appending (adding them). You will have to show that you have done all this. Some students like to make *screen dumps* (prints of everything on the screen) of the files they are working with to show that they have done the work.

Normally data is entered into a database through manual methods – keyboard, mouse and number keys. It is possible, though, to enter data through automated means – generally using a scanner. Documents of data are scanned and automatically entered into the database through Optical Character Recognition software. This saves a considerable amount of time and effort once the system is set up to perform the task.

Databases can also be loaded from files stored separately. See Chapter 24.

Data entry and appending records

When we *append* a record, we simply add another record. It therefore makes sense to tackle *data entry* and *appending records* at the same time, as Microsoft Access works in the same way for both.

Look again at the screen in Figure 11.2. In order to enter data to the database or append a record, the user has to take the cursor to the last record item entered and click on it. The data for each field of a new record should then be typed in.

Amending records

Should the user wish to *amend* a record, the record in question has to be selected (using the mouse again). The field containing the data for amendment is then selected and the new data is entered. In Figure 11.2 the database displays record number 10 (H. Coogan) Sex field as FEMALE. If we wish to change it to male the cursor is moved to the record and field and the required change is typed in.

Deleting records

In order to *delete* a record, it is necessary to *select* it first. Once the record for deletion is selected, the software highlights it. The user then pulls down the Edit menu at the top of the screen and chooses the Delete option. The software proceeds to delete the record.

Maintaining a database can be compared to using a *paper file*. When you first start a file for your portfolio, it's empty! There's nothing you can do with it except put pages into it. Once it has a single sheet of paper in it, though, it can be maintained. You can add more to the file, add file dividers or take paper out.

Evidence collection point

At this point you may wish to start work on the project which will prove to your tutor that you understand this part of the element. If so, turn to page 169 and do Section 1 of the project. This covers the first evidence indicator for this element.

Data handling processes

What exactly do we want to obtain from a processing system? It requires planning to be able to create one; without knowing exactly what is needed, the system cannot be developed to work as required. Once the planning side of a processing system is complete, we need to measure and evaluate the outcomes against our expectations to decide whether or not the system is working accurately and effectively.

In simple terms, a data handling process is a *function* that database management software can perform. The functions include:

- calculating numerical fields and totals;
- converting numbers and characters;
- sorting;
- searching;
- selecting;
- merging – this is performed in the same way as it is in a word processor – two files of data are merged together to create one new one; and
- grouping.

All these data handling processes were looked at in Chapter 10 (Element 3.2). We shall revisit the processes of searching and selecting by looking again at our sports club database. We shall deal with the other functions as we work through this chapter.

Searching

If we wish to find an item of data in the database this process is found under the Edit menu using Microsoft Access.

Microsoft Access produces a new window where the user is invited to enter the data that must be found in the database. In this case we wish to have the software find the name Noel Fitter. Note the software is being instructed to search through all fields, and that the search is to be *case sensitive* – if Noel Fitter were to be typed in as Noel fitter, the entry would not be found, as the surname is incorrect. Having instructed the software to search through the database to find Noel Fitter, it does so and the results are presented in Figure 11.4.

While we have asked the database to search for a particular record here, it is possible to build up a sequence of arguments to fulfil a more detailed search. More generally, searching is the act of locating information in a table or file by reference to a field of each record called the *key*. In the case above the ID is the key that should be used if a record is to be located because that is the only field that is certain to be unique. However the person using the database probably knew that 'Noel Fitter' would also be unique, and so was perfectly safe in searching on that.

Where a number of arguments are helpful in narrowing a search, SQL can be used. SQL stands for 'structured query language'. It is supported by the major database management systems, as discussed in Chapter 25.

Selecting

Alternatively, the user may wish the database to select an entire record. Remember again that this is more important when dealing with large databases as it saves time and effort looking through all entries. Microsoft Access offers this facility, and again it can be elaborated in SQL. At this point, the user may choose either to delete the record or copy it for use elsewhere.

These processes are similar to some we carry out on paper, without the formality, usually, of identifying named processes. But remember a crucial difference: when you amend or delete a record held on computer file you lose all trace of what was there before – though you may, of course, have saved a copy beforehand.

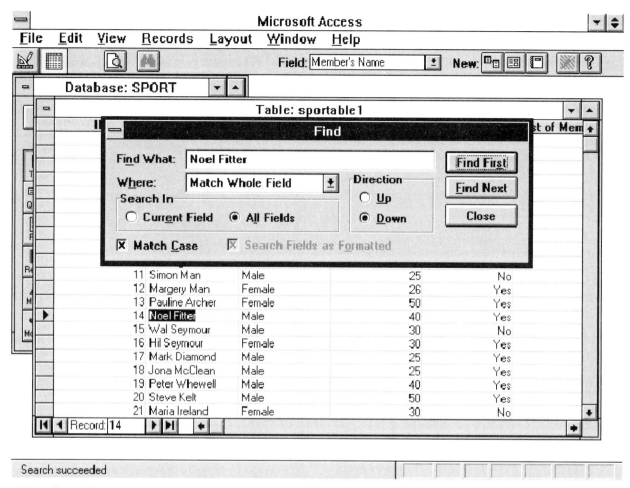

Figure 11.4 Searching a database

The computer carries out the processes very much more quickly than we can by hand, and with complete accuracy.

Database reports

Data handling processes may be used to help create reports. There are a number of different database reports you can create – each using the same information to highlight different points or give different views of the data. Let's look at them in turn.

Operational

An operational report consists of lists of activities that have been carried out on the database. For example, the system manager in charge of a database on a WAN may wish to see at the end of each day who has worked on it, how long the work took and other facts. Rather than asking all users for these details, the system manager prints out an operational report and the software provides the information based upon the transactions.

Summary

These reports provide the user with summary information of data in the database. For example, a credit card company may be interested in knowing how many times their cards were used between 1 November and 31 December the previous year throughout Northumbria. Each credit card transaction will have been automatically entered on a database as it takes place. All the credit card company has to do is run a summary report to find out the exact information it wants. It is likely that there will be very little information in the example here, which will probably state the exact number of transactions that have taken place and nothing else because that is what was requested.

An example of a summary report may be a request to the database management system to summarise members of the squash club according to whether or not they have paid their annual subscription, and the sex of each member.

Data grouping

Any of the attributes can be used, singly or in combination, to specify the contents of a data grouping report. For example, from the database shown in Figure 11.2, the report could yield a listing of all the female members; or all the female members over 25 years of age; or all the female members over 25 who are full members.

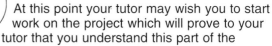

Did you know?

It's possible to buy databases from local authorities with names and addresses of residents who meet your criteria. For example, when you finish your GNVQ, you may get a letter from your local college telling you about the different courses they run. Most people are astounded when this happens, wondering how the college knew they were thinking of doing another course. The college didn't – they sent the same letter to hundreds of other people finishing A-levels and GNVQs at the same time, in the hope some of them would continue their education with them.

Exception

Exception reports allow the user to set limits for the data, and anything beyond those limits is highlighted in a report. For example, credit card companies use this type of database report to find out which customers have exceeded their credit limits; or shops may be interested in exception reports to find out when they have made more sales than were forecast, or for goods that have been in stock for more than a year.

Evidence collection point

At this point your tutor may wish you to start work on the project which will prove to your tutor that you understand this part of the element. If so, turn to page 169. If you have already started the project you may be ready to do Section 2. This covers the second evidence indicator for this element.

Accuracy checks

There are two types of accuracy check that you have to perform. The first is a *validation* check. Each item of data must be valid. For example, rates of pay should not normally be negative, nor should they be unreasonably large; there cannot be more than 31 days in a month; post codes must conform to the rules governing their structure; stock numbers and product descriptions must correspond.

There are two ways you can achieve this – first; by manually checking the entries you make in the database are not too big or unrealistic for the field being dealt with (e.g. if the *age* field has a value of 190 entered, it is obviously incorrect). Secondly, using your PC you must be able to demonstrate you can set up a database so that it allows only *valid* data to be entered. Such specifications are entered into the Options category of Microsoft Access – as illustrated in Figure 11.5.

The second type of check is *verification*. Verification is the process of checking that the data entered is exactly what was intended. In the days of commercial punched-card systems it was normal to verify input by keying the data in twice and comparing the results. Where they differed, one or the other – or, just possibly, both – contained an error.

Visual checks are more usual today, but one way or another the user must be reassured that the right data is finding its way on to the database. Users sometimes decide that spot checks are adequate for their purpose.

Access allows data to be entered twice for this purpose. This has been done in Figure 11.6 in Form mode. Form mode shows only one record at a time rather than all the data in the database. It's easy to put a database into Form mode in Microsoft Access – the user simply has to select the Form icon and the software does the rest. Once New Form has been selected, Microsoft Access takes the user through a series of Menu Wizard screens until the form is developed according to the needs of the user – the results of which are shown in Figure 11.7.

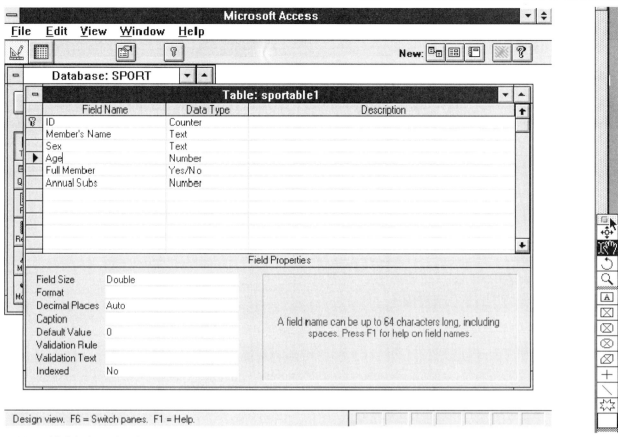

Figure 11.5 Validation checks

Figure 11.6 Form mode

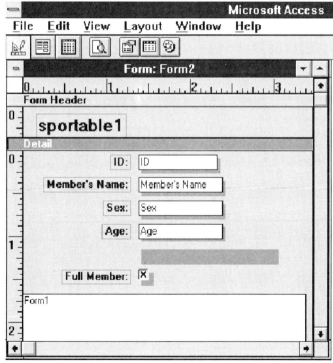

Figure 11.7 Entering data in Form mode

Security checks

Confidentiality

You will need to be sure you don't tell anyone about the data on your database – this is the practice of *non-disclosure*. You will also need to place *passwords* on the database files so that only authorised people can gain access to the database and the information on it. If you look at Figure 11.8, you will see the now-familiar Microsoft Access screen with the *security* option from the menu system displayed. We shall look at each of the security features available to us in the Microsoft Access software.

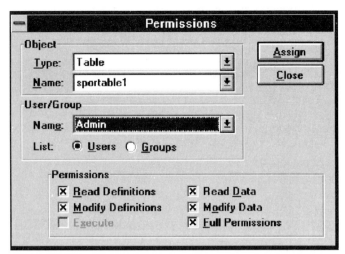

Figure 11.9 Permissions

In Figure 11.11 we are given the opportunity to set and change *passwords*. This feature ensures that before a user can access the data in a database a password must first be entered. It is reasonable to wonder why anyone without permission would even be using the computer in the first place. With this in mind, why is a password required on a database file? Many people may use the same PC each day, and may even use different databases built in Microsoft Access. The way to safeguard the information therefore is to place passwords on the data.

Figure 11.8 Security option

The first option available is *permissions*. This is the facility given to the database writer to allow other users access to information on the database. Figure 11.9 gives an example of permission granted to a group of users called 'Admin' to carry out the operations specified on the screen on the data in the database.

In Figure 11.9 we saw how users could be selected for access rights. It's possible to create user *groups* and specify who has access to what parts of a database. This is shown in Figure 11.10.

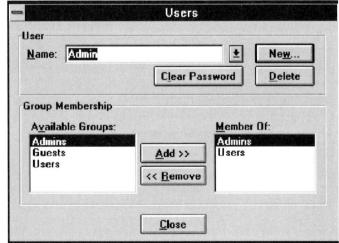

Figure 11.10 Users

Change Password

User Name:	Admin
Old Password:	
New Password:	
Verify:	

OK Cancel

Figure 11.11 Change password

Did you know?

During the Gulf War, a high-ranking army officer used a notebook computer to take down secret details connected with the allies' plans. He left the computer in his car while the car was unattended – it was stolen! Security doesn't just come from software, and devices connected to each computer – simply making sure your data is looked after can also contribute to data security. Fortunately, in this case, the computer was returned to the owner and no secrets were divulged.

Regular file saving

This is the old problem of making sure all data is saved and backed up. You could set the database software to save data every twenty or thirty minutes if you want to limit to that extent the amount of data that can remain unsaved. This can be set by using the File menu, 'save as' option.

Back up

The extent of the precautions taken to back up files ought to correspond to the value of the data and the risks to which it is exposed. For example, data that is regarded as precious could be recorded on magnetic tape or cartridge and stored in a fire-proof safe at a location remote from the place where the original data is held. There could even be two back-up copies of data held separately. If the risks of sabotage or commercial espionage are thought to be greater than those of fire or other disaster, the back-up arrangements will have to be designed accordingly. In places where earthquakes are common, allowance must be made for that type of hazard.

Theft

If you are concerned about theft of equipment or software, as you should be, you will have to take precautions to ensure the PC can't be moved. The precautions that can be taken to prevent both hardware and software theft are covered in Chapter 5 (Element 2.1).

Activity

Place a password on a computer so that each time it's started it prompts the user to input the password before anything else can take place. To do this you will need to use the Set-Up file in DOS. Unless it's your own PC, do remember to take the password off the computer when you have finished as nobody else will be able to use it. If it is *your* PC, don't forget what the password is – otherwise you may have a few problems using it in the future! This is a useful facility – it's always a good idea to use passwords on portable computers as this stops anyone else gaining access to your work.

Copyright

Remember, all information, data and software belongs to someone. The copyright security check is covered in Chapter 5 (Element 2.1).

Did you know?

In some countries the copyright laws are not as strict as they are in the UK. As a result of this it's possible to buy pirated software much more cheaply there than the real item. Don't think that by going away on holiday to a country without regard for copyright will save you money. Copies of Microsoft's Windows '95 were found in a copyright-free country and many people jumped at the chance to buy the pirated software cheaply. What they didn't know at the time was that the software was faulty and caused a lot of damage to their operating systems and other software. If *you* are going to buy software, do make sure it's legal and not a copy.

Access rights

These rights are intended to make sure that only those people who have been given rights to use software can do so – generally, a network file server

167

will check that the user's password is included in its access rights list. If it is, then the user is free to use the software – if not, the user is stopped from using it. This software-based security device can also be used to allow the *user* to establish rights to his or her files and sub-directories for other network users.

Evidence collection point

At this point your tutor may wish you to start work on the project which will prove to your tutor that you understand this part of the element. If so, turn to page 169. If you have already started the project you may be ready to do Section 3. This covers the third evidence indicator for this element.

Did you know?

Anyone trying to access a user number on a computer network that is not his or her own can be detected immediately. Most networks allow the user three attempts to log in – if the third attempt is a failure (due to the wrong password being typed in) the network file server locks the user number in question so nobody can use it. The network manager generally follows up quickly by going to the computer to see who has been trying to breach the security devices.

Evaluating the effectiveness of the data processing activity against its specification

Whenever we have to evaluate the effectiveness of anything, we must think in terms of *reliability, speed, cost, benefit* and *volume*. We do this all the time. Consider buying a car. We look at the price, the colour, shape, the history of the manufacturer (i.e. are their cars notoriously reliable or otherwise?), the size of the car, the size of the engine and the insurance category of the car. This gives us some indication as to how effective it will be in meeting our requirements. It is highly unlikely that 100% of our requirements will be met, but we try to get as close as possible.

There is a great deal here to think of all at once in relation to a data processing activity, so it's best – once again – to break down our evaluation into components and analyse each one in turn.

Before doing this, let's set ourselves a specification to work with:

Data processing specification

You are to enter and process 10,000 records of data, each of 80 characters, into a relational database that is already set up and ready for use, using a 486 SX notebook PC. (The processing requirements have to be imagined.)

The PC specifications are as follows:

Processor:	486 SX
RAM:	4 Mb
Hard disk:	80 Mb, 50 Mb of which are already used
Monitor:	Greyscale
Input method:	Keyboard, mouse
Operating speed:	50 MHz
Time allowed:	3 working weeks

We have to assume that the data processing activity has now been completed and we are in a position to evaluate the effectiveness of the data processing against this specification.

Reliability

When you ran the job did the system perform correctly throughout? This question applies to the hardware as well as to the software. As long as it always did its job then it was reliable – otherwise it wasn't! In this instance, let us assume that the PC was reliable and is considered to be effective. It worked as expected throughout the operation.

Speed

The PC's specifications are not leading-edge technology. A 486 DX2 or Pentium specification machine operating at 160 MHz would have assisted – not in terms of the physical input of data (as this was down to the keying speed of the operator) but in terms of the processing the machine was carrying out.

Cost

We tend to think of how much *money* it would cost to build the system when dealing with cost. However, we should also be aware that there are other costs involved in using systems, as in business there is an old saying – *time is money*. Although it was not the case here, if a system is unreliable and rework has to be done constantly, there is a cost.

A cost that is often forgotten is *human* cost. It's not always easy to place a monetary value on human cost as this includes good will and the effort people put into a job – the cost of buying the equipment has little or no bearing on human cost. At the same time, if the data processing activity is too hard or too boring there may be human cost as it could make the users ill or careless.

Benefit

Here we need to ask the question: How much benefit are we getting from the system? Furthermore: Would we gain any extra benefit from purchasing a different PC? In truth, the PC the task was performed on was adequate. It *would* have made the job faster, though, had the specification of the computer been better. At the same time, it is important to note that as the records are being put on to a computer database rather than being used in a paper filing system, there will be great benefit in terms of speed, accessibility and transferability of the data. From this point of view we can state that there is a great benefit to be gained from the system, but it could still be improved.

Volume

How much data can the system handle? In theory, a database can expand for ever – as long as there are computers big enough to be able to store the information. In this instance, it would probably be advisable to increase the size of the hard disk and RAM in order to make the PC capable of working with a much greater volume of data.

Evidence collection point

At this point your tutor may wish you to start work on the project which will prove to your tutor that you understand this part of the element. If so, turn to page 169. If you have already started the project you may be ready to do Section 4. This covers the fourth evidence indicator for this element.

Evidence indicator project

This project has been designed to cover all the evidence indicators related to Chapter 11 (Element 3.3). It is divided into four sections. Tutors may wish students to complete the

sections at the appropriate points marked in the text. Alternatively, tutors may prefer their students to do the entire project at the end of the element.

Performance criteria: 1–4

Key skills: Communication 3.2
Application of number —
IT 3.1, 3.2, 3.3, 3.4

Scenario
The IT Fanzine Squash & Lager Club has various categories of membership: Junior (less than 18), Intermediate (from the date of the 18th birthday to 21), Single (from the date of the 21st birthday) and Social (where everyone over 18 has joined to socialise with their friends). There are thus six possible membership classes:

- Junior (J)
- Intermediate (I)
- Intermediate and Social (ISO)
- Single (S)
- Single and Social (SSO)
- Social (SO)

Below are the 15 members in four of these classes:

Name	Age	Joining Date	Sex	Membership Category
Jim Henson	51	28/7/94	male	SO
Kim Street	46	28/4/92	female	SO
Paul Jackson	34	22/3/91	male	SO
Pete Davidson	35	18/8/89	male	S
Sue Henson	39	14/2/94	female	I
Kate Spencer	36	22/5/90	female	S
Diane Jackson	35	20/9/96	female	S
Avril Davidson	25	20/12/93	female	S
Bill Donnelley	20	20/1/92	male	I
Luqman Khan	26	2/2/91	male	SO
Alan Lee	17	12/11/90	male	J
Heide Buzan	16	15/10/88	female	J
Karen Joyce	29	18/12/87	female	S
Jo Smith	19	15/2/91	female	I

Section 1
Create a database for the IT Fanzine Squash & Lager Club, showing members' names, ages, joining dates, sex and membership category.

Add the following 11 new members and their relevant data to the database – all of whom are joining the club today. In addition, add another 74 members, to bring the database up to 100 records, using different names, membership details and ages. Start by keying in the details shown on page 160:

Billy Fish	Social	Aged	27
Jon Aster	Social	Aged	28
Mike Thomas	Intermediate	Aged	20
Terry Aster	Junior	Aged	15
Anthony Scale	Intermediate	Aged	19
Tony Scale	Social	Aged	50
Juliet Aster	Social	Aged	42
Simon Lawrence	Intermediate	Aged	20
Margaret Mann	Junior	Aged	14
Philip Scale	Social	Aged	20
Joanne Almond	Social	Aged	27

Add a new category of membership to the database – a family membership that allows three people from the same family to join.

Update your database to make any three members with the same surname members through family membership.

Two members have recently married and have changed their surnames. Diane Jackson has changed her surname to May, and Kim Street has changed her surname to Green. Make the necessary changes to the data.

Avril Davidson has moved away and her membership has lapsed. Alter your database accordingly.

Section 2
Undertake the following data handling processes on your database to produce database reports:

- Find out how many members are over the age of 35.
- Search for all members who joined before February 1994.
- Rearrange all members into alphabetical order by surname.
- Merge together all *Intermediate* and all *Social* members.
- Search for all members who have a family membership.
- Convert all ages into year of birth.

Section 3
Design the following security and accuracy checks to the IT Fanzine Squash & Lager Club database, and write notes explaining what you have done.

- Validity and verification checks.
- Confidentiality (by the use of passwords).
- Regular file saving to ensure the database is backed up regularly.
- Apply anti-theft deterrents for the hardware and software.
- Apply access rights to the software and data files.

Apply these checks where it is practicable for you to do so.

Section 4
Write notes evaluating the effectiveness of the database in terms of its reliability, speed, cost, benefit and the volumes of data it can handle.

Finally, produce three database reports based on at least two of the following – operational, summary, data grouping, exception – to satisfy your own specifications.

Organisations and information technology

Chapter 12

Investigate the safety and security requirements for a data handling activity

As we progress through the rest of this unit, remember that you are laying the foundations for the future. It should by now come as no surprise to you that security is a major issue in the world of computers and data handling systems. The data handling aspects of almost any major enterprise are essential to its success, and the importance of providing security for its data handling facilities is clear. Some security issues have been mentioned in other chapters: here they are brought together.

Where there is reference to legislation, such as the Data Protection Act 1984, do remember that drafting these measures is a very precise activity. The law is an exact profession, and there are dangers in trying to paraphrase or summarise what an Act says. You should refer to the actual wording, and make sure you do not try to interpret it yourself: you'll be sure to get it wrong.

After studying this chapter you should be able to:

1 identify *reasons for protecting data held on individuals* and *organisations*
2 define *health and safety* issues for system users
3 describe *obligations of system users*
4 specify *system security methods*.

Special note

There is only one evidence collection point for this element. It is the evidence at the end of the element, on page 181.

Did you know?

The 'hole-in-the-wall' cash dispensers used by banks require the user to input a PIN (personal identification number) along with his or her bank card to use the bank's services. In future it may be possible to have the user's hand print scanned by the machine rather than using the PIN. This should greatly improve security and eliminate a lot of illegal bank card use.

Reasons for protecting data

In this part of the element, we are interested in the reasons *why* data on computer systems should be protected for both individuals and organisations.

To begin with, what is the difference between holding information on either of these parties on computer rather than paper? In many ways there is very little difference as the same information is still being held and stored. However, as we have seen, data held in computer format is far easier to manipulate, copy and distribute around the world than paper-based information. So what are the main causes for concern?

Confidentiality

This is the requirement to preserve privacy in dealing with personal or organisational affairs. It reassures people that their information on computer is secure. Matters such as credit-worthiness are sensitive, and no one would wish to see them disclosed without proper reason. Similarly, you may not want your neighbours to know what's in your bank account. By keeping records confidential we are protected.

The Data Protection Act 1984 seeks to provide that protection as far as information about living people, held on computer, is concerned. It places obligations on 'data users' who handle such data, and businesses running computer service bureaus with that objective. It also gives 'data subjects' the right to see what data is held.

Activity

Find out what banks do to protect their customers' confidentiality. Your work should be based around:

■ cash dispensers
■ money deposits
■ cheques
■ computer use
■ bank and credit cards
■ telephone banking.

Legal

The Data Protection Act, 1984, provides protection for individuals on how data may be kept and used. Data may be kept only for specific purposes, the individual's agreement is generally required, data can be accessed only by authorised personnel, and the subject has right of access to copies of data. The main points of the Act are as follows:

1 Any organisation holding personal data in a computer system must register with the Data Protection Registrar, stating clearly what details are to be included and for what purpose.
2 The data must be obtained fairly and legally and held only for the purpose stated.
3 Only necessary data should be included – in other words, extra, irrelevant data is not allowed – and it must be accurate, up to date and kept only as long as it is needed.
4 The data must not be given to anyone who is not entitled to it.
5 The data must be protected against loss or disclosure to unauthorised users.
6 The data subjects – the people to whom the data refers – are entitled to see what information is held on them, with certain exceptions.
7 If data held is inaccurate the subject has the right for it to be corrected, and in the event he or she has suffered personal damage through incorrect or lost data, there is a right to compensation.
(A student pack containing further information can be obtained from the Office of the Data Protection Registrar, Wycliff House, Water Lane, Wilmslow, Cheshire SK9 5AF.)

There are other Acts which aim to provide security for individuals and businesses:

■ The Consumer Protection Act, 1987, covers personal injury and damage to personal property. It provides for redress against manufacturers whose products cause injury or damage, including manufacturers of computer software.
■ The Copyright, Designs and Patents Acts 1988 reinforces long-standing principles aimed at protecting the work of playwrights, musicians, and artists, so that software, data held electronically and integrated chip design are also covered.
■ The Computer Misuse Act, 1990, is intended to safeguard the privacy of data held on computer file by making hacking a criminal offence.

Activity

Look at an application form for a credit card or an insurance policy. In the corner of the form there will be details concerning the Data Protection Act. How does this affect the applicant, and what rights does the applicant have under the Data Protection Act with the application form you have chosen?

Moral

Morality is concerned with the distinction between right and wrong. Moral conduct that is wrong may or may not be illegal; and it may or may not breach local rules; but we can picture moral conduct which is neither illegal nor in breach of rules but which can be damaging. For example, staff working on computer systems may be tempted to talk about work they are doing when they know the details are supposed to be private.

Businesses, too, are capable of behaving immorally. They may try to acquire commercially sensitive information from a competitor, or interfere in some way with the smooth operation of a competitor's systems or networks.

Data held on individuals

Criminal

Anyone who has ever been arrested by the police will have a criminal record – any convictions following the arrest will also be held. There are good reasons

for this – the police may need access to information on people at short notice in the future. They may wish to send the information to other forces or around the world – again, computers make the task easier. Previous convictions may be taken into account for securing certain jobs. For example, if you were taking up a job at MI5, a search would be made of your background to see if there is evidence that you have had connections with any organisations that might put the country at risk. Even prospective foster or adoptive parents have to be screened and accepted by the police computer.

There are safety issues too for this type of computer use. All teachers have to be *screened* against a police database before taking up a new job to check that the teacher doesn't have a history of violence.

Did you know?

The police use computers all the time to help them collect information and track down criminals. They now have a computer with details of faces on it. If someone has seen a suspect and can only remember one or two facial features, he or she can look at a number of pictures of facial details on a computer, select the ones that are closest to those of the person he or she has seen and tell the computer to check its database. The computer looks into its files to find any known criminals with features matching those highlighted, and the pictures of known criminals are shown on the screen. People can then be brought in for questioning, with the police being more certain they have the right person.

Educational

All schools keep records of their pupils. In the past the records were paper-based, but are now likely to be kept on computer. As well as holding a pupil's name, age, form, exam results and home address, the records may include information such as school reports, behaviour records, attendance and general well-being of pupils.

If a pupil changes school, the records may go too, to make sure that the pupil's past is always there in case the teachers need information from it. It is likely that a child's records may be used to show parents how much he or she has improved over time, or used to help provide a reference for a future employer.

With continuous assessment now widely used in schools, colleges and universities, there is a role for data handling systems in recording and accumulating marks.

Employment

Very often the personnel department in a company looks after employment records. They will include qualifications, courses attended, previous jobs, days off ill, addresses and may also hold details of pension entitlement, staff appraisal notes and any disciplinary matters. Although these records may be used to help provide a reference to a future employer, they are unlikely to follow an employee around in the same way educational and medical records do.

Financial

Banks hold financial records on customers showing account details, borrowing arrangements and charges.

There are financial records that can be checked by anyone. If someone owes money and fails to pay it back, the financial institutions keep each other informed though computer systems operated by credit reference agencies. If someone has a bad track record, the chances of another bank lending money are remote.

Did you know?

It costs approximately £70 every year for a bank to keep a current account running for each customer despite the use of computers. If computers were not used, banks would have to employ more people, and customers would have to bear the extra cost.

Medical

Medical records are kept by doctors to keep track of all illnesses and prescriptions the patient has had over a lifetime. They are transferred around the country from doctor to doctor if the patient moves. Hospitals also maintain records of patients.

Some lenders require details from medical records before they take on a new client. An example is someone taking out a mortgage to buy a house. The bank or building society may want to see medical records before granting the mortgage – just in case the person is a health risk. Permission is needed from the client before this can take place.

Social

All manner of clubs and societies keep records of their members on computer. The records could be confidential if, for example, they held details of applicants for membership who were rejected, or subscription and failure-to-pay figures. If the body is wholly recreational it would probably be exempt from registering with the Data Protection Registrar under the Data Protection Act.

Data held on organisations

These aspects of data handling are fine for individuals, but surely it's not the same for organisations? In many ways it is. Organisations, though, have a different emphasis from individuals.

Commercial

Commercial data is held by companies on anything they feel is useful. It includes information on products, customers, prospective customers and suppliers. This can take many forms, but will generally include contact names and addresses, product information such as order numbers, production descriptions and historical information on orders placed and received. All but the smallest businesses use computer systems for at least some of these tasks. *You* probably have some commercial data – company accounts, car brochures? What about addresses or telephone numbers of companies – even the *Yellow Pages* could be seen to be built on commercial information.

Did you know?

The DVLC in Swansea is a government agency that holds records of all car registrations in the UK. When anyone buys a car, new or second hand, the registration document has to be sent to the DVLC so they can update their computer, and reissue the document. This way, the government gets statistics on how many cars are being bought and sold in the UK, and what makes they are.

Financial

Many people think of finance only in terms of bank statements that are posted to us each month reporting on transactions and giving the balance.

Although this type of financial data is protected by security measures, it is not as important as other data used in the world of finance. The government uses financial data all the time to help in running the economy. Government departments such as the Inland Revenue and Customs and Excise hold financial data on companies to keep records of when they paid their taxes and duties – and if they paid the right amount!

Legal

In a similar way to financial information being held on companies, the government is interested in any illegal activities a company has been involved in and may keep records of these activities. A company is bound by the Companies Acts to work within certain legal guidelines, such as an obligation to remain solvent, to lodge an annual financial statement, to have a chairman and company secretary. When a company is started, the company directors should be aware of their obligations.

Activity

Your local video club is worried about computer security issues and, knowing you deal with computers all the time, have asked you to make recommendations to help. All club members have personal details stored on computer – names, addresses, age, sex and driving licence number. If anyone was to find these details out, they would know who has a video player at home – a particular security problem.

1 Make detailed notes on how the video club can protect the data on the computer system from unauthorised access.
2 Give examples of other organisations or businesses that use similar security systems, stating any improvements you would make to them and why.

Health and safety

Eye strain

If you look at a computer screen for too long it could hurt your eyes. Every hour it is advisable to leave the computer and have a rest. This will help your eyes have a break. It's a good idea to have your eyes tested regularly by a qualified optician if you use computers a lot. It is also possible to buy computer monitor filters that polarise the image coming from the screen which may reduce eye strain. There are many on the market and you should check which is best for you before buying.

If you work for someone and use a computer, your employer has legal obligations that must be met:

- First, the VDU desk must not reflect any light, and must be a given height above the floor – big enough to hold the PC and all peripheral equipment, as well as any paperwork you need to do the job.
- Secondly, the keyboard has to be separate from the VDU, and must be capable of lying flat or at an angle – this is why PC keyboards have 'feet' at the back to tilt them.
- Thirdly, screen angles must be adjustable, as must the brightness and contrast.

Under European Union directives, employees using computers with screens also have, in some circumstances, the right to:

- eye tests paid for by the employer which may be requested on a yearly basis
- part payment of any lens prescription paid for by the employer if they are needed as a direct result of working on a computer.

Radiation

Radiation from screens is something else you should recognise. Manufacturers have been aware for many years of the commercial risks of allowing their equipment to emit levels of radiation that medical authorities consider could be harmful.

Modern monitors emit low levels of radiation and are said to be safe. Radiation figures, for all sides of the devices, not just forward from the screen, can be obtained from the makers. Customers can choose those devices which declare the lowest levels, if they so wish.

Stress

For most people, working with other people is more natural and more congenial than working with machines.

Working exclusively with computers throughout office hours can understandably become stressful. Managers are increasingly aware of the risk to employees of long spells in front of their PCs, and are introducing breaks in the work to allow a change

of job, or at least an opportunity to circulate and exchange a few words with other people.

Boredom can lead to errors, and to stress. Variety in tasks is desirable. If stress is allowed to develop, perhaps by the need to achieve performance targets in a job that is essentially dull, over a long period, it can lead to prolonged illness and absence.

Did you know?

By taking a plane from Scotland to London, the average person is exposed to more radiation than they would be from an X-ray at the dentist!

Ergonomics

Ergonomics is the study of factors affecting the performance of people in their working environment: for example, the effect of heat, light, noise, equipment and other intrusions on an individual's performance at work.

Working environment

Are the chairs and desks at the correct height for you? Do you need an angled foot-rest? If the table or chair you use while operating a computer is at the wrong height, this is likely to cause problems after a while. The Health and Safety at Work Acts (1974 and beyond) and European Union directives state that all chairs used while working at computers must have castors for free and easy movement, and must be capable of moving up and down and being set at

Figure 12.1 An ergonomically designed office

different levels. They also need rests for backs and necks.

If you work for too long at a computer, you may suffer from back strain owing to the posture you take up. In 1994 there were an estimated 81 million working days lost due to back injuries, although PCs can't take the blame for all of them!

Is the room you work in lit well enough?

Working areas should ideally be kept at a temperature within a degree or two of an agreed level though in some computing areas this may be impossible on sunny days in summer. Taken with the other problems using a computer can create, you may not want to be in front of one for long on a warm day. It's a good idea to get as much fresh air as possible if it's warm, and drink a lot of fluids (but **not** alcohol) as this stops the body becoming dehydrated.

Heat

Apart from maintaining office areas at a comfortable working temperature, computers have specified maximum and minimum operating temperatures. Rooms containing large numbers of PCs may have temperature problems on hot days, especially if there are south-facing windows. There may be a problem if you take a computer from a cold area into a warm one – the components get condensation on them which may damage the machine. If you ever do have to take a computer from a cold room into a warm one, leave it for a few hours to acclimatise to its new environment.

Noise

Noise in itself is irrelevant to the average computer. After all, this is one of their great benefits – they can work in noisy areas where *we* can't. It can wear you down, though, when you are trying to use a computer. Always try to use a computer system in a quiet environment. Printers can cause noise problems – especially dot matrix printers. They can, however, be placed in silencer boxes that reduce noise by up to 90%.

Poor equipment

It's not always possible to use the best equipment – no one can afford to keep on upgrading his or her machines. This doesn't mean that old equipment has

Figure 12.2 An angled keyboard

to be poor equipment, though. Whatever computer you use, take care of it. If you keep the monitor clean it won't glare so much. If the keyboard is cleaned regularly, using a silicone-based spray, then it won't become sticky and hard to use. Never have liquids near the computer. If they spill, not only is it dangerous but it can also cause computer problems. Cola and other fizzy drinks are especially good at destroying computer keyboards.

A key to keeping computers running is to keep them clean. Regularly clean the screen – use disposable wet-wipe screen cloths from your local computer store for best results. Never use water. When not being used, put a screen dust cover on the monitor – it keeps dust and insects away from working parts. Use a small hand-held vacuum cleaner to suck the dust from the keyboard, and when not in use use a keyboard dust cover. It's a good idea to use high-quality diskettes to prolong the life of the disk drive – choose branded disks that are 100% certified error free.

Repetitive strain injury

Have you ever typed for an hour or so and found your wrists or fingers were sore afterwards? This is repetitive strain injury, or RSI. You get it by doing the same job for long periods using the same muscles. It's not just computer users that get it – dentists can, as a result of working in the same position all day long, as can just about anyone doing a job that uses the same muscles for long periods, and is repetitive. If you suffer from it after using a computer, rest for a few hours – the pains will generally go away.

If the pains persist, next time you use a computer you may find using a wrist-rest helpful. This is a foam pad placed in front of the keyboard that the user rests on while typing. Microsoft sell a special keyboard that is angled and set to eliminate strain injury through typing. There are also special mouse mats available that support the wrist and hand, making it more comfortable to use.

Physical stress

If you work in an office using a computer system, you are less likely to encounter physical problems than someone working on a building site. There are still potentially risks around, though – anyone leaving a filing cabinet or door to a cupboard open is inviting trouble. Be wary of uneven floors and badly fitted carpets too as it's easy to trip on them whilst preoccupied with the job you're doing.

Electricity poses a variety of hazards. All electrical equipment should be inspected for electrical safety at least once a year. Plugs should be withdrawn from sockets when that is operationally practicable, and switched sockets turned off. Only trained technicians should take the covers off electrical equipment.

Wires themselves have their dangers – anyone tripping over a wire can pull heavy equipment on to themselves with nasty consequences. Wires that *have* to run on the ground should be covered by rubber cable bridges that hug the carpet and ensure they are safely out of reach when walked on. Any other cables should be fastened together with cable ties.

Hazards

Electrical

Most computer labs are set up for use with circuit breakers. If there is an electrical problem, the circuit breakers immediately cut off all electricity supplied to the room – this way nobody is hurt. If anyone is ever electrocuted – try to switch off the source of power and call for medical assistance immediately.

Fire hazards

In the unlikely event of your PC bursting into flames, what should you do? If you are in a computer lab, there should be at least one fire extinguisher. In the event of fire you won't have time to read the instructions on the side, so make sure you read them when you first start using the room. Your tutor should issue you with safety instructions at the start of your course. Take note of them and follow up anything you are uncertain about.

If you tackle a fire, be sure not to put yourself in more danger – it's better to get out of the building

and watch it burn down than for you or anyone else to be hurt. **Never** use a water-based fire extinguisher on an electrical fire – this will make it worse and more dangerous for everyone.

Obstruction hazards

Have you ever seen anyone putting boxes of stationery in the middle of a room or passage, or leaving furniture in a temporary position, or using a computer with wires trailed across the room so everyone has to walk over them to pass? These are obstructions and potentially dangerous. Sooner or later, someone will trip up and hurt himself or herself. Under the Health and Safety at Work Act, this is illegal as it places people in danger. Not only that, if your computer is suddenly turned off because someone has tripped over the wires and pulled the plug out, you will lose all your work! Always check before you use a computer that it's not posing an obstruction risk to those around you.

Activity

As a representative of your local health and safety committee, you have been invited to give a talk to a youth club about the health and safety issues they should be aware of when they meet each Friday night. Facilities at the club include video and pinball machines, cash registers for the refreshments counter, lighting, a small office (fitted out with standard office equipment) and a car maintenance workshop. Usually up to 60 people meet on a Friday night.

1 Prepare notes for your presentation including all relevant issues as you see fit.
2 Present your notes to a group of no more than five. Discuss how effective your notes were in comparison with the notes made by everyone else. Could you improve the details to be included in the presentation?
3 Having selected the best points from your group, prepare a handout and OHTs for the presentation.
4 As a group, practise the presentation using a video camera. Play it back to see any mistakes made. Practise again, only this time don't make the same mistakes!
5 Make your presentation to the other groups and your tutor. Have them complete a comments sheet as to how effective it was. Evaluate the experience.

Obligations of system users

As computer system users, we are all obliged to follow certain rules of practice. These rules may look repetitive but they are important to bear in mind – let's look at them.

Confidentiality of data

While using a computer it is important to remember that a lot of data is likely to be confidential. This is particularly relevant if you are working for a company. It is wrong and possibly illegal to take the company data and show it to anyone outside the organisation. Information may not seem very important to you, but it may be very important to a competitor.

Always remember that it's easy to copy or download data to another computer – especially using Internet facilities. Never put yourself in a position where you casually deal with confidential data and use file transfer facilities at the same time – you could accidentally send confidential information around the world in a matter of seconds, and put both your job and the company you work for at risk.

Accuracy

We already know that inaccurate data is of little use. While working with data, we need to be accurate at all times to make sure the job is done correctly. If we

enter data into a company computer system inaccurately, it would make everyone else's job more difficult and the data might be unusable.

Right of individual to disclosure

Earlier we learnt how anyone with information on a computer system has the right to know what it says about him or her. At the same time, we have the right not to have this information shown to just anyone without our permission. This is why, upon applying for a credit card, we must sign a waiver giving the credit card company the right to check any records of us they see fit. This should make sure no information can be used to assess us without our knowledge.

Copyright

When using software or data, we are obliged *not* to abuse the position of trust we have been put in. We should never take copies and break the copyright ©. If we do abuse the position, and are found out, we may be prosecuted.

Responsible attitudes to uncensored or private materials

In a similar way to dealing with the rights of disclosure of individuals, if we ever come across private or uncensored material, we must not show it to anyone who could take offence from it, or who could use it to disadvantage others. An example of this could come from the Internet where it is possible to find offensive photographic material such as pornography. By showing it to minors a law is being broken. Another example could be if we were to work for a company doing jobs for the Ministry of Defence, such as British Aerospace. By telling anyone outside the company anything related to the job, the well-being of the company and, possibly, the safety of the nation, may be put at risk. This may, additionally, be illegal and in breach of the Official Secrets Act.

Did you know?

There is growing concern about the type of material that can be found on the Internet. Whilst most of it is of use to the business community and general computer enthusiasts, some material is offensive and dangerous – at one point there were even details describing how to make a bomb. In May 1996, the Technology Minister called for a voluntary code of practice for Internet providers.

System security methods

We looked at security methods in Chapter 5 (Element 2.1) and shall do so again in Chapter 15 (Element 4.3). There are some system security procedures we need to study: regular file saving, back-up and retention of source documentation, and there are other security measures that help to protect whole installations as well as our own PC systems.

Control of access (logical and physical)

Logical access control is based on software controls and passwords. Physical access control relies on passcards, identity cards (used in clubs and at work), gates and grilles (stopping anyone entering without an identification card to give access), guards and perimeter fences.

Forced recognition of security

When starting a new job, certain companies require new employees to sign a contract on working practices. This may include the Official Secrets Act if the company works in a military or government-related field or the signing of a non-disclosure agreement. Anyone breaking these agreements is likely to lose his or her job immediately, and may face legal action – the safety of the country may have been put at risk!

Virus checking

Computer viruses can come in two forms – nuisance and damaging. *Nuisance* viruses come in many different formats – none of them cause any real damage to the computer but all annoy the user. Examples include balls bouncing around the screen while working on software such as a word processor, or a tune being played by the computer every ten minutes. *Damaging* computer viruses include those that destroy data stored on the hard disk drive and those that reformat the hard disk, for example, on Friday 13th. The Jerusalem virus slows the computer down until it can't be used and then deletes the files. The Casino virus shows a one-armed bandit game – if you don't win, it reformats the hard disk drive.

Viruses can be erased if everything is deleted. The preferred alternative is to use software designed to help users detect and remove viruses. There is, of course, a running battle between those who build and distribute new viruses, and those who build and distribute software to counter all known viruses. If you want to rely on anti-virus software you will have to update it frequently.

Modern virus-removing software can be loaded on to the computer and told to run whenever the computer is in operation – in the *background*. This means the computer constantly checks itself for all known viruses – if one is ever detected then the software instantly removes it. This is ideal as the computer user never has to worry about viruses once the software is loaded – the computer does all the work from then on.

Did you know?

Formatting a hard disk is generally known to be the best method of removing unwanted code and data from it. However, *some* viruses can still exist even when a hard disk has been formatted. To combat this, a variation of the formatting procedure, called HDFORMAT, can be used to delete **everything** from the disk. If you ever decide to use this command in DOS, be very sure you know what you are doing.

Computer viruses are generally spread by diskettes being used in an infected computer and then being used in another machine, although the Internet is making it possible to spread viruses far more quickly between computers. Viruses have been known to infect whole networks, and with the Internet there is a real threat of a virus infecting millions of computers around the world.

If you are concerned about viruses on your computer, you should:

1 prevent others from using your hardware and software
2 not use stolen or pirated software
3 not share files or programs with other users
4 always write-protect your diskettes
5 not use 'shareware' software
6 install and regularly use virus-checking/eliminating software on your computer.

Back-up procedures

We know we should always back up our own information. Any data handling activity being done

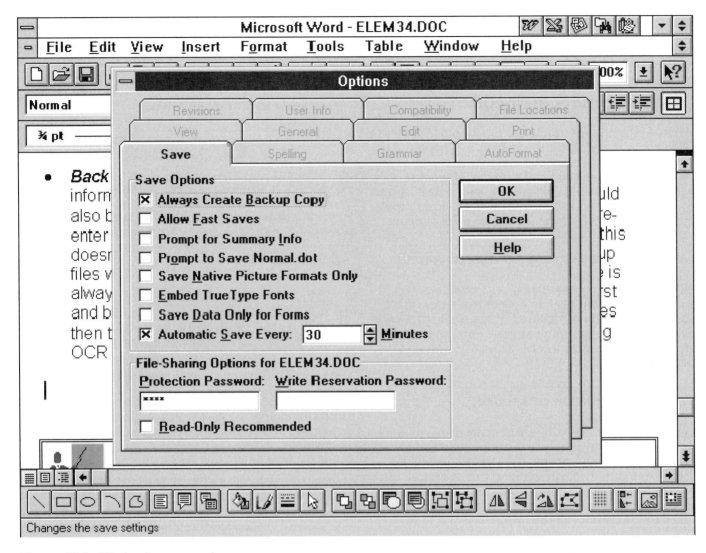

Figure 12.3 File back-up procedure screen

for a company should also be backed up – if we lose *their* data, it costs them money for us to re-enter it. It is our responsibility to make sure we take security steps so this doesn't happen. It's possible on some software to have it create back-up files on the hard drive whenever it saves work so that if the original file is damaged, there is always the back-up file to turn to.

In Figure 12.3, the file back-up procedure is set so that the word processor software automatically creates a back-up file of the work being done. This Options screen is arrived at by using the file menu at the top of the screen – **FILE, SAVE AS, OPTIONS**.

The alternative method is to save the work on both the hard disk and a diskette – this way, should the

hard disk break altogether, and it can, the diskette version can be used. But what can be done if a file is accidentally deleted – can it be retrieved? Generally, the answer to this is *yes*. In actual fact, when a PC appears to delete a file, it doesn't really delete it! Odd as this sounds, it deletes only the first letter in the file name. The rest of the file is left complete and untouched on the hard disk. *You won't* see the remaining file, but it is kept on the hard disk until the space it is occupying is needed for another purpose. It will only be deleted fully if you format the hard disk or diskette, or *write* a new file on top of it. This last way is just like recording with an audio or video tape – if you record over something then you've lost it for ever!

So how do we recover a file that's been accidentally deleted? We can either use Windows utilities software such as Norton Utilities, or we can do it in DOS. Let's look at the DOS method of undeleting a file.

In Figure 12.4, we have entered DOS and told it we want to use UNDELETE. DOS searches through its directories to find all the files which have previously been 'deleted', and which are still held on disk in their truncated form. One by one DOS asks the user if each file is to be **UNDELETED**. In the case of **?CDIMP.HLP** the answer is **YES** because we recognise it as the truncated form of our file **PCDIMP.HLP**. DOS asks for the first letter in the file name and when we supply it, the letter 'P' in this case, DOS automatically restores the file back to its original directory.

C:\WINDOWS>undelete

MS-DOS directory contains 4 deleted files.

Of those, 2 files may be recovered.

Using the MS-DOS directory method.

?CDIMP HLP 3564 6-15-93 3:29p ...A Undelete (Y/N)?y

Please type the first character for ?CDIMP .HLP: p

File successfully undeleted.

Figure 12.4 Reversing a file deletion

Always remember that if the worst turns to the absolute worst, back-up files don't exist, so you can't **UNDELETE** them: but as long as you have paper copies of the files then they can perhaps be *scanned* into the computer and worked on again (using OCR software). If you don't have any hard copies either, then get cracking – you have to start again from scratch!

Did you know?

It's now possible to back up work without the use of diskettes or tape cartridges. The alternative is a special electronic card, costing about £12, that can hold about as much data as a hard disk. The equipment to link the cards into a computer is a bit more expensive, though – over £100. The cards are small and portable and are used in a similar way to diskettes, and once the hardware is bought, it's a cheap and easy way to store massive amounts of data files.

Audit trails

More and more companies are using audit trails now to be able to trace every step in production and distribution, and to be able to follow every financial transactions in detail. Audit trails have to be planned when applications software is being designed. A similar approach is followed with computer security. Anyone working on a computer system will have to be logged on. The file server keeps records of the times and dates when each employee was using the system. Should the system fail, it should be possible by tracking back, to find out if anyone in particular was responsible. This is not just to pass the blame to one person – it can help the system manager find out what that individual did to cause the problem. The problem can then be corrected and the system altered so as to avoid it in the future.

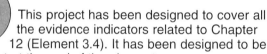 Evidence indicator project

This project has been designed to cover all the evidence indicators related to Chapter 12 (Element 3.4). It has been designed to be carried out at the end of the element.

Performance criteria   1–4

Key skills	Communication	3.1, 3.2
	Application of number	–
	IT	3.4

Scenario
The Accurate Accounts Co. is about to start work for a major new client. The company directors need to know about all the latest details regarding data handling safety and security requirements.

You are employed as a consultant from Data Handling Safety Ltd to give a presentation to the Board of Directors at the Accurate Accounts Co. to include the following:

1   Reasons for protecting data held on both individuals and organisations by the Accurate Accounts Co., including confidentiality, legal and moral reasons. Define health and safety issues for system users at the Accurate Accounts Co. Be sure to cover all aspects we have dealt with in this chapter.

2 At least four relevant obligations of system users at the Accurate Accounts Co.

3 At least four relevant system security methods that can be used at the Accurate Accounts Co.

Use presentation software and hardware if possible to enhance your presentation. You will benefit from using OHTs, flip charts, white boards, and by producing a handout for the company directors on your presentation.

Your talk should last no more than 25 minutes.

Organisations and information technology: Unit test 3

1   All the following are external functions within organisations *except one* – which?
   a   Customers
   b   Purchasing
   c   Suppliers
   d   Legal and statutory bodies

2   An organisation with only a few grades of staff is a
   a   Commercial organisation
   b   Public service organisation
   c   Hierarchical organisation
   d   Flat organisation

3   A high-street clearing bank may be *all but which* of the following?
   a   Commercial organisation
   b   Industrial organisation
   c   Hierarchical organisation
   d   Flat organisation

4   Which of the following is an objective of a data handling system?
   a   Verification checks
   b   Batch processing
   c   Validation checks
   d   Speed

5   Information can appear in the form of
   a   Industrial organisation
   b   Flat structure
   c   Verbal communication
   d   Verification

6   Batch processing is
   a   Data items being processed together as a group
   b   Faster than single-user processing
   c   Very often done using CAM
   d   Slower than any other method of production

7   Which of the following is a type of information?
   a   Customers
   b   External
   c   Operational
   d   Internal

8   Which of the following is *not* a type of function in an organisation?
   a   External
   b   Legal

   c   Internal
   d   Design specification

9   As a computer system user one is obliged to
   a   Check for viruses
   b   Hold data on individuals
   c   Observe copyright laws
   d   Be aware of radiation levels

10   MICR stands for
   a   Magnetic Ink Character Recognition
   b   Magnetic Ink Capture Recognition
   c   Magnetic Ink Character Resolution
   d   Magnetic Input Character Recognition

11   An objective for a *bookings* data handling system is to
   a   Allow multiple screen entry to a database
   b   Introduce Windows software to allow data to be shared more easily
   c   Allow bookings to be made from more than one terminal
   d   Allow touch-tone telephones to be used with a computer system

12   MICR is a method of
   a   Sorting records
   b   Fast input of data into a computer system
   c   Fast printing
   d   Fast turnaround of data

13   Which of the following is *not* a data handling process?
   a   Convert
   b   Sort
   c   Calculate
   d   Computer-aided design

14   File maintenance activities include
   a   Converting
   b   Searching
   c   Deleting
   d   Calculating

15   Turning data from a spread sheet into a database format is performing which data handling process?
   a   Converting
   b   Sorting
   c   Searching
   d   Calculating

16 A sales order is different from an invoice because
   a The sales order is sent by a firm placing an order for goods
   b The sales order is sent by a firm receiving an order for goods
   c The invoice appears before the order
   d An invoice is sent by a firm placing an order for goods

17 Operational information is
   a Information relating to the process activities performed in an organisation
   b Information relating to the running of an organisation
   c Information derived through marketing activities
   d The way CAD and CAM interact

18 A confidentiality system security check could include
   a Passwords and non-disclosure
   b Identification cards
   c Attaching the computer to a wall
   d Screening system users prior to being allowed to use the system

19 File maintenance can include
   a A comparison of alternative methods of operation
   b Examining data for accuracy
   c The use of passwords and other security measures
   d Appending to a file

20 The most common method of data capture in modern shops is
   a Bar code reader
   b Mouse
   c Keyboard
   d Voice

21 A database summary report provides a
   a Database test report
   b Synopsis of data in the database
   c Print of a database
   d Set of data beyond set limits

22 The operation of finding required data from one field in a database is known as
   a Calculating
   b Manipulating
   c Merging
   d Searching

23 Accuracy and security checks can cover *all but* one of
   a Spell checking
   b Grammar checking
   c File maintenance
   d Thesaurus

24 Validation is the method of
   a Examination of a data entry to confirm it is in a database
   b Checking suitability of data for entry
   c Examination of a data entry to confirm it is authentic
   d Checking the hardware and software are effective for the exercise

25 Verification is done by
   a Checking the hardware and software are effective for the exercise
   b Checking a data entry to confirm it is in a database
   c The operator amending entries
   d The computer user reading and checking entries

26 The type of data held relating to an individual may be
   a Commercial
   b Personnel
   c Supplier
   d Legal

27 Access must be restricted to any data which is
   a Inaccurate
   b Closed
   c Inconsistent
   d Confidential

28 In the event of an electrical fire, which extinguisher should be used?
   a Water
   b Carbon dioxide
   c Foam
   d Sand

29 Which of these might help to mitigate the hazard of repetitive strain injury while keying?
   a Use a mouse
   b Use a keyboard rest
   c Use a typewriter
   d Use of a trackerball

30 Swiping an ID card through a bar code reader to enter a library is an example of
   a Confidentiality of data entry
   b Physical security
   c Audit trails
   d Logical access restriction

The demand for communications facilities seems to be remorseless: the appetite of enterprises and individual users insatiable. Users call for digital and analogue channels, to carry binary data, voice and other sound traffic, and images, from one user to another, both across networks and directly. The growth in services, both public and private, is strong and continuously changing. This unit addresses fundamental communications issues that will help you to understand the detail and the significance of future developments. The first and third elements are mainly theoretical; the second and fourth largely practical. Together they introduce you to important terms and operational techniques in the field of communications.

■ *Element 4.1 (Chapter 13) covers the concept of computer networks; and components, standards, parameters, and modes of communication.*

■ *Element 4.2 (Chapter 14) gives you the opportunity to demonstrate that you can prepare equipment and software to transfer data; and that you can make the*

transfer, check it and provide a log of the communications activities.

■ *Element 4.3 (Chapter 15) focuses on your gaining an understanding of computer networks, involving components, topologies, data flow control methods, and management functions including the maintenance of security.*

■ *Element 4.4 (Chapter 16) asks you to demonstrate that you can access a network in accordance with the local standards of your organisation, carry out data file processes, and management tasks. You will also have to send and receive electronic mail, install a new user on the network, and set and modify access rights.*

In addition to the knowledge and skill you can acquire from your tutor you will find relevant information in many books on communications equipment and practice, and every week in articles in IT journals.

An external test forms part of this unit.

Chapter 13

Investigate electronic communications

This chapter looks at electronic communications. Electronic communications are an important aspect of IT, having given us the facility to send and receive information, perhaps over great distances. You can find resources to help with this element by visiting your local library and selecting books on data communications or by obtaining information from an Internet service provider.

You may be able to reinforce the knowledge you need for this chapter by tackling Chapters 14 and 16, at the same time. The work for both these chapters are practical and will give you a good working knowledge of what is required here. However, it may not be possible to do this as access to the Internet and other electronic communications is not always easy. If this is the case, some case studies would help with your work in a more theoretical way.

After studying this chapter you should be able to:

1 explain *network services* used for electronic communications
2 describe the *system components* and *standards for electronic communication*
3 explain *protocol parameters* and *modes of electronic communications*.

Let us look first at computer networks, briefly, then run through some of the important services now available over networks.

Did you know?

Owners of Psion palm-top computers can buy software that allows them to transfer money by linking in to their bank's computer, typing in the cheque details and pressing the return key.

On 3 July 1995, Swindon became the first town in the UK where it was possible to buy goods and services without money or a credit, or debit, card. The system is called Mondex and utilises a computer network, allowing people with Mondex electronic cash cards to ring their bank and deposit or withdraw money over the phone from their own homes. The card holds data relating to how much money is held on it. Each time it is used, the value of the purchase is subtracted from the balance carried on the card. It works in the same way as cash, only it's a card! Every member of the trial scheme is issued with a special card reader that shows how much money is *on* the card, a calculator that works out how a transaction will affect the balance remaining on the card and a special phone that the card is inserted into so it can communicate directly with the bank.

Network services

What is a computer network? Computer networks existed before PCs were invented. These early networks, of which the US Department of Defense's ARPA network is an example, were expensive, and too inconvenient for widespread use.

When PCs arrived users wanted to be able to communicate with the users of other systems, and to have access to remote data. These facilities that users wanted led to the drive to establish the whole field of network technology and services.

We should note, though, that there are still purposes for which a mainframe computer linked to a number of 'dumb' terminals is suitable. Many such network systems exist. Their characteristic is that all communication is to and from the one mainframe.

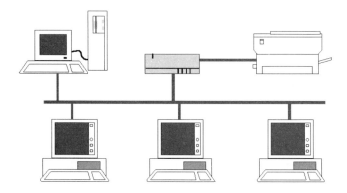

Figure 13.1 A local area network (LAN)

As PC networking became established, ways were devised of extending the maximum range over which computers on a network could be linked. The practice of including a PC with high speed and large capacity in a network, to hold shared code and data, became general. This machine is known as the network 'server'.

Compact PC networks, linking PCs in a building or cluster of buildings, are called local area networks (LANs) (Figure 13.1). Networks stretching further afield normally use a different communications technology, and are known as wide area networks (WANs). The Internet is the largest and best-known example of a WAN. We will investigate computer networks in more detail in Chapter 15, (Element 4.3).

Did you know?

The Walt Disney Corporation is developing a small town in Florida to celebrate the year 2000. However, this will be no ordinary town. As well as having to meet standards of living and cleanliness, every household will be connected to a special computer network allowing occupants to communicate with each other and with facilities in the town such as the hospital and school. The network will have special electronic noticeboards where people can leave messages for one another, and generally let inhabitants know anything of interest that has happened.

House-building firms in the UK are starting to include computers in their executive homes. Some are even installing cabling connecting the homes together, to allow each home to be linked to other homes or to network services such as the Internet.

Now that we know what a network is, what *services* can be used on one? Let's look at them one at a time.

Electronic mail

Electronic mail is commonly referred to as email. It can work in two ways – first, through a local area network or LAN. All network users are connected to the same email software. Let's assume there are two users on the network – Emira and Suzanne. Both of them have a special *area* in the file server – a mail box similar to a letter box in a house. If Emira sends Suzanne an email message, it leaves his PC and goes straight to the file server. It sits here in Suzanne's area or mail box waiting until she is ready to read the message. Once Suzanne reads the message the system won't tell her it is waiting for her again. It's just like sending a letter through the post, only it's done electronically between computers.

This example shows how email works on a very small scale but – secondly – what about using it from a person in one town to a person in another? Certainly, the principle's exactly the same, only this time when Emira sends a message to his distant friend, Jim, and it reaches the network file server, it is sent out to a regional WAN file server, and then on to the next and so on until it reaches the regional file server on Jim's own network (Figure 13.2). There are many systems that differ in detail from the one described, but the general scheme of email communication over distances is similar.

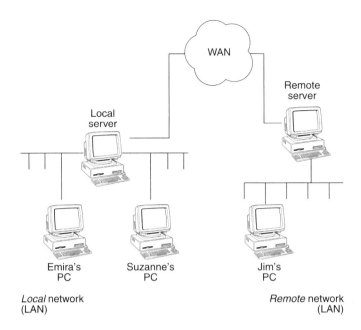

Figure 13.2 Communication with local and remote users of LANs

more Internet users work on other Internet facilities, there is convenience for them in using it for email too.

The Internet had its origins in the USA where users of local academic networks decided to link to each other on an informal scheme. The usefulness of the arrangement soon led to its expansion.

Now the dominant component of the Internet is the World Wide Web (WWW) which has become a market and an information source on a gigantic scale. Electronically published material including software, text and graphics is traded; bookings can be made; and details on a vast range of goods and services can be obtained. WWW can be used from most countries in the world.

A new industry dedicated to supporting users has grown up around the Web. Companies offer 'browser' and 'navigator' packages to help users locate information they want; they offer to design Web pages for would-be advertisers; and as 'service providers' they handle the interface between users and the Internet.

We should note that there are two ways of becoming an email user. One can sign up as a customer on a public service such as BT's 'Gold', or the Internet or make use of a service established within a company or other groups.

One of the most important mechanisms for handling email is the Internet, which is discussed below. Its importance for email is based on its continuing rapid growth, which is constantly extending its reach. Also, as

Organisations have developed email for their own staff within one site. Then, with WANs, they were able to send messages to staff in other places. Now emailing is almost as common as faxing.

Look at Figure 13.3. It shows an example of email software. The `In Box` will show all messages that have arrived for the user to read. The `Out Box` shows all the messages the user has sent. Each message sent and received shows the address of the sender/receiver first, and then the date, time and title of the message for reference purposes.

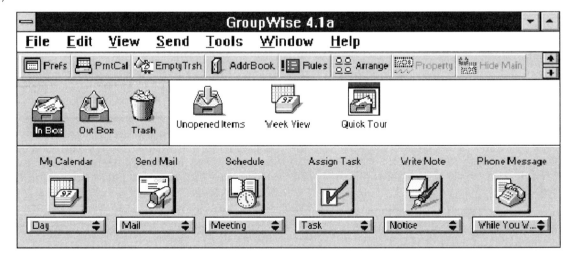

Figure 13.3 Email software

Advantages	Disadvantages
It's fast to send information or messages to people – far quicker than using the post	It may be expensive to be connected to an email service
It's convenient: messages can be sent without leaving your desk, and the recipient can open the mail when that is convenient	It costs something in telephone bills to use email
It's possible to attach files with your email message	PCs may need modems to be connected to email
It's cheap to send information	If your computer or telephone breaks then you can't email anyone
It's easy to use, the messages sent can be filed or erased, and statistics of email usage can be accumulated without difficulty.	Files sent by this method can be damaged and have to be sent again.
	It is not always obvious when a message has not reached the recipient.

The results of a LAN or WAN email system are similar, though not necessarily exactly the same, because there are many email software packages in use offering slightly different facilities. In order for email to work, each person on the email system has a unique email address. Always check for accuracy when typing in an address as more than one organisation may have a similar address.

The advantages and disadvantages of email are shown in the table above.

Did you know?

It is estimated by Ernst & Young, the international firm of accountants, that over the next three years up to 15 per cent of bank branches will close due to the sudden interest people have in *virtual banking* over the Internet. By using this rather than traditional methods of banking, IT replaces traditional transactions where customers speak face to face with bank staff.

Owners of Psion palm-top computers can purchase PsiWin – a software package that allows files to be transferred between the hand-held computer and a PC. What makes it so special is that the tiny computer has a built-in word processor, spreadsheet and database as well as personal organiser software. The software bundles are compatible with Word, WordPerfect and Word Pro, Lotus 123, Excel and Quattro Pro and the Lotus Organiser Pim on the PC. This means a Psion owner can produce reports while away from a PC and download them later. It's essentially a mini-network between the devices.

In June 1996, Kodak released an inexpensive digital camera able to take pictures of 'photographic quality' for £350. After research carried out in the USA, Kodak believed half the people taking snaps have a PC at home. They also believed that half these people would

like a second camera to take snaps that could be put onto their PC. When the pictures have been downloaded on to disk, they can be integrated with an Internet home page, or even be sent to family and friends around the world using email. The camera can hold 16 half-resolution pictures or 8 at full resolution. They must then be loaded on to the PC so more can be taken. The camera itself will not produce excellent pictures in low light, but in future other models will be made with built-in flash units.

Conferencing

The concept of being able to hold discussions with business partners who are far away, and ideally see them at the same time, has long been an attractive idea. Now that communications technology can support remote conferencing it is being widely used.

Video conferencing was the first method of conferencing using IT facilities. It allows a number of people to hold a meeting with colleagues in another room, perhaps hundreds of miles away, and even to work with documents and drawings which are in only one of the rooms.

Rooms used for video conferencing are sometimes called 'studios'. The equipment is expensive – £100,000 in the early 1990s was not uncommon. A typical system consists of a number of video cameras positioned around a room. They are generally on rotating mounts so they can turn to focus on anyone talking in the room. Another camera is often included so any still pictures can be shown, and a PC will be available so that graphics can be created and shared.

Until recently, companies using video conferencing facilities had to be able to transmit the signals to a satellite, which in turn sent the signals to the receiving party. At the same time, the receiving party

Figure 13.4 Video conferencing

had to transmit their signals via satellite. This allowed both sides to be able to see and talk to each other at the same time. The use of satellite time sometimes required booking and added to the expense.

It is now possible to use telephone lines to connect the two parties together for a video conference with the same results as before but much less expensively. It's common for both to have at least two TV monitors in the room during the conference – one showing themselves (so they can move the cameras accurately to focus in on whoever is talking) and one showing the other party.

Large companies can justify the cost of remote conferencing because it became possible to see and talk to colleagues around the world at any time of the day. It also made it cheaper to hold meetings with people around the world without having to leave the office and without the cost of airfares. Imagine buying ten business-class plane tickets rather than paying for the cost of a telephone call!

Teleconferencing is less expensive. It is intended for an individual with a PC on the desk. It is possible to use teleconferencing equipment in a similar way to video conferencing equipment. The quality of the video image is not as professional, though, and it's not possible to move the camera smoothly or to focus in on an individual: teleconferencing is to video conferencing what a point-and-shoot camera is to a single-lens reflex.

Anyone teleconferencing places a small video camera on top of his or her computer monitor, along with a microphone. The sound and image produced are manipulated by Windows software and transmitted down a telephone line to a receiving party using the same equipment (or at least compatible equipment). Anyone who is confident with Windows will be aware of the way several working windows or items of software can be used at any one time. Not only does teleconferencing allow the PC user to continue using more than just one piece of software but it also allows the two people to use each other's software tool. For example, if Joe is conferencing with Yasmin and wants to illustrate a point, he could use a drawing package in Windows to draw whatever he wanted. At the same time, Yasmin could make alterations to it on her PC.

The great advantage teleconferencing has over video conferencing is the cost. A teleconferencing package can be bought for about £500. This includes the camera, software and microphone. Added to this is the cost of a telephone call (that *can* be expensive depending upon where in the world you are calling), but even this is far cheaper than using a satellite link. It has enabled the average PC user to talk face-to-face with others around the world, cheaply and efficiently.

Did you know?

Some universities in the UK intend to have teleconferencing facilities on each lecturer's desk so students can talk to them and see them from their halls of residence. In the Australian outback, teachers are using these facilities to teach children hundreds of miles away, without ever having to travel!

Activity

In a group of no more than four contact a few companies that use electronic conferencing facilities. Find out how much each system cost to purchase, how much it costs to run, and what savings the company makes. Do the advantages outweigh the disadvantages?

Did you know?

Video conferencing and teleconferencing became firmly established as a method of face-to-face communication during the Gulf War. Through the use of this technology, it was possible for President George Bush to see and talk to his generals in the field, getting the latest information on the war. It also allowed him to see and talk to his ally commanders around the world to discuss the war and the tactics being used.

Bulletin boards

Are you a member of a team, club or society? If you, then the chances are there's a noticeboard you look at from time to time to check what is happening. This is an old-fashioned bulletin board – people place items of information, bulletins, on it for others to see and for people to respond to.

At this point in the book, you won't be surprised to hear that there is an IT version of the bulletin board (Figure 13.5). A computer-based bulletin board works in a very similar way to the old-fashioned version. A centralised computer or file server acts as a storage area for computerised bulletin messages on which system users place information. Other users can link in to this bulletin board and look up any information or advertisements that may be there. Access to bulletin boards can be restricted, in some software, to named individuals or named groups.

Bulletin boards are on the Internet as well as on local area networks. When someone places a notice on the bulletin board asking for help or advice it is possible to receive a response to the request within an hour – even from somewhere as far away as America, for example.

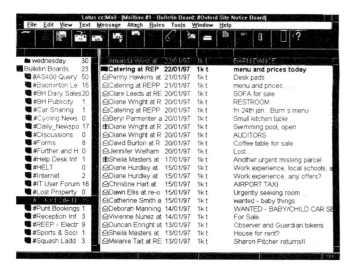

Figure 13.5 Electronic bulletin board

Activity

Find a bulletin board on the Internet. List the facilities it provides. How easy is it to interact with the bulletin board you chose? Compare your choice with that of a friend.

File transfer

Most computer users have had the experience of working on a file on a diskette when they decided they wanted it on the hard disk to make their work faster. By copying the file from one disk to the other a file transfer took place. The information or data from the file on the diskette was sent within the computer to the hard disk where it was stored again.

Often it is convenient to carry out file transfer over a computer network. Network management software for LANs and WANs provides facilities for the transfer of files. There are checking procedures to confirm the accuracy and completeness of the transmission, and procedures for retransmission if corruption or failure occurs.

You should recognise that the transfer of a very large file takes a long time, with a corresponding likelihood of some transmission failure arising. For example, a file of 10 MB transferred over a 19,200 bits-per-second link would take more than one and a half hours.

You may be concerned about who can read the file once it's transferred down the telephone line. The simple answer is that only the person it's addressed to (using the email address system) can read it. No one else has access.

In order to transfer a file using an email facility, it's necessary to stipulate:

1 any security procedures that have to be met. You may want the message to be encrypted so if by chance anyone other than the intended receiver was to see the file, it would be meaningless;
2 which network and service the file is to be sent through – is it run by British Telecom, Mercury or a cable telephone network?
3 to whom the file is being sent, and that person's email address.

Did you know?

It's possible to connect a notebook or laptop computer to a standard desktop PC using a cable and special software called Laplink.

Once this connection is made, both computers can transfer data to one another as though each hard disk drive was shared.

Interacting with databases

We have looked briefly at databases (and will look at them later in more detail). Some databases are interactive. This means that although they hold a good deal of data themselves, they can communicate with other software to obtain more information than is already stored. For example, we may set up a database about cars, with details on it such as engine size and the price. A CD-ROM we own may hold pictures of cars. While the database does not itself hold the pictures, if we ask it for information on a Ford Escort, it can show us both the stored information and also a picture of the Escort by interacting with the picture file on the CD-ROM. This is illustrated in Figure 13.7.

Similar systems are used commercially – if you go to a large record shop and ask for a CD that's not on the shelves they check on their computer to see if it's in stock at the back of the shop. If it's not, the computer database can interact with another store's database elsewhere in the country to see if it's in stock there. If it is, then the CD can be ordered.

While some commercial databases interact with other databases, some don't but are still responsive. Anyone using Ceefax or Oracle on TV is interacting with a database. This makes it interactive even though the database works alone. Information is stored on a database that is constantly transmitted over airwaves by the TV stations. The signals are picked up only if a home TV is fitted with a special receiving device. When the user types the page

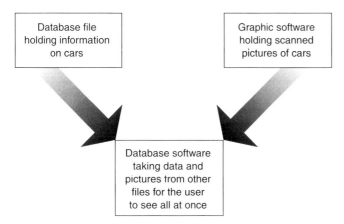

Figure 13.6 Interacting with databases

number required into the handset, the TV receiver works its way through the broadcast signals until it comes across the required one. It then displays it.

 Activity

Create a database of the names, ages and sex of students on your course. If you are fortunate enough to be able to arrange the use of a PC disk-based camera (an electronic imaging device that stores its pictures on diskette camera and not on film), take pictures of each student.

Set up the database so that whenever a student's name is typed in to the database, his or her picture is also displayed. This is an example of database interaction, or consolidation – information from different places being used, or consolidation together by the database.

Direct interaction

In its simplest form, an example of direct interaction is two friends talking to one another over lunch. If we want to get a bit more technical, two people talking to one another over a telephone network is similar. In the world of IT, the equivalent is one person's computer ringing through to another computer and sending information direct to it.

The most general form of direct interaction occurs where two users can conduct a dialogue over a network. The sending and receiving computers will hold the information in digital form: it will usually have to be altered in form for transmission over a network, unless the computers are close to each other, in a LAN.

If the network uses either private or public telephone lines the information has to be carried in an analogue form, superimposed on a carrier wave, as discussed in Chapter 14, (Element 4.2). This requires a modem at each computer. Alternatively, if transmission takes place in digital form the information in binary digits may have to be assembled in a particular way for transmission.

The telephone system was originally designed to carry voice traffic, and it does this admirably. It can also carry data converted to analogue form and, if the quality of the lines is good enough, it can carry video images. A digital network can also carry voice, data and video.

Did you know?

Orange, the mobile telephone network provider, believes that in years to come we will move around with mobile video phones in the same way we use normal mobile phones now. Just imagine going for a walk and being able to speak to, and see, another person anywhere in the world!

Evidence collection point

At this point your tutor may wish you to start work on the project which will prove to your tutor and assessor that you understand this part of the element. If so, turn to page 198 and do Section 1 of the project. This covers the first evidence indicator for this element.

System components

Computer systems can't be put together with just any old components that come to hand, especially when it comes to electronic communications. The type of system being used makes a difference to the components employed. Can they be bought easily then? Certainly – computer shops sell all the equipment you may need and we need to study each item.

Until quite recently, local area networks were used only in companies that could afford to spend a lot of money on IT. It's now possible to network two computers together if you wanted to. If you ever decide to do this, it costs as little as £80 to buy all the equipment you would need, provided the PCs are in the same building. If you want to network more than two PCs then you need more equipment, and of course the price goes up.

These are the components needed for any network:

- a network file server
- network management software to run the system
- network cards, or adapters, to link each PC to the network, for LANs
- network cable
- network applications software – this is slightly different from the applications software used in PCs as it is for use by several network users at a time.

Look in a copy of *PC Direct* or other PC magazines for the current costs of networking equipment.

Let's look in more detail at the equipment and tasks an electronic communication system has to manage.

Data terminal equipment

A bus or train terminal is a place where people get on or off. Data terminal equipment (DTE) is the hardware that puts data on a network and takes it off. *Generally,* this equipment is a PC, although any piece of equipment connected to a network, such as a printer or scanner, can also go under the name. Why? Because data is sent from a PC to a printer on the network. By taking this data from the network, and interpreting it correctly, the printer can print the text the user wants.

The term data terminal equipment is used by the CCITT (the International Consultative Committee for Data Communications) to describe the device at the end of the communication chain.

Data circuit terminating equipment

The DTE has to be connected to the network in some way. This connection is known as an interface. It would be nice to be able to plug a cable into the back of a computer, and away it goes! Sadly though it's not that simple. If you look at the back of a PC you'll see there are a number of ports or sockets that plugs can go into, so which one should the network plug into?

In order to make sense of the information coming from the network cable into the back of the PC, the interface has to be a piece of hardware. This has the correct socket to take the cable's plug, and can do the job of translating the data into something useful to the PC.

So what's a practical example of data circuit terminating equipment? Something we've dealt with before is an ideal example – a *modem*. This takes analogue information from a telephone line and translates it into a usable format for the PC.

The term data circuit terminating equipment (DCTE) is also used by the CCITT.

Connectors

We see connectors all the time in everyday life. An electric kettle is connected to the mains by a cable with a plug at one end to go into a wall socket, and a socket at the other end to plug the kettle into.

Connections to a computer are similar. We can divide them into two main categories.

Devices, typically printers, that need to be able to receive data at high speed have *parallel* connections: that means that the bits making up one character travel side by side, reaching the device at notionally the same instant. The standard for this kind of connection is known as 'Centronics'. It has a 36-way plug at the printer end, and 25 pins at the PC end.

Other PC connections are *serial:* that is to say the bits travel serially, arriving one at a time. There are three main standards:

1 VGA connection is to a 15-pin socket, linking the monitor to its PC.
2 Communications, or other serial devices, use the 9-pin socket in the PC which is commonly called an RS232 interface.
3 Keyboard and mouse have sockets which are similar to one another, and normally have 5 pins.

The pins on all these connector plugs are delicate,

and care must be taken not to bend them.

For most uses several of the pins and their connecting wires are not needed. In the so-called 'null modem' connector used for communication between two PCs close to each other, a special cable has to be supplied with both ends having the same arrangement of pins.

As in other aspects of IT, developments are continuously taking place to satisfy the demands of users for greater speed and capacity; new names for the interfaces will be introduced, and new techniques adopted.

Software

Software is needed for all types of computer-based communication. Examples include system software, user interface software and communications software such as Terminal in Windows (Figure 13.7). Terminal allows you to connect a computer to other

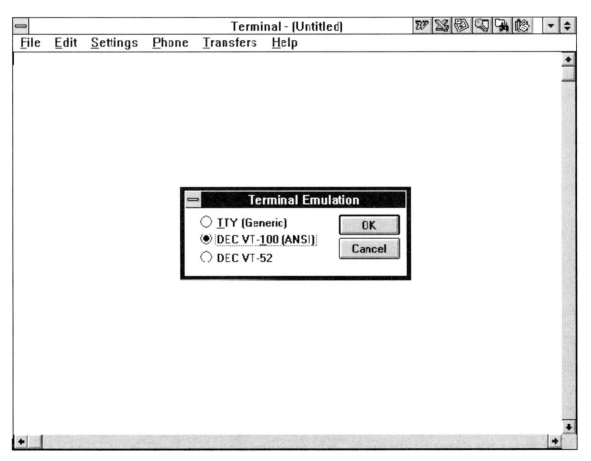

Figure 13.7 Terminal in Windows

computers and exchange information through a modem. It has the task of directing data to the hardware interface so the system as a whole works effectively.

Cabling

Computer cables vary according to the job being done. The fastest and in some ways the best type is fibre-optic cable. This allows data to be transferred at almost the speed of light – the text of the *Encyclopaedia Britannica* could be sent down fibre-optic cable in a fraction of a second, and it does not emit electro-magnetic radiation. It is, however, an expensive medium and it has a physical limitation of being unable to tolerate sharp bends or corners.

The two other common forms of cabling are co-axial cable similar to that used to connect a TV set to a roof aerial, and unshielded twisted pain (UTP) which resembles electric light flex.

Most LANs currently installed have a transmission capability of 10 million bits a second. Traffic at this speed can be carried over UTP, which is very much less expensive than co-axial or fibre cable. LANs requiring higher rates for transmitting their traffic would need co-axial links.

Fibre is installed for busy telephone links, partly because of its advantages noted above, and also because it is a compact way of providing a large number of channels. As the cabling of the houses in the UK proceeds, enabling a huge take-up of new cable-based services to occur, the use of fibre is being extended.

All three types of cabling require termination equipment to ensure that connections to PCs operate reliably. LAN connections are made directly to the port from the communications card which itself is held in an expansion slot inside the PC.

Did you know?

If you suspect that a network cable is faulty and causing the network to stop working, it's possible to use testing meters to see if the cable is in fact broken. The meters are simply attached to the cable and an electronic pulse is sent down it. Any glitch is highlighted. This is far cheaper than replacing the cable *in case* it is broken, and less trouble than putting up with a network that keeps breaking down.

Standards for electronic communication

In some aspects of day-to-day life we accept standards as natural and desirable. In the UK we drive on the left, and cars have the accelerator pedal on the right; cheques, bank notes and coins are standard sizes; telephone dialling, ringing, and engaged tones are standard for each public service operator, or for individual countries. Without standards there would be chaos, and possibly dangerous chaos. But of equal importance, without standards progress towards unified systems would be slow or non-existent.

In IT, and especially in networking which may have an international dimension, standards are absolutely crucial. The International Consultative Committee for Data Communications (CCITT) has no power to enforce standards, but it does propose standards for communications protocols and interfaces. You may have heard of the V24 interface standard. That is the CCITT recommendation for modem standards that has been widely adopted. The RS232 standard you may also have met is the principal standard for serial data transmission.

We now look at standardisation in two areas of importance to computer networking.

Data representation

You probably realise that in computers data is held in binary form. You can think of this as being 0s and 1s, or as 'on' and 'off', or even 'north' and 'south' if you find that helpful.

A *character* inside a computer is represented by eight binary digits (or 'bits'), accompanied by a checking bit called a parity bit. In this form the character is called a 'byte', derived from 'by eight'. All this is standard, for all PCs in all countries. When a key is pressed on a keyboard a chip in the keyboard translates the character desired into a serial bit stream and passes it to the PC for storage as a byte.

There are 256 possible arrangements of eight bits, each of which can assume either of two values. There are thus 256 possible characters that can be handled within a PC.

The transmission of data outside a PC follows the American Standard Code for Information Interchange (ASCII). This provides for seven bits plus one parity bit for each byte, allowing 128 different characters. This, too, is standard. (We look further at the way ASCII is used in the paragraphs on protocol parameters, below.)

 Activity

In ASCII code the name of one of the authors becomes :

1010011	S
1000101	E
1000001	A
1001110	N

1001110	N
1000001	A
1010101	U
1000111	G
1001000	H
1010100	T
1001111	O
1001110	N

Using reference books, find out what your name is when converted into ASCII code.

Data circuit connections

We have just looked at the role of CCITT. An important area of standardisation is that of data circuit connections. Data being transmitted over any medium is represented by the alternation of voltage levels. CCITT recommendations prescribe upper and lower voltage levels for each of the two bit values. In addition to the data traffic there is a large amount of control traffic, establishing the electrical connection and monitoring its behaviour. Standards for all these voltage levels are essential if users are to be free to mix types of PC, if software writers are to limit the number of versions of their products, and if manufacturers are to be sure that their equipment will interface with other equipment.

Evidence collection point

At this point your tutor may wish you to start work on the project which will prove to your tutor and assessor that you understand this part of the element. If so, turn to page 198. If you have already started the project you may be ready to do Section 2. This covers the second evidence indicator for this element.

Protocol parameters

There are certain parameters of protocol for electronic communications that must be followed by equipment being used in communications systems. Why? Think of all the email networks that exist around the world. What about the number of fax machines? How useful would they be if they used different formats for communicating? If manufacturers worked to different standards, the chances of people being able to communicate effectively with one another would be limited – no one would have any faith in the systems and would stop using them.

In a similar way, in the late 1970s, there were three different types of video machine on the market – VHS (now the home standard), Betamax and Philips 2000. Each did the same job but worked to different recording principles. The Philips machine was the first to leave the market. Despite giving the best quality of recording, according to many, the company failed to see the market for home movies and so cinema releases never made it on to their format. Betamax fared slightly better, but most households opted for the VHS system as video libraries were stocking more VHS films. Once VHS had become the industry standard, nobody bought any other format.

To stop this from happening in the world of communications, a standard was introduced. This way anyone on the Internet or using fax equipment can contact someone else without having to worry about his or her equipment being set up right.

Transmission rates

This is quite simply the speed at which data is transmitted through a system. It's measured in *bits per second* (BPS) – the number of data bits or control bits that can be sent through the communication system every second. The theoretical maximum rate of bits per second is called the *baud rate*. If you look at advertisements of modems, you will see a baud rate of either 28,800 or 14,400. The 28,800 baud is obviously faster, although if you were sending data at this speed but the receiving modem could work only at a top speed of 14,400 baud then you would be no better off than if you too had a 14,400 baud modem.

As a comparison, 110 BPS will send 10 characters of text every second. And 1,200 BPS will send 120 characters a second, and 4,800 BPS will send text at 480 characters a second.

195

The speed of transmission across a link or over a network will be governed by the speed of the slowest devices that are in the sequence of connections. For example, it is quite usual for fax machines or modems to operate at different speeds at opposite ends of a line: there is no point in spending more money to buy a device that is faster than those with which it will be working.

Flow control

When a PC sends information to a printer (just for example), it's very similar to you talking to a friend. You don't talk without stopping, do you? If you did, your friend wouldn't be able to understand everything you said. In the same way, PCs send information to peripheral devices, such as printers, in chunks so the devices have time to understand it.

Peripheral devices have buffer memories so that information sent from the PC can be stored. However, buffer memory is limited in size – if a large amount of data was sent without a break, the peripheral device wouldn't be able to cope with it all. To stop this happening, the information sent undergoes *flow control*. This is a scheme under which the computer sends data to another device. When the buffer is full, a signal is sent back to the PC telling it not to send any more until told to do so. Once the buffer is empty, the PC receives a signal telling it to start sending more data. This is illustrated in Figure 13.8.

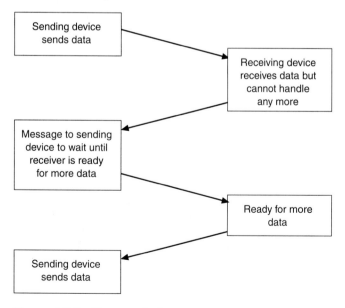

Figure 13.8 Flow control

Number of data bits

If you worked out how to spell your name using ASCII code, you would have noticed there were seven binary digits that made up each letter or special character. There is also an extra bit used to check that the data has been sent without an error. This is with value 1 called the parity bit. Both ends of the communication chain agree that there must be either an odd or even number of bits in each byte. If parity is to be even, and there is an odd number of bits, then the parity bit is set to 1 to make an even number of bits. As an example, the letter 'A' is represented by 1000001 in ASCII. If even parity were being used the parity bit would be 0; if odd parity were being used the parity bit would be 1.

A large proportion of the corruptions in data transmission are single-bit errors which are detected by parity checking.

Modes of electronic communication

Terminal modes

In Figure 13.3 there is an example of an email system screen. The information in the lower box shows any messages that have been sent out on the email system. Although it doesn't show the entire message, it gives enough information to tell the user to whom the message has been sent. This is *echo* – a checking mechanism so the user can be sure the email message went to the right person. The command ECHO OFF prevents the data entered by a user from appearing on the screen. The entry of a password is normally inhibited in this way.

If you have a particularly important document to be emailed, you can check the system works by sending a copy back to yourself. Either type in your email address at the CC (carbon copy) or BC (blind copy) point. For important documents the BC is the one to use as it does not disclose to the addressee that the copy has been sent.

PC display units have line lengths of a fixed number of characters. *Wrap* is a feature that automatically arranges the characters that overflow a line. They are not lost but appear as the first characters of the succeeding line.

A computer such as a PC may be connected to a network it was not designed for but has to work with. It's possible to write program code to make the

PC behave like a terminal that *was* suitable for the network – when this takes place, the computer *emulates a network system terminal*. Widely available is a free terminal emulation package for PCs called 'Kermit'. Seen from a mainframe, a PC running Kermit appears to be a 'dumb' terminal.

If you type an assignment on a word processor, you will notice how, as you get to the end of a line, the cursor automatically moves to the next line. If a word is too long to fit on one line it will, again, move it to a new one. This is the *carriage return* and *line feed* facility.

Transmission modes

Simplex is data transmission in one direction only. A computer can be used to send out messages to a terminal such as a remote printer but the printer cannot send any data back (Figure 13.9).

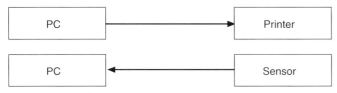

Figure 13.9 Simplex transmission

Duplex (or *full duplex*) is data transmission if possible in both directions simultaneously (Figure 13.10).

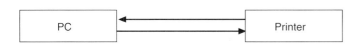

Figure 13.10 Duplex (or full duplex) transmission

Half duplex is data transmission in both directions but not simultaneously (Figure 13.11).

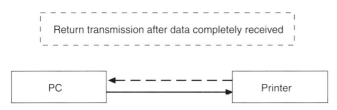

Figure 13.11 Half duplex transmission

In duplex mode, two DTEs can communicate with each other at the same time at the same rate. Under *asymmetric duplex,* one channel may communicate faster than the other DTE.

Did you know?

Bill Gates, the founder of Microsoft, is having a house built in America. Although there is nothing unique about this, his interests in technology are evident throughout. When a visitor enters the building, he or she is issued with an identification badge that must be worn at all times. Next to each door is a sensor that reads data from the badges. If the badge being worn is not allowed into the room in question then the door simply won't open. If it is permitted, then access is granted!

We saw above, when looking at connectors, that binary data could be transmitted serially or in parallel.

Most data movement *outside* a PC or other computer is *serial*. The data and parity bits are fed one by one into a communications channel (Figure 13.13). The cabling required is less expensive than that for parallel connections, but imposes more of a limitation on speed.

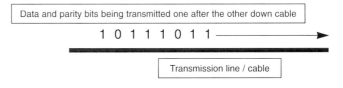

Figure 13.12 Serial transmission

All data movement *inside* a PC is in *parallel*. When you hear of a 32-bit bus or PC you know that the 'data path', as it is called, carries 32 data bits in parallel, in addition to the parity bits of the four bytes making up the 32 bits.

Outside the PC parallel transmission is normally limited to eight bits – seven ASCII data bits and a parity – being transmitted side by side. The connectors and cables have many more than eight lines, pins and socket terminals to allow them to accommodate command signals, reference voltages and spare capacity for future developments.

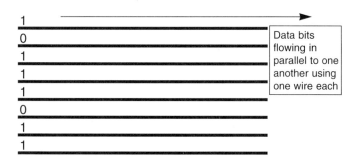

Figure 13.13 Parallel transmission of an ASCII character

Eight lines are needed as each bit is sent at the same time down its own line. This is used in a bus structure (Figure 13.13).

At the same time as being sent in serial or parallel, data transmission can be either *synchronous* or *asynchronous*. It's easier to look at asynchronous transmission first.

With *asynchronous* transmission, one character is sent at a time, with each character following a *start bit* and ending with a *stop bit*. The data bits of the character come in between (Figure 13.14).

The device that receives the data at the end of the line recognises the *start* signal and continuously reads the bits that follow until it reads a stop signal. Microcomputers *generally* use this type of transmission as it's efficient and economical – unless large quantities of data are being transmitted. Asynchronous equipment is very much less expensive, though generally slower than synchronous equipment.

With *synchronous* transmission, data is sent from one machine to another at a *constant* rate. Therefore start and stop bits aren't needed to go between each character. The rate of transmission is controlled by a system clock.

| Start bit | 8 data and parity bits | Stop bit |

Figure 13.14 Asynchronous transmission

Synchronous transmission makes better use of communication links because the time taken up by the start and stop bits on an asynchronous channel represents 20 per cent of the line capacity even if one character follows another immediately.

Evidence collection point

At this point your tutor may wish you to start work on the project which will prove to your tutor and assessor that you understand this part of the element. If so, turn to page 198. If you have already started the project you may be ready to do Section 3. This covers the third evidence indicator for this element.

Evidence indicator project

This project has been designed to cover all the evidence indicators related to Chapter 13, (Element 4.1). It is divided into three sections. Tutors may wish students to complete the sections at the appropriate points marked in the text. Alternatively, tutors may prefer their students to do the entire project at the end of the element.

Performance criteria: 1–3

Key skills:	Communication	3.2, 3.3 3.4
	Application of number	–
	IT	3.3

Section 1
Contact two or three companies that use electronic communications both internally and externally. Two of them should use the conferencing communication techniques we have looked at so far.

Interview managers and staff, asking how they use the equipment and how often. Find out how it has affected the ways in which they have operated over the past five years.

Using details and examples from the companies you contacted, write a report that illustrates the different network communication services that exist.

Section 2
Write a report describing the system components and standards for electronic communications.

Section 3
Explain the purpose of protocol parameters and modes of electronic communications for network services.

Chapter 14

Use electronic communications to transfer data

In Chapter 13 (Element 4.1) we looked at how electronic communications and network services work. In this chapter we put this theoretical knowledge into practice. You will need access to either a wide area network facility, a LAN or two PCs and a null modem. This null modem will make two computers connected together 'believe' they are communicating over a network. Due to the practicalities of transferring data using a WAN or LAN, you are more likely to be issued with two PCs and a null modem for your communication activities. At the end of this element you have to perform a practical demonstration showing you can use the hardware and software necessary to transfer data electronically.

After studying this chapter you should be able to:

1 prepare and connect *hardware* for electronic data transfer;
2 access *software* for electronic data transfer;
3 configure *controls* and *protocols* to match a remote station;
4 undertake *data file transfer*;
5 undertake *interactive electronic data communication*;
6 maintain a *communications activities log*.

Special note

There is only one evidence indicator project for this element. It is at the end of the element, on page 213.

Did you know?

The Deputy Prime Minister, Michael Heseltine, has been trying to get computer manufacturers to give cheap or free PCs to schools and public buildings to make the UK more computer literate. One of his aims is to provide 250,000 PCs for schools by getting a discount of £500 off each PC. The computer manufacturers are interested in this as they think once children use their hardware in schools, they and their parents may stay loyal to the make.

Preparing and connecting hardware

For data to be transferred electronically there must be a continuous path for each item of data to follow. As we shall see, that path does not need to be open throughout its entire length at any one instant, but it must exist. We shall also see that the path does not need to be exclusively of copper wire: fibre-optic or radio waves travelling through space are sometimes the best choice of medium.

We looked at each of the items of hardware earlier, and we don't need to go into any more detail here. Before you even attempt to connect any of the items together, be sure you know what each piece of equipment is, and the job it does. That way you will increase your understanding of the data communication process, and you are less likely to damage anything.

The golden rule when it comes to connecting a system together is to have all the equipment to hand. You don't want to be half way through connection to find some part is missing – searching at this point is annoying and time consuming. It is sound advice to lay out all the equipment so you can see it – preferably in the order in which it has to be connected together. If you want to, build a checklist of all the parts and tick each one off as you assemble your hardware. Table 14.1 gives an example.

PC	✔
Monitor	✔
Keyboard	✔
Mouse	✔
Modem	✔
Telephone socket for modem	✔
Cable connecting modem to PC	✔
Other cables	✔

Table 14.1 Hardware for data communication

If your hardware is going to be connected to a wide area network, make a note of this too, with a picture to remind yourself of how it all has to come together. in Figure 14.1 we have a picture of an *ethernet* type LAN. This acts as a visual guide indicating what you

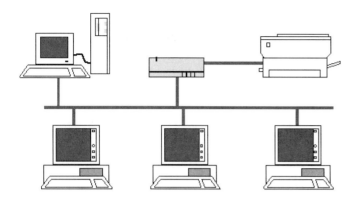

Figure 14.1 An ethernet network and its components

will be connecting together.

There are, however, other items of communications hardware that must be considered.

Data terminal equipment (DTE)

DTE was dealt with in some detail in Chapter 13 (Element 4.1). DTE equipment is the side of a network interface that represents the user, usually following a standard such as RS232C or X.25. DTEs are therefore usually PCs, but can be any equipment through which a user communicates with a network.

Data circuit terminating equipment (DCTE)

Again, DCTE was dealt with in detail in Element 4.1. Any hardware device that is connected to a network has to be *interfaced* to it in some way. This means the DCTE hardware has to be connected to the network and set to work in line with the network requirements. An example is a computer modem being used to take information from a telephone line for a fax transmission, for the receipt of e-mail or for file transfer.

You will have to make sure that the DCTE is connected to the correct communication ports in the back of the computer. The PC must then be told which ports are being used. Ports are the sockets that connect hardware such as printers and scanners to the PC. Generally, the PC ports are present but disconnected from use by the operating system, and have to be activated if they are to be used. When deactivated, the PC is slightly faster and more efficient as it doesn't have to deal with the ports as well as everything else in the system.

If we wish to make changes to the hardware set-up,

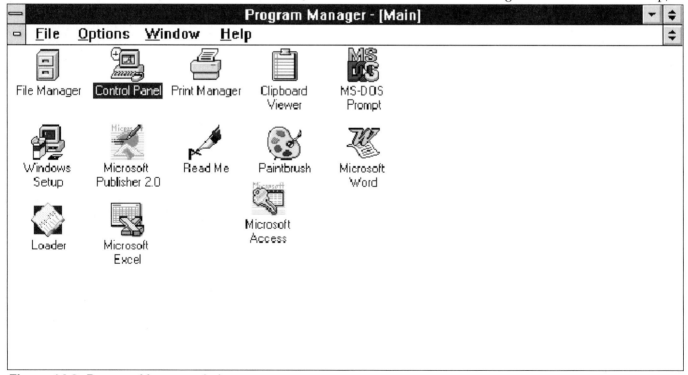

Figure 14.2 Program Manager window

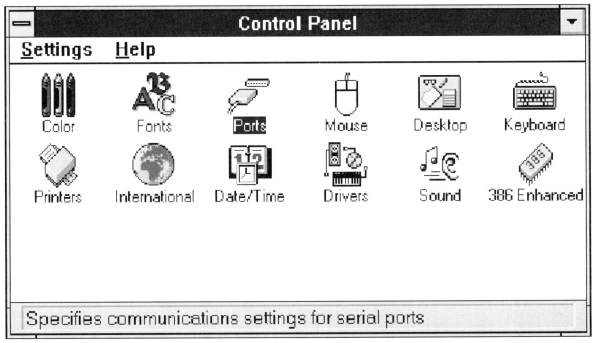

Figure 14.3 Control Panel window

starting from the Program Manager window (Figure 14.2), we select the Control Panel icon. In this instance we are interested in altering the way in which the PC ports work. So having selected the Control Panel icon, we are presented with the Control Panel window as illustrated in Figure 14.3.

This window allows us to alter settings for hardware such as the mouse, printer and keyboard, as well as the ports. As it is the ports we are concerned with, we select the appropriate Ports icon (either double-click with the mouse or press Return once the icon is selected).

In Figure 14.4 we see the Ports window showing **Com**1 to **Com**4. These are serial ports. PCs do not necessarily have as many as four. Generally one is used for a mouse, one for a keyboard and one is available to connect the serial cable from the modem to the PC. An LTP port is for a parallel connection.

If we select Settings in Figure 14.4 we are presented with the window as illustrated in Figure 14.5. Most communications applications require standard port settings, and these again are presented in Figure 14.5.

The meaning and use of each of the settings for the Com ports are given in Table 14.2.

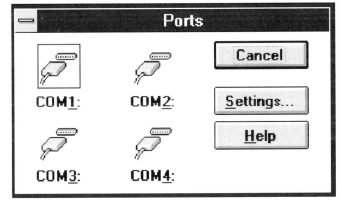

Figure 14.4 Ports window

Figure 14.5 Settings window

201

Table 14.2 Settings for Com ports

Setting	Meanings and use
Baud Rate	Identify the data transfer rate for your device
Data Bits	Identify the number of data bits to use for each character – most being transmitted in 7 data bits
Parity	Identify the type of error checking being used – odd, even or none
Stop Bits	The number of stop bits that will follow each asynchronous character
Flow Control	Identifies the method for controlling the flow of data. Xon/Xoff (handshaking) is the standard software method

Whilst preparing hardware for electronic data transfer, ensure it is compatible with hardware at the other end of the transmission – there's no point in trying to transfer data using one type of modem if the person receiving it is using another, incompatible modem.

Wide area network

Wide area networks are those that exist outside the immediate neighbourhood and require more than a simple cable to connect equipment. They require the services of a telecommunications carrier for their links. British Telecom, Mercury and cable phone service providers such as Nynex offer such facilities.

The links may be short wavelength radio, satellite, underground cables, or overhead cables; in general the user of a WAN does not know what medium is carrying the data traffic, and is not concerned about it. The equipment attached to, and forming part of, a WAN can consist of a variety of DTEs, DCTEs, processors and transmission media.

There are a number of different services each of the telecommunications companies can offer. Your choice of which of the competing services to use will depend on cost and range of services, and reputation. You will need to have some idea of the volume of traffic you will want carried in order to make an accurate comparison of costs.

In addition to these public WAN facilities there are many WANs built to serve particular enterprises; a large company is likely to have its own WAN, as is a government department or agency. Some companies with their own WANs find they have surplus capacity, and rent part of that capacity to other users.

Did you know?

As the costs of telecommunications are important to organisations, companies that specialise in finding the cheapest route for large-scale users of long-distance connections are being formed. The calls may be voice, fax or data communication of any kind.

The service involves a computer search through the required communication routes around the world to see which telecommunication provider offers the best price and service. These services are common in the USA but new in the UK. According to details published in 1995, one of these companies, Logicall, can make savings of 20% using this PC-based system. Communication experts believe the service could provide savings of hundreds of millions of pounds a year for UK businesses in the future.

Connecting cables

When selecting your cables, make sure they are suitable for the job. As a specific example, if you are connecting one PC directly to another PC by a cable acting as a null modem, so there can be direct data communication between the two machines you must check the cable carefully.

If two plugs in a network connection are wired in exactly the same way, the connection will not work as the pins used to transmit from one end will arrive at the other end's 'transmit' pins whereas they ought to arrive at the 'receive' pins.

The cables therefore have to be crossed over in the plug so the information arrives at the right pin and the control signals sent with the data work as intended. Don't worry if you don't like making alterations to wiring – null modem cables can be bought.

Most cables needed for routine working over communication links can be easily acquired.

Did you know?

Electronic pagers are a one-way form of electronic data transfer. Rather than using wire or cable, they send signals over radio waves. The data is transmitted from a central transmitter. The pager being addressed recognises the electronic call sign, receives and decodes the message, and then may display the message to the user. Although very effective, electronic pagers are used only to receive and not transmit information. If you ever need to transmit information, get a mobile phone instead.

Accessing software

Operating system

PC and network operating systems provide many facilities to support data communications.

Perhaps the most widely used facility is for the transfer of data to a printer. If you use Windows '95, the operating system will automatically find out which printer is being used in the system set-up and configure the PC to communicate correctly with it by installing the appropriate printer driver. In earlier

versions of Windows (such as Windows 3.1), it is necessary to select the appropriate printer driver manually. An example is shown in Figure 14.6, which is reached through the Program Manager screen and then the Control Panel window in the same way that we obtained the Ports window.

Turning to data communication external to a single PC configuration, DOS makes it possible to transfer data without the need to use Windows. When using the Internet or other communications software, transport protocols are required. The universal protocol for use with the Internet is called Transmission Control Program/Internet Program (TCP/IP). It ensures data is delivered to the correct address securely. As well as using passwords and other security devices, it is possible to *encrypt* files – this is a method of changing a text message into a

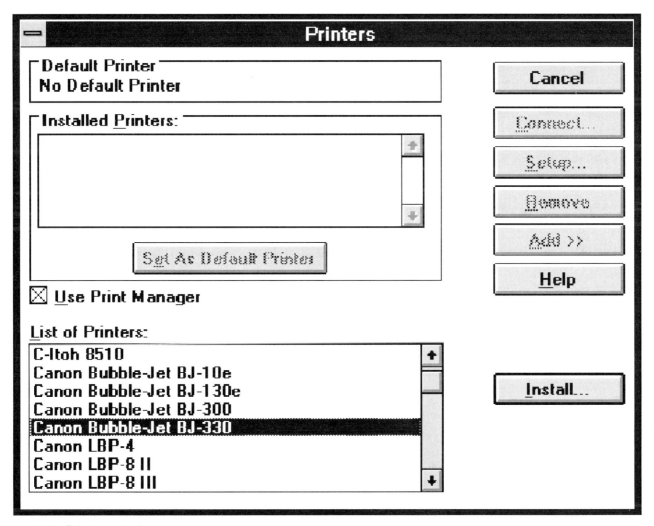

Figure 14.6 Printers window

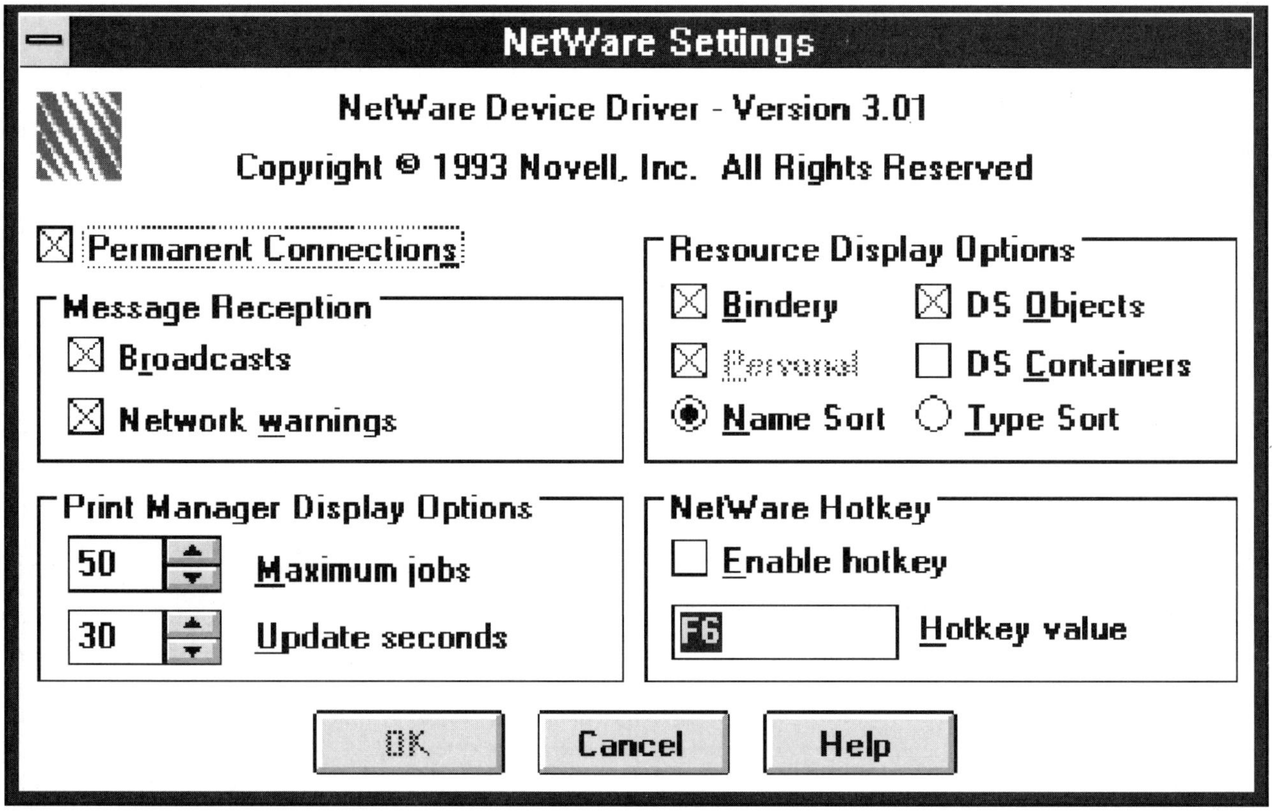

Figure 14.7 NetWare settings

coded one that has to be decoded by the receiving equipment before it can be used and understood.

An example of network operating system settings, in this case Novel's 'NetWare', is illustrated in Figure 14.7 – found through making the selection available on some networks from the Windows Control Panel, shown in Figure 14.8. As it's a Windows-based system, it is a simple process of clicking on the appropriate icon to make a selection.

We have placed the meanings and uses of the main options available in Figure 14.7 into Table 14.3.

Table 14.3 NetWare settings options

Permanent Connections	This option allows the user to make the PC a permanently connected part of the network
Message Reception – Broadcasts	This option allows the user to turn the PC on or off in respect of the receipt of information or messages coming from the network. Such messages may include details such as failed prints, etc
Message Reception – Network Warnings	This option allows the user to specify if any warnings from the network are shown, such as when an e-mail has failed to transmit correctly – the user is informed so corrective action can be taken
Print Manager Display option – Maximum jobs	This is the maximum number of files or items of work that the Print Manager can store while the PC is performing other tasks
Print Manager Display Option – Update seconds	While the Print Manager is operating, it updates its present workload at the required number of seconds
NetWare Hotkey – Enable Hotkey	This function allows a key stroke or series of key strokes to be stored in computer memory on a permanent basis, so that when actioned the NetWare settings are made available to the user – it is a simplified and quicker method of access.
Network Hotkey – Hotkey Value	This is the key used to activate the NetWare Hotkey

Communications software

Communications software is the set of instructions that controls the hardware devices used in the process of providing communication. All data communications facilities need appropriate network management software. Whatever the technology of the network the software has to

- establish logical data paths;
- check accuracy of each transmission, and arrange retransmission if necessary;
- exercise flow control, to avoid congestion and loss of data; and
- maintain statistics on traffic volumes over all links, and on network reliability.

It is easy to think of communications software as being simply for e-mail. As well as executing file transfer operations of various kinds, it is now common for businesses to communicate by fax direct from a PC, rather than from a separate fax machine. As well as needing a modem and telephone line, the PC requires faxing software. Any data being transmitted or received is treated in the same way as it would be if the PC was communicating with a printer or other peripheral device. An example of the fax software set-up is found in the Control Panel as illustrated in Figure 14.8

In a similar way to other hardware devices, if a fax modem is to be linked in to a PC, the software must be informed which communication port is being used. COM 1, 2, 3, 4 are the addresses by which the software identifies the serial ports. We can see from Figure 14.9 that the faxing software is set up on the H: drive of a LAN. It's possible to set it up on any other drive if need be by selecting the Add option. Once this is done, it is necessary to configure the new connection through the use of the Setup

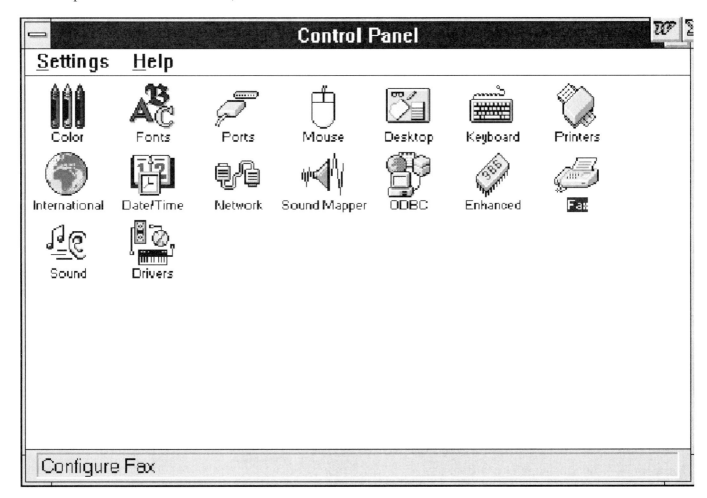

Figure 14.8 Selecting Fax in the Control Panel window

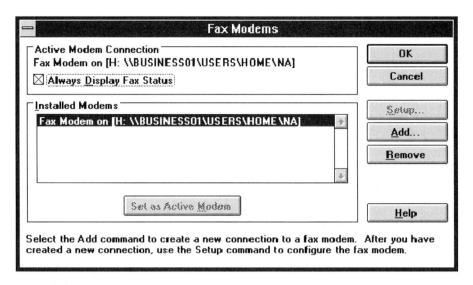

Figure 14.9 Fax Modems window

command. By selecting Add in Figure 14.9 port options are presented and a selection can be made, as illustrated in Figure 14.10.

If you're worried about communication software, go back to Chapter 13 (Element 4.1) and remind yourself what was said about it. E-mail, on the Internet for example, uses a simple address for each user of the communications network, and allows data to be transmitted to that address, which can be anywhere in the world.

Networks need communications software to help them meet their objectives. Some of it will be carried on communications cards which fit into slots inside PCs; some will be installed in a server or other network management computer.

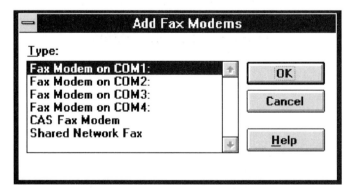

Figure 14.10 Add Fax Modems window

Did you know?

Motorola, the computer chip manufacturer, has a salesforce that carries portable computers when meeting customers. These computers allow customers to design a pager to their own specifications, to connect to the telephone system via a modem and also to the pager factory at Boynton Beach in Florida. Pagers can then be made to individual specifications in just two hours. These techniques, and this application of technology will, in future, allow Motorola to manufacture and deliver customised products, designed by customers in their own locations.

Controls

Before we progress any further, what exactly are system controls? They are the rules a computer system obeys to fulfil a particular role. The system controls can be altered according to the needs of the end user, but *generally* work according to *default values* – a standard, predetermined set of values set by the operating system software.

You need to demonstrate that you can configure the system controls.

Binary transfer

All data transmitted digitally is transmitted in binary over telephone lines it is sent in an analogue representation of binary. Most messages are made up of characters which can be sent as ASCII coding, in binary, character by character. However, some files need to be presented in their binary structure. Graphical and image work will have this requirement. If the network to be used cannot handle unstructured binary files a software facility to break the data into pseudo-characters has to be invoked. A message like that shown in Figure 14.11 is displayed on the sender's screen.

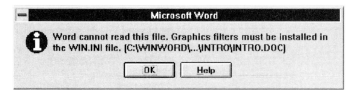

Figure 14.11 The network unable to handle binary code

Over the Internet binary files must be sent as text because much of the equipment on the Internet can cope only with 7-bit ASCII. Conversion can be carried out with a UU encoder, with a UU decoder at the other end.

In general, binary transfer, like all data transfer, relies on the hardware and software being compatible throughout the route from the sending DTE to the receiving DTE.

Did you know?

It costs just a few pence to fax an A4 sheet of paper. The exact cost depends on the time of day, the distance, and the speed of the transmission. If you consider that to send a single-sheet letter through the post costs 26 pence by first-class post, it is not only faster to fax but it is also likely to be less than a third of the cost.

Modem commands

Like most hardware, modems need protocols to ensure they work correctly. The baud rate setting must be correct in the software. Information is sent at the speed which you specify in the window Settings for COM 1 shown under Modem Commands. Modems have some features that allow files to be sent automatically with every page in a standard layout when performing certain tasks, such as using them to fax data. An example is a header or company logo – once set up in the protocol, the top of each page can have a company logo sent without the user having to include it with the information in the fax report itself.

Terminal preferences

When using a terminal, there are two types of transmission that can be used – synchronous and asynchronous – dictated by the characteristics of the devices attached. The synchronous terminal sends data in blocks, that is as strings of bits. Asynchronous terminals send and receive data character by character.

You can also choose attributes such as echo, carriage return/line feed and translation. You find these choices on the Terminal Preferences window which you reach through the Settings menu of the application's Control menu.

Terminal emulation

Terminal emulation was dealt with in Chapter 13 (Element 4.1). It makes a PC behave in the way that a "dumb" terminal would behave providing the correct protocols have been set up.

In order to configure terminal emulation correctly, it's important to know where the protocol configuration screens exist. From the Program Manager in Figure 14.12, choose the Terminal icon.

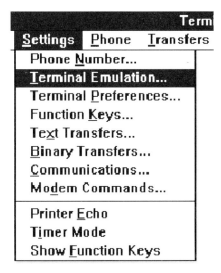

Figure 14.12 Terminal window

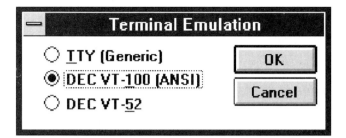

Figure 14.13 Terminal Emulation window

In Figure 14.12 we can see the Terminal software has been opened and is ready for use. As we are interested in terminal emulation here, it is found under the Settings menu option.

In Figure 14.13 we can see the Terminal Emulation window setting options. If you are unsure as to which type of terminal to emulate, set your PC to DEC VT-100(ANSI) – the standard and most common setting. To use this, though, you must press the Scroll Lock key on your keyboard. Once the selection is made, the terminal software alters your system so that everything belonging to it performs as specified.

Did you know?

Anyone thinking they can use the Internet at work may be taking a big risk. The company Network General has released a software package called Sniffer Network Analyser that monitors the percentage of network use credited to the Internet. This means it can determine how much time system users are spending on the Internet instead of working on their in-house tasks. Not only this, Sniffer Network Analyser can identify the biggest users on the network system! The software can save companies a lot of money in terms of telecommunication bills as employees will spend less time on the Internet.

Protocols

Formally, a protocol is an agreement that lays down the procedures used to transmit and receive data by co-operating machines. In the context of this element the term protocol relates to the baud rate, data bits in each character, the parity, the stop bits, the flow control method, the connection port used and carrier detect. All these matters, except carrier detect, were covered when we were looking at COM 1 settings earlier in this chapter.

Carrier detect

Analogue signals such as those carried over a telephone line are created by alterations in the voltage superimposed on a much higher frequency of regular voltage oscillations. This underlying oscillating frequency is called the 'carrier' or 'carrier wave'. The signals bearing the data we are sending cause temporary changes to the carrier. These changes are called 'modulation'.

Before devices on an analogue-based network transmit or receive data they check that the connecting channel has its carrier present. This checking process is called 'carrier detect'.

As long as the system protocols are configured correctly you should have no difficulty. But there's a good chance that it won't work first time – there's so much that you're trying to do, it's very easy to forget something accidentally. Go back and check that *everything* is set up in the way it should be. If everything is OK, what about the hardware – is any of it faulty? Have you plugged the electricity in and turned all the hardware on?

The computer you use will actually tell you if something is wrong. It probably won't give a detailed explanation, but it will give some type of coded message saying that its configuration is wrong and has to be fixed before it can do its job. Go to your user manual and find out what the code means.

Did you know?

The computer manufacturer IBM is hoping to pave the way for a revolution in computing, by making its newest computers respond to the user's voice. Although it's already possible to word process using voice-recognition software, IBM's new machine will make it possible for users to tell their computers what they would normally have to type in or point at with a mouse.

Data file transfer

In order to obtain the evidence required to show that you have transferred data files, there is a set procedure you will have to follow.

Identify the data file to be transferred

This means that once your system is up and running and the software is working, you need to select a file of data that you can send over your communications network.

Select the destination the file will end up in

This is where you have to put in the address of where the information is to go. The address of the destination might be a device address, such as that of a printer or plotter; or it might be the address of a PC which could be on your LAN or it could be remote. A good example of a destination is an e-mail address.

Establish a communication link

When you use a fax machine, there are beeps and other noises that it makes just after it has rung through to another fax and the other machine 'answers the telephone'. This is the two machines establishing a communication link. In a similar way, when you use a communications network, you must establish a link with the computer to which you are sending the information.

Data file transfer undertaken

Most of the work in establishing a data communication link is done for you by the software and hardware. Once you have told the system which file is to be transferred and where it is to go, it will generally link in this operation with the actual data

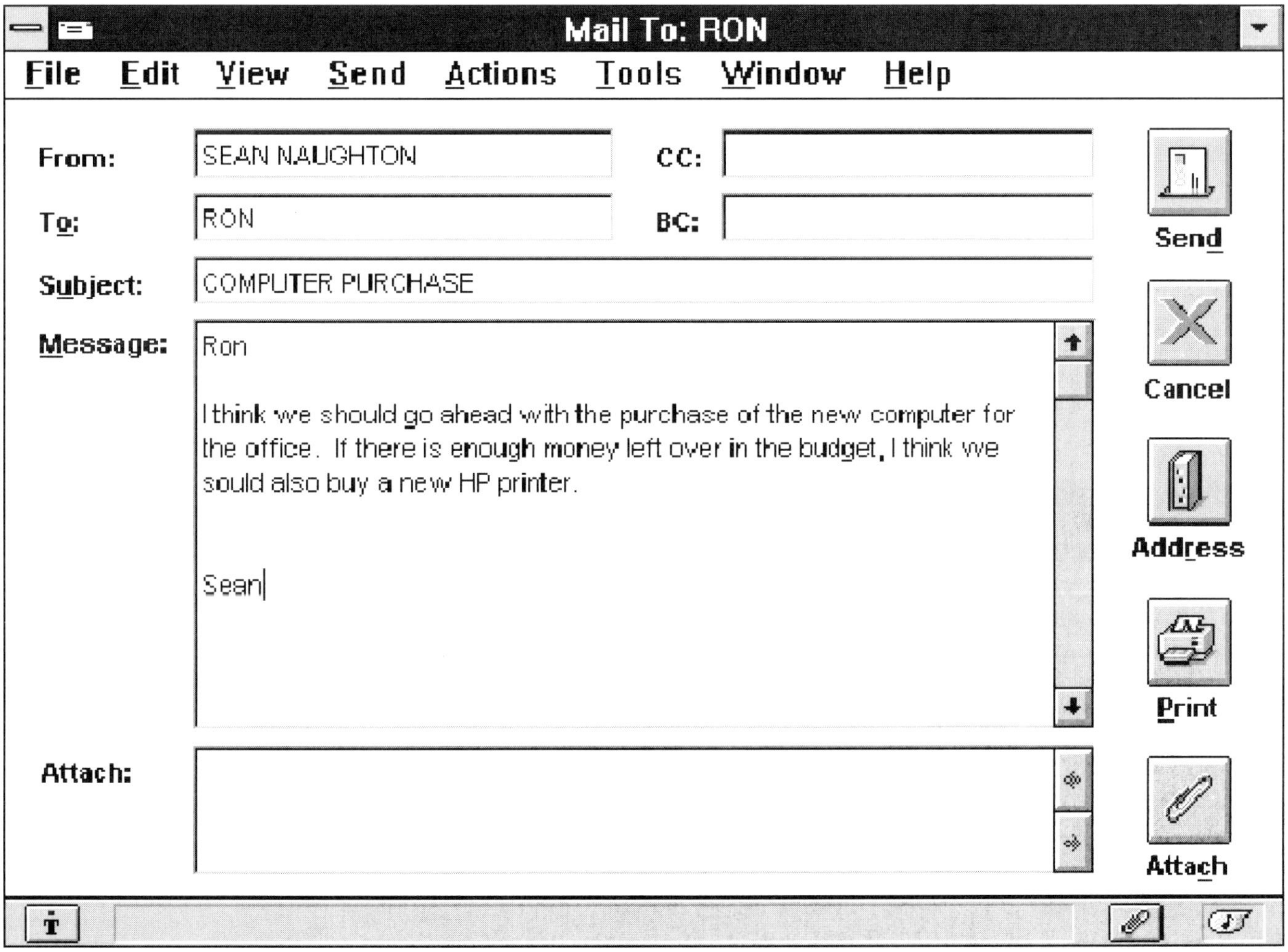

Figure 14.14 Creating an e-mail message

209

file transfer operation. If the communication link is established, it will automatically start transferring the data. If a link can't be made, you will get a message saying so, and no data file will be transferred. This might occur because the receiving machine is switched off, or because of a link failure.

Close the communication link

Once the data file has been transferred you will want to close the link between your computer and the other. This is done through the software. Most software will issue a message telling you the file has been transferred and asking if there's anything else you wish to send; if the answer is *no,* it will cut off the communication link automatically for you, but whether or not the link is closed down automatically you should check that it has been closed to avoid unnecessary line charges.

It's possible to transmit a binary file through e-mail and ensure it retains its original format, including diagrams, pictures and text. As an example, we can look at how a Word for Windows 6.0 file can be selected and transmitted. In Figure 14.14 we can see an e-mail message has been created but not yet sent.

By clicking with the mouse on the Attach key prior to sending, we can assign a file to be e-mailed with the message being typed.

Having selected this Attach option, a new window is presented (as in Figure 14.15) that provides us with the option to attach either a file or an object. In this case we wish to attach a file so the Attach File key is clicked on with the mouse. We are then presented

with a new window **Figure 14.16** showing the files available on the hard disk that can be attached. In this case we have chosen to attach a file called `elem53.doc`. The required file is shown (along with its directory details) in a new window.

Finally, we are taken back to the original message that was typed in. The difference can be seen in Figure 14.17, where an icon representing the attached file is presented in icon format in the lower-left corner of the window.

Interactive electronic data communication

You will also need to follow a set procedure when undertaking interactive electronic data communication as follows:

1 Select a destination for the communication.
2 Establish a communication link.
3 Send and receive data – this is the interaction.

As mentioned earlier, you may select your destination in a number of ways. For the transmission and receipt of data files, the communications software may be set to allow automatic connection to the destination. Alternatively, the software may allow this to be done from a menu or a function key. You may want to undertake interactive communication over a direct telephone link to another user, requiring a telephone number, or by connecting a null modem cable between the PCs.

The communication becomes interactive when some kind of dialogue is established. Both ends must engage in the transmission and receipt of data.

Activity

Find a friend who has a PC with a modem. Alternatively, try to borrow a notebook PC and modem from your tutor and take it home. Set up the hardware and software so that it's ready to *receive* incoming data.

Back at school or college, use a PC (and any other hardware and software you feel necessary) to send files to your friend's PC (or the one you borrowed). When you get back home, retrieve the files you sent, and print them. Take them back to your tutor for assessment.

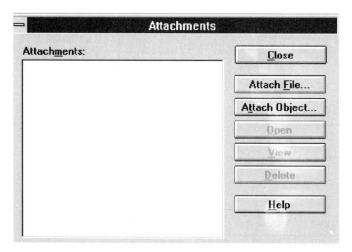

Figure 14.15 Attachments window

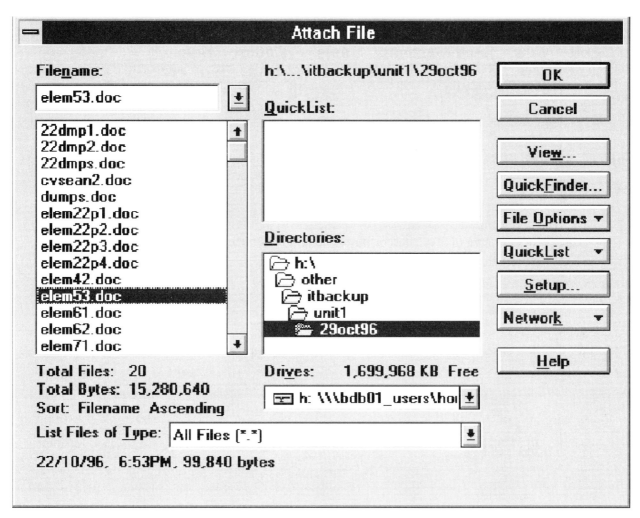

Figure 14.16 Attach File window

Maintaining a communications activities log

Any data communication activity requires a log to be kept. It's sensible to use a log in case anything goes wrong. You then have a record to check each action you made. In this case, the points that should be included in your log are:

■ date of communication;
■ time taken on line;
■ amount of data transferred;
■ names of files transferred; and
■ destination names and locations.

Did you know?

PC makers are working together to create an international database that will hold information such as component serial numbers on individual computers. It's hoped that the database will work on the Internet, and will allow police to find the owners of hardware that has been stolen and recovered by them. Compaq, Hewlett-Packard and ICL are the manufacturers backing the scheme. The FBI is very keen, and police forces in UK may well support the project.

Create a table along the lines of Table 14.4 to use as your log.

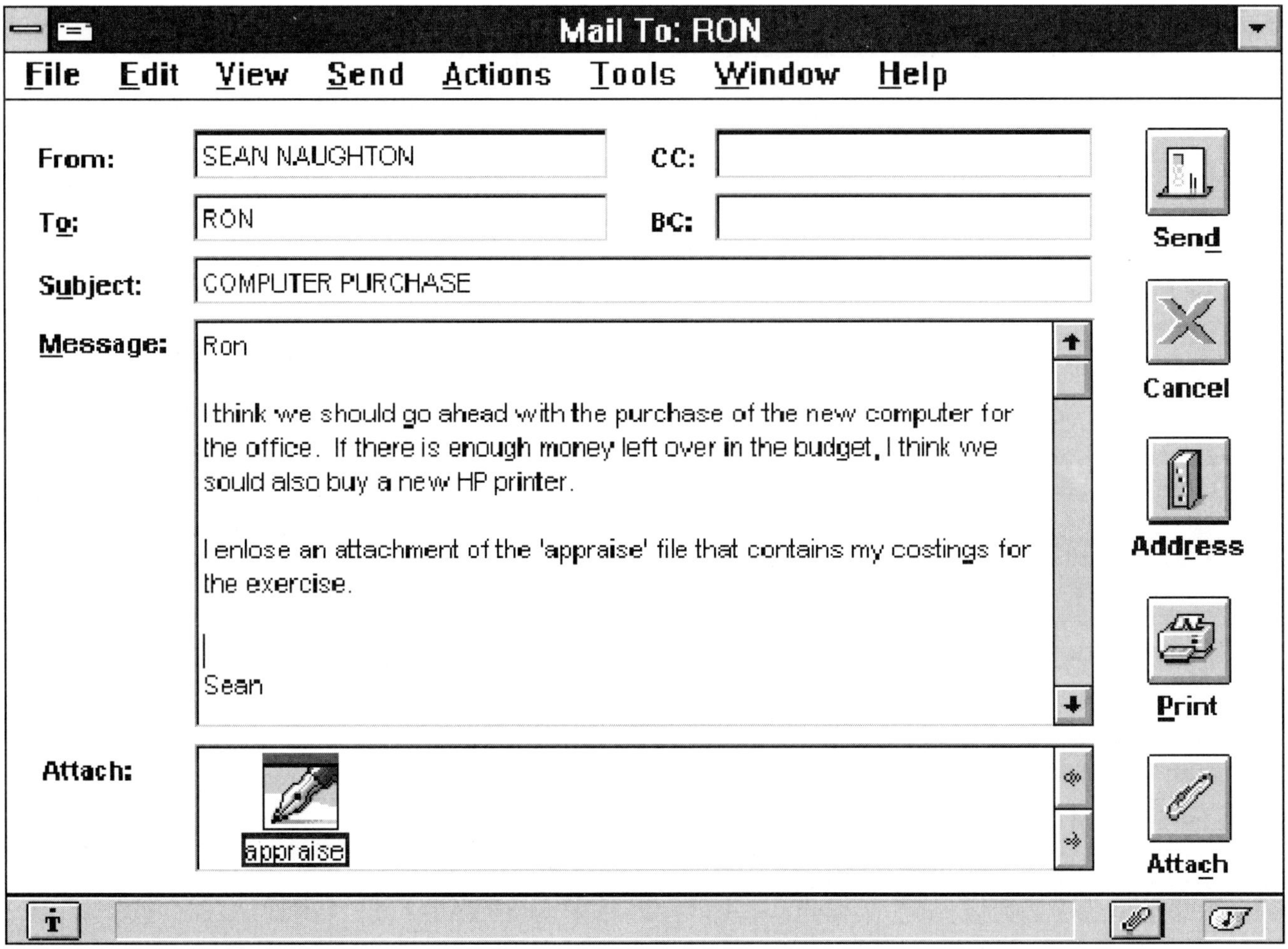

```
┌────────────────────────────────────────────────────────────────────────┐
│ ▬ ▭                          Mail To: RON                            ▼ │
├────────────────────────────────────────────────────────────────────────┤
│  File   Edit   View   Send   Actions   Tools   Window   Help             │
├────────────────────────────────────────────────────────────────────────┤
│                                                                          │
│  From:   │ SEAN NAUGHTON        │      CC:  │                    │        │
│                                                                    ┌───┐ │
│  To:     │ RON                  │      BC:  │                    │  │   │ │
│                                                                    └───┘ │
│  Subject: │ COMPUTER PURCHASE                               │     Send   │
│                                                                          │
│  Message: │ Ron                                          ▲ │    ┌───┐   │
│           │                                              │ │    │ X │   │
│           │ I think we should go ahead with the purchase │ │    └───┘   │
│           │ of the new computer for the office. If there │ │   Cancel   │
│           │ is enough money left over in the budget, I    │ │            │
│           │ think we sould also buy a new HP printer.     │ │    ┌───┐   │
│           │                                              │ │    │   │   │
│           │ I enlose an attachment of the 'appraise' file │ │    └───┘   │
│           │ that contains my costings for the exercise.   │ │  Address   │
│           │                                              │ │            │
│           │ |                                            │ │    ┌───┐   │
│           │ Sean                                         ▼ │    │   │   │
│                                                                          │
│  Attach:  │  [appraise icon]                          ◈ │     Print    │
│           │                                            ◈ │              │
│           │                                              │    Attach    │
├────────────────────────────────────────────────────────────────────────┤
│  [i]                                                         [∅]  [⌂]    │
└────────────────────────────────────────────────────────────────────────┘
```

Figure 14.17 Mail To: window

You may be lucky in the software you use for communications – some software has its own communications data log facility. Maintaining a log is essential if you are using a public wide area network so that you can check your bills.

Table 14.4 Communications activities log

Date	Time on line	Data volume	File names	Destination
21/2/9–	2.34 minutes	1.243 Mb	Learn.Doc	01782 123458 Jim Quartz on file server BC208987
22/2/9–	5.24 minutes	2.345 Mb	Advance.XL	01798 213243 Assam Pradeep on file server NA1426N3
23/2/9–	2.12 minutes	0.978 Mb	Adv.DB	01782 123234 Suzi Collings on file server MF354234
23/2/9–	2.12 minutes	0.978 Mb	adc.db	01798 213243 Mike Rossi on file server L29385K2

Activity

Connect two PCs and modems using suitable software and appropriate cable. Test the system to see which of these you can do:

■ Send and receive data.
■ Send and receive graphics.
■ Send and receive animation.

Evaluate the system, pointing out strengths and weaknesses. Which type of data was the fastest for sending? Why?

Evidence indicator project

This project covers all the evidence indicators related to Chapter 14 (Element 4.2). It has been designed to be carried out at the end of the element.

Performance criteria: 1–6

Key skills:

Communication	3.2, 3.4
Application of number	3.3
IT	3.1, 3.2, 3.3, 3.4

Scenario
Direct Computer Communications Ltd is a company based in Hull specialising in the supply and set-up of computer equipment for clients around the UK. As Direct Computer Communications Ltd's head of sales, you have travelled to a firm in Perth who are interested in the transfer of data throughout the company's PCs, both within the office building and outside over telephone line connection.

1 Collect all the necessary equipment to demonstrate how hardware is to be connected for electronic data transfer. Ensure all connections are correct and make a note for Direct Computer Communications Ltd's future reference.

2 Using software supplied on the computer system made available to you prepare to transfer electronic data.

3 Select a remote station to transfer data to. If this is another local PC, be sure any details regarding null modem cables are taken into account. Match the controls and protocols so you can send data to this station. If you use a remote station on a WAN, keep a record of the controls and protocols you must meet to transfer data successfully for reference of those at Direct Computer Communications Ltd.

4 Select at least one data file and transfer it to the remote station, explaining how the process works to your audience as you perform the task.

5 During this exercise, take detailed notes of any settings, configurations and protocols you implement. Be prepared to answer questions from Direct Computer Communications Ltd regarding the decisions you made during the system set-up.

6 Make a presentation to the board of directors and employees of Direct Computer Communications Ltd, showing how you set the system up, and why you used the configurations.

7 Make, or obtain from the software you are using, a log of the data traffic you have sent and received in file transfer and interactive transactions.

Investigate computer networks

Computer networks are now found in every part of the economy, including, of course, education. Networks potentially provide notable benefits for their owners and users: mainly, more convenient working practices, shared resources and improved security. You should try and visit a number of organisations using networks, to get a feel for the range of possible forms they can take.

The work you covered for Chapters 13 and 14, Elements 4.1 and 4.2, will be directly relevant to this element and also to the next one. Chapters 15 and 16 (Elements 4.3 and 4.4) are sometimes taken together.

After studying this chapter you should be able to:

1 describe and give examples of types of *networks*
2 describe the *components* which form *networks*
3 describe network *topologies*
4 describe the *benefits* of using computer *networks*
5 explain the different *data flow control methods* on a network
6 explain network *management activities* and *system security methods*.

Did you know?

Before the advent of PCs, when mainframes were the only type of computer being used by companies, system users were storing data files in their own user file areas. It was discovered that the same data was being used and stored on the mainframe several times by people all over the company because there was no standard database for them.

To overcome this problem, standardised databases were introduced, ensuring all data was stored in a format everyone in the organisation could understand and use. This format worked well until PCs came along and reversed all the hard work!

At first, PCs were introduced into companies alongside mainframe computers. They did not interact with one another and so, as a result, data was stored several times on different machines around the organisation – the problem that had been overcome had returned. It was only when PC networks were developed that a standardised format was reintroduced and used effectively again.

Types of networks

There are very many kinds of computer networks, but one of the main categories into which they fall is based on the size of the area a network has to cover. Within this categorisation by size are local area networks (LANs) and wide area networks (WANs). We look first at LANs.

Local area networks

LANs link items of computing equipment that are sufficiently close to each other to avoid the need for signals to be amplified or for an external provider of communications services to be involved. Often it is said, as a guide, that one kilometre is the maximum span for a LAN. A LAN typically links PCs and other resources which can be shared between the users.

The links between the items are most commonly cabling, either unshielded twisted-pair (UTP) or co-axial cable (co-ax). An alternative to the use of either of these physical media is the use of short-wave radio or infra-red links, both of which are gaining in popularity.

PCs on a LAN are called *workstations*. They can be normal PCs, or they can be PCs without a diskette drive, without a hard disk or without both. We shall look at these options, and also at the two main strategies for communication on a LAN. They are called *token-passing* and *bus* technologies. Token-ring networks are described on p. 00. A bus type arrangement is one in which the LAN items are all connected to a single conductor, or bus.

Some of the PCs on a network are usually dedicated to particular tasks. They are called *servers*. Files of data and software are held on a server's hard disk to be shared by users through their own workstations. This would be a *file server*. A printer or a plotter could also be shared, and be controlled by a dedicated PC. A PC controlling a printer server, or printer would be a *printer server*. A file server and a printer server, or print server could be amalgamated in a small LAN. There may be a *communications server* if there is a special need for one. In contrast to LANs with servers, there can also be *peer-to-peer* LANs in which all workstations have more or less equal status. They would share the tasks of the servers.

You will be getting the flavour of the wide range of choices the planner of a LAN has available. In deciding upon the design for a particular LAN the planner has to consider the role the LAN will have to play. More is said about the choices and the issues later in this chapter.

Wide area networks

WANs can span areas with no distance limitation. There is no set pattern for WANs. They can link individual users to one another, individual users to remote computers or LANs and LANs to other LANs.

The links are likely to be run by an external body such as a telephone service operator. The links themselves are metal wires or cables, radio links over the earth or satellite links. The Internet is a WAN.

Broadcast

The word *broadcast* has different meanings, depending on its context. Here a broadcast service is a data service such as the TV Ceefax service, or some radio transmissions. More generally it refers to any communication in which information from a sender can be picked up by many, unspecified users. Thus signals sent from a satellite are broadcast, as are those on a bus-type LAN.

Public switched data network (PSDN)

A PSDN provides a communications facility for digital data that is fed from a sender to an address on the network in the form of standard-length packets. No computing service is provided. Users need to have *packet-assemblers/disassemblers* (PADs) to interface with a PSDN. The PSDN standard for packet-switching, as it is called, is CCITT's X.25, and revisions of it. The best-known PSDN is BT's Packet Switch Stream (PSS).

Public switched telephone network (PSTN)

In the UK the PSTN is largely BT's national telephone system. As deregulation moves forward other PSTNs will become established by other public service operators.

The PSTN was designed for voice, but is now a carrier of huge amounts of data. The upgrading of lines and the replacement of the mechanical Strowger switches in telephone exchanges by System X digital switches have made the efficient handling of data possible.

Integrated services data network (ISDN)

The ISDN is an international network for carrying digital data over the telephone system. It is intended to carry voice, data, fax and video signals, but the quality of the telephone lines limits what can be done satisfactorily.

The basic ISDN service, which is the service taken by most users, provides two 64-kilo-baud channels for digital traffic, and one 16-kilo-baud channel for call management functions on the network.

An attraction of ISDN is that it accepts digital traffic directly, with no requirement for PADs or other special equipment. In a company, for instance, once an ISDN exchange is installed all users can communicate with remote users without having to use modems, in full duplex mode.

Private WANs

Many enterprises, including many companies, have their own private WANs. A company that has a head office, sales offices, factories, and depots spread across the country or internationally could decide to set up a private WAN. Airline and tour operator reservation centres might link over private WANs to their principal sources of bookings. Banks use WANs to link their branches. Most private WANs use the PSTN, but many have dedicated phone lines as their links.

The joint academic network JANET is an example of a private WAN. Other examples are Compuserve, CIX and Delphi, to which it is necessary to subscribe in order to use their services.

Did you know?

The global pharmaceutical company SmithKline Beecham is conducting first-round job interviews using video conferencing equipment. Rather than paying for an applicant to travel to the interview, the company is saving considerable sums of money by using a video and television link. It is especially useful when applicants live in other countries. The only difference between having a face-to-face

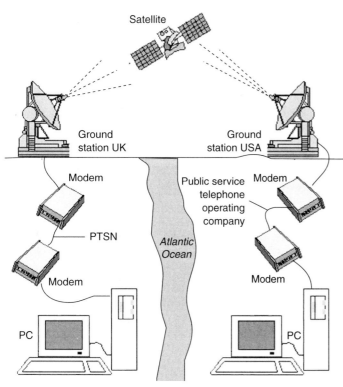

Figure 15.1 WAN using satellite links

interview and a video-based one is that both parties have to get used quickly to the time lag the equipment creates between one person finishing talking and the other replying.

Did you know?

A digital mobile telephone made by Nokia can be linked into a notebook PC to allow anyone on the move to link into either another PC, the Internet, a local area network or a wide area network. In many ways, the fact that the PC can link into a distant local area network makes it part of a wide area network automatically, as it is extending the use of the local area network.

Evidence collection point

At this point your tutor may wish you to start work on the project which will prove to your tutor and assessor that you understand this part of the element. If so, turn to page 226 and do Section 1 of the project. This covers the first evidence indicator for this element.

The components of networks

Workstation

Any PC or computer terminal forming part of a LAN is called a workstation. The workstations use software and other hardware on the network to help produce what the user wants, for instance CAD drawings, spreadsheets, word processed documents and database reports.

Data transmission media

Data is carried by metal, glass or through the air and space. Metal is the medium for UTP and co-ax, glass is the medium in fibre-optic cable (Figure 15.2), and air and space support radio and satellite communications.

Metal is plentiful and inexpensive; fibre-optic cable has very large capacity (or *bandwidth*, to use the term for the amount of traffic that a channel can carry), is immune to radio frequency interference, and does not itself emit radiation; radio and satellite communication can cover very large distances at reasonable cost.

Workstation to media connectors

We have referred to PADs as needed to connect a workstation to a packet-switched digital data network. For a LAN workstation the connection from the cable is made directly to a network card installed in an expansion slot, usually through a T-piece.

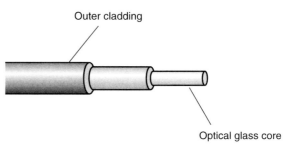

Figure 15.2 Fibre-optic cable

Did you know?

It's possible to buy a computer mouse that works without wires. A receiver is plugged into the back of the computer. This holds an infra-red sensor. The mouse hand-piece holds an infra-red transmitter, just like a TV remote control. Any movements made by the mouse are picked up by the sensor and interpreted by the computer in the same way as a regular mouse.

The type of data transmission media used in connecting a network can have a big impact on the standard of the network, its accuracy, the speed it sends data at and how easy it is to install, and build additional workstations into the network.

Network cards

We've looked at workstation to media connectors. We know that at one end they connect to transmission media, but how do they connect to a PC?

Network cards, or network interface cards (NICs), are devices much like other printed circuit boards that are held in expansion slots inside the computer. The other end is connected to the workstation to media connectors on the outside of the computer. It's just like an electricity plug being connected to the wires of a hairdryer, and then being connected to the socket in the wall which in turn is linked into the house electricity system. NICs come in different shapes and sizes, for instance, modern notebook PCs use network cards the size of a credit card.

File servers

In a network, individual PCs tend not to store any of their own files – the file server does (*some* network PCs have their own hard disk drives, but most don't as doing so increases costs, and defeats one of the objectives of having a network). The server holds all the operating system files that make the PCs and LAN work, the applications software used on the PCs, and the data used on the system.

Activity

Write to companies that manufacture network components, and ask them for rejects of any network components they may have. When you have collected at least one example of each of the network components discussed in this element, as a group, create a visual display showing similarities, differences and how the components work together in a network.

You would assume that the file server is no ordinary PC. You'd be right! File servers need to be able to work with very large amounts of data – the hard disk drives are measured in Gb (gigabytes). They also have to be able to respond to the needs of possibly hundreds of users at the same time. They must therefore be able to work very quickly. But there's still more to most file servers than these basic facts. They are designed to deal with many different commands from users at the same time. If a network is very busy it will probably slow down – *you* may have come across this yourself at some time. Great reliability is needed: if a file server fails all users will lose service.

DOS and Windows were not designed to run busy network file servers – the number of tasks the file server has to perform means specialist operating systems are required. There are a number available on the market – a popular one is Netware by Novel. As well as running the individual PCs in a network (and all the usual tasks expected by each user such as formatting and printer control), it is also capable of

1 noting the load of all hardware and software so everyone is allowed to use the network facilities fairly;
2 maintaining security; and
3 keeping track of the software being used (so that any special software licences that require payment each time the software is used can be paid for), keeping track of who is on the system and for what length of time, and monitoring what each user has done on the network – any illegal or immoral activity must be stopped immediately by the network manager.

If you use Windows on a network, you believe it's the same as Windows on a PC. As far as you're concerned it is, although it is different internally.

Did you know?

In 1995, US Department of Defense systems were attacked 250,000 times by computer network hackers. One of the most serious attacks was made by a 16-year-old schoolboy in London. In 1994, he worried US officials by attacking their systems in

Korea – they thought that if he attacked the systems once more there could have been a war between the USA and North Korea. Just in case you are so impressed you too want to hack into the US defence systems – don't! The boy in question was arrested in 1994 as a result of his actions.

Printer servers

Printer servers control printing in the network. When a networks PC sends data to be printed, the data is received by the file server and passed on to the printer server which acts as a queuing device. Generally, all print work is carried out by a designated printer, possibly the one nearest to the workstation making a print request. This is also known as the default printer. It is possible to select different printers on the network, as each printer may have particular characteristics of speed and print quality. When the user sends data to be printed, the address of the new printer can be selected by the workstation user, and the work is done at the required point.

Software

When a PC is turned on, anyone may be able to use it. It's not the same with a PC on a network – turning the PC on allows the user to type in a password – if the password is wrong then he or she can't use that workstation. Passwords are issued by the network manager to safeguard the network. It's expensive to run, and the operating system allows *sharing* of specific software. This means that anyone on the network can use the same software at the same time. It's not a good idea to let just *anyone* use the system, so only approved users are given access.

However, it's highly unlikely that any system user could gain access to the operating system – this is normally reserved specifically for system managers. The system manager can intervene in various ways. For example, he or she can change users' passwords, change access rights, modify parameters at the file server and vary allocations of file space for individual users.

Multiplexer

Traditionally, any cable or data transmission medium carries only one signal at a time. Look under the bonnet of a car and you will see how this happens – why else are there so many wires? It's because lots of signals are needed and they each have their own wire. A multiplexer is a device that allows a number of signals to be transmitted at the same time over one cable.

The purpose of multiplexing is to reduce cost and bulk by allowing several relatively low-speed transmissions to share one channel capable of carrying more than one transmission – that is, having greater bandwidth. A multiplexer is a device for concentrating and distributing the individual transmissions.

This sharing can be carried out in various ways. In *time division multiplexing* each input channel is allowed a slot of time to itself on the multiplexed channel; in *frequency division multiplexing* and *amplitude division multiplexing* the cable resource is shared by tuning the signals to be superimposed on the carrier wave. Where there is more than one frequency used at a time the technique is called *broadband* working.

Auxiliary storage

This is the name given to storage devices that are external to the computer itself. Auxiliary storage is used to extend the capacity of the installed secondary storage, or to maintain copies of the data in secondary storage.

The devices used for auxiliary storage can be streamer tape, cartridge tape, writeable CD-ROM, or external hard disks.

If a hard disk breaks or is faulty, copies of all work are safely backed up and can be accessed.

Bridge

Local area networks are not always run by one file server – it's common with a larger LAN for a number of file servers to be linked together to form a more powerful network. This is particularly useful if an organisation is made up of several different departments, each having its own system requirements.

If each department is given its own file server then it can be devoted exclusively to its needs. This ensures the optimum use of computer facilities, but creates another problem – the benefit of sharing data on a network has been stopped as each department's file server is not directly connected with any other. Some facility is required to allow several file servers to co-exist in the same network.

This is possible by using a bridge to connect similar file servers running under similar protocols together. For speed and data capacity, fibre-optic cable is likely to be used as the bridging data transmission medium. It is possible, though, to use metal wire to do the job, but this *may* have some of the disadvantages discussed earlier in this chapter.

If two different types of file servers need to be bridged, a *routing* device is used. This acts as an administrator in a separate working area or zone.

When bridges are used, the file servers being linked may be several hundred metres apart. The data signal sent down a line can travel only short distances before it begins to distort, or become alternated. The signal may have to be regenerated by a repeater.

Gateway

If a local area network is to be expanded into a larger LAN or a wide area network, a gateway is needed. This is the door between two arenas – the LAN and the WAN – in the same way that *your* front door is the link between *your* house and the rest of the world. Services such as email have gateways to enable PCs and LANs to connect to each other or to a mainframe.

A gateway works by using a modem and software to allow data to be sent from the local area network (to somewhere else), and to receive data from elsewhere. It opens and closes in the same way as a door.

If you have ever used the Internet and received a notice saying the 'gateway is down' this is telling you that the gateway connection to the Internet wide area network facilities is not working.

Evidence collection point

At this point your tutor may wish you to start work on the project which will prove to your tutor and assessor that you understand this part of the element. If so, turn to page 226. If you have already started the project you may be ready to do Section 2. This covers the second evidence indicator for this element.

Network topologies

What exactly is a *topology?* In simple terms, it's the way that the nodes or hardware on a network are physically arranged or connected. The most common topologies are ring, bus, star and tree.

Ring

In a ring network the hardware in the system is joined together by cable in a ring shape. This type of network does not necessarily need a file server as the computers are in a direct link with one another and together do the work the file server *would* do if it was present. This is illustrated in Figure 15.3.

In Figure 15.3, if workstation A sends data to workstation C, it goes in an anti-clockwise direction. Workstation B receives the data before C and checks to see if any of the data message is intended for *its* use. If it is not, a device in workstation B *repeats* the message and sends it along the cable to the next computer in the network. As the next computer *is* C, this process will not be run again. Had it not been, the data would continue until it reached its required destination.

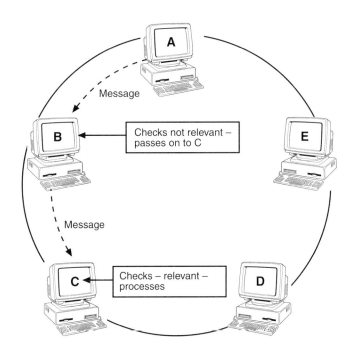

Figure 15.3 A ring network

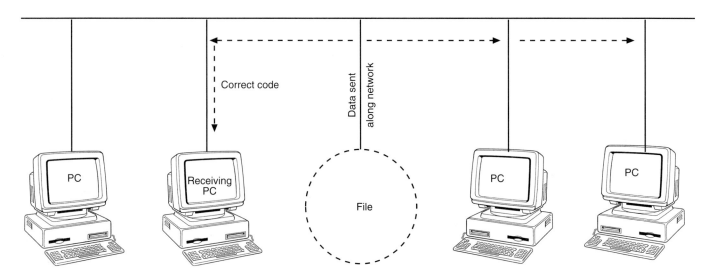

Figure 15.4 A bus network

On the surface it would appear that this process would be slow. Data transmissions pass through each workstation interface with a few bits delay. It's possible for the start of a data transmission to arrive back at the original sending computer before the last part of it has been sent – this is obviously not slow!

If you read further into this subject, you will come across a variation on a ring network – the token ring network. Before any data can be transmitted from a workstation, it must hold a *token* that travels constantly around the ring.

The ring arrangement looks as if the whole network is vulnerable to one link failing; but this is usually not the case because the routeing of the cables builds in some redundancy.

Bus

In a bus network, data is sent from one point along a single cable. Computers are connected to this cable and can receive the data sent down it. All messages are sent with a code for the address of the receiving piece of hardware. This makes sure only the intended hardware receives the message. However, if it is not switched on, that data is lost! It would have to be sent again. Let's look at an example diagram in Figure 15.4.

The usual bus technology LAN is called Ethanet. It has that name because it was not intended to be restricted to any particular medium. Strictly it is a broadcast system because all workstations receive every message.

Star

In a star network, the file server is needed to act as a central controlling device. All messages are sent to it and passed on to the destination intended. This is like a letter you post to a friend: before it arrives it goes through your local sorting office to determine which part of the country it is to go to. When it arrives in that part of the country it is sorted again

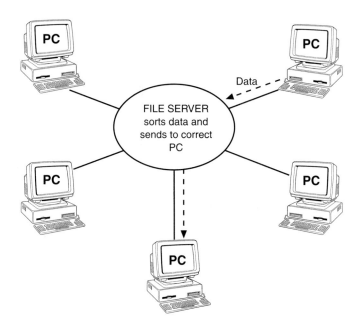

Figure 15.5 A star network

into the correct post code area to be delivered by the postman. This topology is shown in Figure 15.5.

Star topologies tend not to be used as much as other topologies because each time a new workstation is added to the network, extra cable must be added to link it to the file server. There are advantages to star networks, though: if a node or cable breaks down, only one workstation is affected – all the others continue to work as normal.

You should take careful note of the structure of a star network – don't assume just because the network cabling system forms the shape of a star that it is a star topology. It's quite likely that other network structures will look like a star in layout, but in reality be working as a different topology. This would be the case if redundant cabling was included in a ring topology to give extra resilience. That is, to be able to keep the network serviceable if one link should fail.

Mesh

In some cases where reliability is of great importance extra links are added to provide a choice of routes for data to reach its final address. Such an arrangement is called a mesh topology.

Tree networks

In a tree network, large volumes of data processing are done by a mainframe or minicomputer. Smaller, lower-level processing is done by mini or microcomputers. Tree networks are commonly used as wide area networks. They are intended to reduce the costs of transmitting data by having different types of work done at different levels. In other words, transactions are directed by the network to processing facilities best able to handle them efficiently and economically.

The networks we have looked at so far are fairly expensive to build. What happens if you need to link only a small number of computers together – in a number of offices or at home, for example? It's possible to build a network quite cheaply (at around £100 for the hardware per PC). Software is loaded into each PC in the network and network cards and cable link the PCs together. This is a peer-to-peer network.

Activity

Using computer magazines or any other source you feel is appropriate, find out how much it costs to build each of the networks we have dealt with. Put your findings into a table and make a comparison, highlighting (in your view) the best network for the money.

Evidence collection point

At this point your tutor may wish you to start work on the project which will prove to your tutor and assessor that you understand this part of the element. If so, turn to page 226. If you have already started the project you may be ready to do Section 3. This covers the third evidence indicator for this element.

The benefits of computer networks

Sharing

The biggest benefit of a network comes from sharing – software, hardware, resources and data. This saves money – the hardware has to be bought only for the system as a whole rather than for each individual user. It also saves time as data can be moved around from user to user quickly and efficiently without needing to transfer it on disks. This makes life far more convenient for each system user. We shall look at some examples to illustrate the benefits of using computer networks.

Software

Rather than storing a copy of applications software on each machine and having to go to each one in turn every time there is a software update, it's far easier and more convenient to store the software once on a file server and have PCs access it on a network. For example, if you use a computer each day at work, rather than having a hard disk on your PC with word processing, spreadsheet and database software, you can log on to the organisation's network and use the appropriate software when needed. As it becomes available, and once it has been tested, any software that has been upgraded is put on the network. If there are hundreds of PCs in the organisation, it would take weeks for the network manager to go to each one in turn and load up the new versions. By loading them once on to the file server it saves time, effort and money, and the software works just as well as it would if it were on the hard disks of every workstation.

Hardware

If an office is shared with other colleagues, rather than each person having a printer and scanner next his or her PC, there can be one of each in the room. Each person has access to them through the computer network. This is cost-effective as these peripheral devices aren't used all the time and are expensive. It makes more sense to share them.

Resources and data

An example of a benefit here can be seen when one needs to work closely with a colleague using the same data. If a database is created, but updated on only one of the two PCs, there will immediately be two versions. Shared data on a file server eliminates this possibility.

Did you know?

Organisations with large WANs, linking perhaps hundreds of PCs into their networks, have to invest substantial sums in the equipment. Even if the PCs do not contain disk drives, the total cost is still high.

Manufacturers are competing energetically with each other to produce network computers, or NCs, that will perform the functions that network users need, but will be very much less expensive than the PCs currently available. Microsoft's proposed offering, called 'Net PC', is to be an Intel-based machine having Windows facilities and interface but no end-user expansion slots.

Central services

By using a network, a company can make sure that all aspects of their computer system are looked after centrally by the same people all the time. This gives the added advantages of *security, support* and *maintenance*. The system manager can control who uses the network and place security devices on it to ensure no unauthorised access is gained. This is particularly important as, when network systems grow, it becomes easier for hackers to strike and gain

access to restricted areas. Centralisation can take this into account and take steps to prevent it from happening.

Any problems people have when using the network can be sorted out by a central help-line support facility. This is preferable to individuals owning copies of user handbooks and trying to sort out problems with their own PCs. Changes on one PC could theoretically damage other parts of the network.

The risks of viruses entering a network are minimised if there is only one, closely controlled, point of entry for new software.

Finally, by keeping the network running centrally, the network manager can ensure that software maintenance is kept up from a central point rather than by moving to different computers around a building.

Efficiency

Computer networks make the use of computers more efficient. They eliminate wasted time by ensuring users have access to what they need when they need it, rather than having to ask other people if they know where data is, copying it on to diskette and then loading it up on to their own PC. There are economies in having standard usage practices, security procedures and support.

Teamworking

By setting up a network the members of a team can have access to the same data and information. As certain projects in businesses are conducted in teams, this can be useful.

It may also be cheaper to use a local area network or wide area network than to support team operation in any other way.

Evidence collection point

At this point your tutor may wish you to start work on the project which will prove to your tutor and assessor that you understand this part of the element. If so, turn to page 226. If you have already started the project you may be ready to do Section 4. This covers the fourth evidence indicator for this element.

Data flow control methods

Imagine going to a library only to find that all the books are in a pile in the middle of the floor. How would you find what you need? In a similar way, if all the data in a computer or computer network was on the hard disk in a totally random and haphazard way, it would be very difficult to find what you need. This is why data is controlled – without this control it could be anywhere. Uncontrolled data defies the main aim of computers – to speed up the use and manipulation of data, and to make jobs easier.

There are two main data flow control methods for networks. The first is *reservation* and the other *contention*.

Reservation

If you ring up your local cinema and have them put two tickets for a film aside for you (providing you can pay for them over the telephone using a credit card), you are making a reservation. The tickets have been assigned to you and will be waiting for you to pick them up. *Some* data flow control methods in a network work in a similar way – allowing the user to *reserve* slots on the network and to send information at the reserved time.

Token ring

This is a network designed by IBM. The PCs are connected to the network, with a *multi-station access server* controlling the entire network. It exercises control over the flow of message data round the ring by allowing only one item to be using the ring at any instant.

If there is no traffic between workstations a token passes from one workstation to the next continuously. If a station needs to transmit; it must first capture the token and substitute for it the message to be conveyed. When the message reaches the destination workstation it is stripped out of the ring and a token substituted. The new token continues to circulate until there is a requirement for another message to be sent. Some advantages and disadvantages of token ring networks are shown in the table following.

Advantages	Disadvantages
One part of the system can fail or the cable can be cut; the signal will then trackback on the network	Token ring networks are generally more expensive than other networks. For example, if twisted-pair type cable is used, four cables are needed
Token ring networks are supported by IBM software – this makes the network flexible and open to use by different systems	They are more complicated than other networks – four cables (if twisted-pair cable is used) makes it harder to put together

Time slots

This is similar to reserving plane ticket – you are essentially reserving a slot on a plane to fly to a destination at a certain time. In a similar way, it's possible to reserve time slots in a network to send or receive data. What are the advantages and disadvantages of time slots?

Advantages	Disadvantages
On a busy network, it guarantees that once a time is reserved, the user will be able to use the system (once that time arrives)	You may need longer than the length of time you've been allocated in your time slot. If that occurs the network manager has to increase the slot time, or messages have to be broken into segments for transmission
No one can use the network exclusively – stopping others from using it all the time	You have to wait for your time slot to come up before you can use the system

Polling

Polling is a process under which stations are invited, one at a time, in an agreed order, called the polling list, to transmit. If a station has nothing to send the invitation is extended to the next on the list. This is shown in the table overleaf.

Contention

With reservation networks time is put aside for users to send what they want on the network. With contention the computers on the network compete to use it. This really means that the first computer that logs on and asks the network file server for data uses the file server first – once this computer has done its

223

Advantages	Disadvantages
If all computers on the network are the same, their bids will give them equal priority to use the network	Not all computers have the same needs – some may be given rights by the network manager for preferential bidding to use the network – other users miss out as a result. The network manager constructs a polling list which favours some computers at the expense of others, in order to maximise the effectiveness of the network
Having the computer bid for network time means the user doesn't have to think about it	If the user doesn't have to bid for network time then he or she may not know how the system works – any failures will be hard to detect

Table 15.1 Polling advantages and disadvantages

task, the others compete for file server time – it's a case of *first come, first served*. Although this has advantages, it causes the network manager problems in certain areas of the network.

Collision avoidance and *collision detection* mean almost the same thing. They apply to Ethernet LANs. You may come across the term *carrier sense with multiple access/collision detection* (CSMA/CD) in literature on Ethernet. This is how it works.

Each workstation on the LAN monitors the network. When one of them wants to transmit a data packet it does so if no other transmission can be detected on the bus at that instant. If during the interval between deciding to transmit a packet and that packet actually arriving on the network some other device starts transmitting, a collision occurs. Both workstations notice the collision, and back away.

After a random time interval, normally different for each device, the transmissions are made again, this time without collision. Naturally, the more workstations there are sharing the bus the more collisions occur, and the more time will be lost in recovering from them.

CSMA/CD is well established and used generally on Ethernet LANs. It works well and has no obvious disadvantages.

So now we know the basic facts, how do we decide which type of system to choose? First of all, look at the advantages and disadvantages of each method. Is there any one method that appears to be best for you? If so, then the question is answered. If not, then you will need to analyse everything in a bit more detail. Does every network user have a good working knowledge of how the network works, as this can

make a difference? Is there a network manager who works on the network all the time, or does he or she have other jobs to do? By analysing all factors such as these it's possible to narrow down the options until you find your ideal network.

Evidence collection point

At this point your tutor may wish you to start work on the project which will prove to your tutor and assessor that you understand this part of the element. If so, turn to page 226. If you have already started the project you may be ready to do Section 5. This covers the fifth evidence indicator for this element.

Management activities and system security methods

A network manager is the person in charge of everything that takes place on a network. This may be a job you aspire to, but it is not always as easy as it sounds. When anything goes wrong, the network manager is responsible for getting the network up and running again – quickly, as the network users don't want to be without their computers for even half a minute. What's more, it is impossible to plan what you are going to do when the network breaks down as nobody knows *when* problems will occur or *what* they will be.

Things going wrong may be as minor as a plug inadvertently being pulled out, or as serious as a power surge blowing fuses in the file server leading to corrupted disks, hackers breaking into an organisation's network or the loss of the file server hard disk. This would bring a network to a halt for hours or even days.

Here are the jobs a network manager has to do:

Check network activity levels

Make sure the network is being used by the correct number of people. If the network is being overloaded by the users (i.e. too many people using the network at the same time and making demands on its hardware and software resources so that it is very slow at responding to instructions), then it needs updating, or some kind of rationing of demands must be imposed. This may involve adding an extra file server to share the work the present servers are doing, or upgrading the server so the network can work faster.

Conversely, the network may not be being used much and it is up to the network manager to find out why.

If a network is too difficult to use, money has been invested in a computer system that is not suitable for the people who need to use it, so something would have to be done, such as training the system users, or making a *help desk* available.

System reporting

Periodically network managers run system reports to show how the network is set up and being used. Typical items to look out for include what access rights users have on the network, who is using what software the most and any illegal activities taking place on the network (such as software pirating by system users). It also shows if any illegal or unlicensed software is being run on the network (important, as it will have to be removed or the right to use it paid for by the organisation), or if anyone has been trying to 'hack' into the network. If anything has taken place that shouldn't, the network manager is responsible for taking corrective action. Another job system reporting does is to propose areas of improvement for the system. Is it possible for new software to replace anything on the network, or if some people don't use the software they have access rights to, can the network manager save money by not paying for a user licence for it?

It is common practice to run a system report at the end of each working day so that the activities that took place are recorded. As software becomes more advanced, a greater part of the reporting task is done without the network manager having to oversee it. Details of what can and cannot take place on the network are loaded into the reporting software and it checks the day's activities alongside the list.

Security

The network manager is in charge of system security – ensuring only authorised people use the system, issuing passwords and user identification numbers, and checking the system for viruses and people trying to hack into it.

Did you know?

If you use a friend's password to let you enter the computer network at school or college you are almost certainly breaking security regulations. If you are caught, there is a good chance you will be banned from using the system.

Storage

The network manager has to allocate how much storage space the system users can each have to store their files on the network. The network manager also has to be aware of how many files are stored – if they are of no use to anyone they should be *purged* or deleted. You may have experienced this at school or college – when the IT tutor finds the network hard disk drive too full, all students are asked to remove any files they don't use any more to give the network more space. This is called housekeeping. If no one deletes files, the chances are the IT tutor will delete files on everyone's behalf! There may be a policy by the management which states how long files should be kept on the network hard disk before they must be archived.

System configuration

As well as the setting of passwords, the rights of access to the different servers on the system and the printer queues for each individual network user; systems are configured according to the needs of their users. For example, a project-estimating department that calculates how much construction will cost requires computers that run several spreadsheets at once. Although a standard computer may be capable of doing this job, it may be too slow to do it effectively. Each computer in the department would be altered so it could work faster, and each one in turn would have to be configured accordingly.

Planning is an important part of the system manager's responsibilities. The pattern of demand, the characteristics of new hardware and the launch of new software all bear upon the nature of the network that best meets the needs of users and the enterprise as a whole.

We've looked at the network manager's job, now let's see what system security methods exist. Remember, the security of the operation and the resources are probably of crucial importance to the organisation.

Control of access

Examples of mechanisms for controlling *physical* access are passcards (perhaps with a picture and a magnetic black strip on the back to allow use of the computer when passed through a reading device), identification cards (to allow staff to pass through the security guard gate of the building), gates (possibly with combination locks on or those that work with identification cards) and grilles (simply metal bars stopping access to equipment).

Examples of restricting *logical* access are software controls (such as passwords to start work on a PC or network, or even to gain access to individual files) and hardware controls (an example being a printing card to allow a user to print on a certain printer).

Forced recognition of security

This is concerned with making sure employees are aware that data on the network is of a sensitive nature and should not be disclosed to anyone outside the organisation. An example is the Official Secrets Act that anyone working in a security-sensitive field is required to sign. Even the catering staff at Harwell can't divulge menus or purchasing patterns in case foreign agents find out how many people are employed there! Many companies have non-disclosure agreements written into their contracts, stating that it is the duty of each employee not to divulge any information. Anyone ignoring this is disciplined. This shows that even companies that are not openly security sensitive are careful about the information they generate.

Evidence collection point

As this point your tutor may wish you to start work on the project which will prove to your tutor and assessor that you understand this part of the element. If so, turn to page 226. If you have already started the project you may be ready to do Section 6. This covers the sixth evidence indicator for this element.

Evidence indicator project

This project has been designed to cover the evidence indicator related to Chapter 15 (Element 4.3). It is divided into six sections. Tutors may wish students to complete the sections at the appropriate points marked in the text. Alternatively, tutors may prefer their students to do the entire project at the end of the element.

Performance criteria: 1–6

Key skills:		
	Communication	3.2, 3.3
	Application of number	–
	IT	3.2, 3.3, 3.4

Section 1
In a group of no more than four, make a presentation to an audience describing and giving examples of types of networks. Rather than giving a technical presentation, use graphics and any other visual aid you can to express each network in practical terms. Use examples from everyday life that members of the audience will readily understand and relate to.

Section 2
Choose two networks from the examples presented in Section 1 of this project. One must be a local area network and the other a wide area network. Describe the components which form the selected networks.

Section 3
In a group of three, film a five-minute report on video showing the different network topologies that exist. The video should not be straight narrative, but should include graphical illustrations as well as practical live footage of the way the networks operate.

Section 4
In a group, discuss the benefits of using computer networks. One member of the group should take notes of all relevant points so they can be word processed into a list to be handed to your tutor. Ensure that the benefits include those shared (software, hardware, resources, data), central services (security, support, maintenance), efficiency and teamworking.

Section 5
Explain the different methods of data flow control for networks including reservation (token, ring, time slots, polling), and contention (collision avoidance, collision detection).

Section 6
Explain the following network management activities and system security methods:

Network management activities:
- check network activity levels
- system reporting
- security
- storage
- system configuration.

System security methods
- control of access (physical, logical)
- forced recognition of security.

Chapter 16

Use a computer network

Now you have an opportunity to put into practice the knowledge you have gained from Chapter 15 (Element 4.3) on networks. This element requires you to use a network and undertake file management activities on a network. To gain the evidence required in this element, you need to have access to a computer network. Arrange with your tutor to use your school or college's network or if possible with a local business.

After studying this chapter you should be able to:

1 access a computer network in accordance with an *organisation's standards*
2 undertake *data file processes* and *file management* activities
3 modify the *access rights* of other users to own files
4 *access* network applications
5 send and receive electronic mail
6 *install* a new user on the network.

Special note

There is only one evidence indicator project for this element. It is at the end of the element on page 239.

Did you know?

Novell's Netware is possibly the most common type of computer network software. Although Novell dominates the market, there is one area they don't command in the same way – the market of schools and colleges, many of which use a network designed and built by Oxford-based Research Machines – the NIMBUS network. It was designed with education in mind, and there is even software available to help students tackle parts of the National Curriculum and to use simple but powerful packages such as databases. Some local education authorities provide other kinds of network software free to schools and colleges in their areas.

Access a computer network

In attempting to safeguard security and protect copyright, special procedures exist within some organisations. It is not possible simply to sit down at a network computer and use it – you must have authorisation. Without it insisting on only authorised users having access anyone could reach material stored on the network, possibly with serious consequences.

The first point below, log in, looks at one aspect of network security. Other aspects were discussed in Chapter 15 (Element 4.3).

Log in

To gain access to the network, you usually have to type in your user identification number (ID) and password. The ID is normally set by the network manager and can't be changed. The password is first set by the network manager, but can be changed by the user. Different networks allow users to change passwords at different times. It is not uncommon for networks to prompt users to change their passwords every six to eight weeks. This is an extra security procedure just in case anyone discovers an individual's password – regularly changing it makes it more difficult for hackers to break in. There is always one thing to remember when this happens – the new password! Don't write it down, though, as it may be found by someone else.

Display and access files

There are two ways of displaying and accessing files, both of which will depend on what type or make of network you are using. In the past, once the user logged on to the network, the screen display looked much like a DOS screen. Files were displayed by typing in the appropriate command – DIR or its equivalent. Over time, networks have become more user-friendly, and the opening screen has started to display a menu option system whereby the user may choose the software that is required.

Since Windows has been introduced on to networks (called Windows for Workgroups), users have had the option of using the operating system to display files or file manager software. This is accessed by double clicking on the icon or by accessing an application

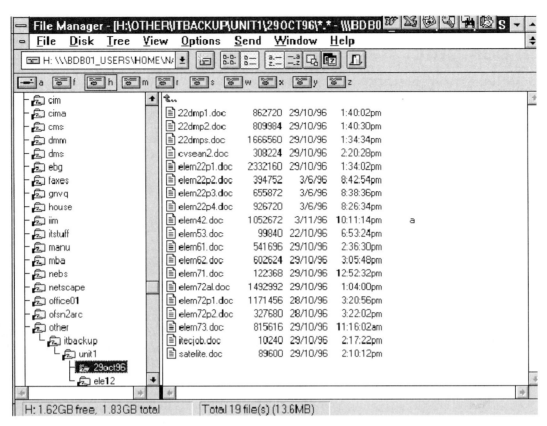

Figure 16.1 A directory tree displayed by Windows File Manager

and *opening the file*. Figure 16.1 shows File Manager software illustrating directories and files stored. Figure 16.2 shows how files can be displayed from Word for Windows, by selecting FILE and then OPEN from the menu at the top of the screen. The user can select the directory and file that is required.

Display and access applications

Applications are executable files. That means that in a list of files provided by DOS on giving the command DIR will all carry the suffix, or 'extension', .EXE. Under DOS, when you have identified the file name for the desired application followed by .EXE, select it and press 'Enter' in order to get in to the application.

By accessing Windows for Workgroups, all Windows-based applications software is shown by icons, in the same way it is in Windows on a PC (see Figure 16.3). From here, using the mouse, and *double clicking* on

the required icon, access can be gained by the user to the software application. Alternatively, using the *arrow keys* on the keyboard to direct the cursor to the required icon and pressing the *return key* will have the same results. For this operation you will not be conscious that you are on a network.

In the unlikely event that you are unable to access the icon window of your choice, but still need to access a software application, use the menu system at the top of the screen to help. Pressing the Alt and W keys at the same time will open a menu selection box giving you access to each of the main software applications on the screen. Selecting the one of your choice will take you to the icon window.

When we looked at displaying and accessing files under Windows, a network opening screen and menu option were suggested. Very often this offers a pointer to a screen displaying the software applications available. By pressing the number next to the application you want, the operating system launches it for you.

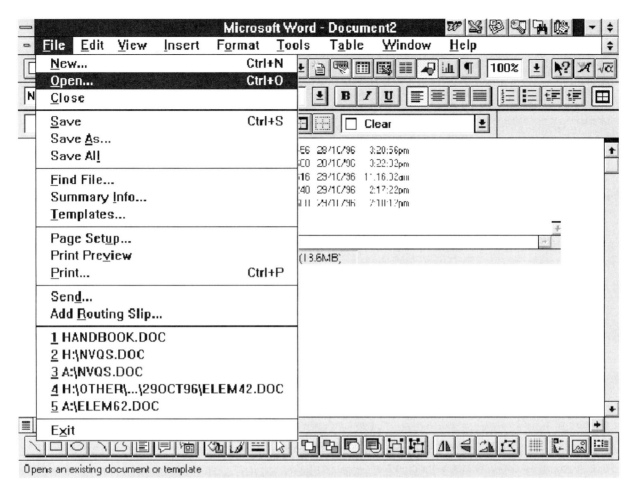

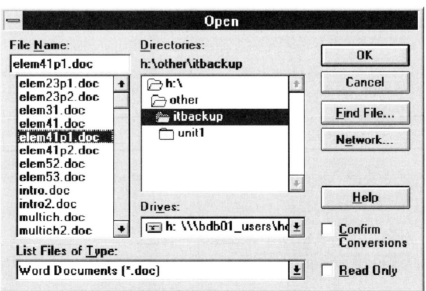

Figure 16.2 Selecting a file through Word for Windows

Figure 16.3 Application icons under Windows for Workgroups

Organisation's standards

User identification

How are users identified by the network? Is entering your user ID sufficient, or do you have to key in your password as well? Is the system controlled solely by software, or also by physical identification such as swipe cards?

Security conventions

These are the conditions, which may be contractual, to be satisfied before access to the computer network is granted. This may involve signing documents before passwords and other logical requirements are made available. Physical access may also be controlled. Remember that security conventions change from one network to another.

Copyright requirements

This has already been covered earlier in this book in Chapter 12 (Element 3.4). You are not allowed by law to copy any material produced by someone else without his or her permission. Although we tend to think of copying only in terms of photocopying, scanning information or even typing and copying out of a book is exactly the same as far as the law is concerned. Exceptions to this are granted only through the organisation buying a licence to copy a percentage of the material in question (for example, schools and colleges can buy licences to copy 5% or 10% of certain printed material wanted for research or academic purposes).

Procedural requirements

Does the network you are using come under any procedures that have to be used at all times? Examples include BS5750 – the quality standard, where all activities must be logged. If so, the user must complete the appropriate documents to ensure the procedure is adhered to.

Allocated workspace

Does each network user have only a limited amount of storage space for files on a network file server? The answer is obviously *yes* because all storage space is limited in some form, but by how much?

It would be nice to state how much workspace each user is given. It's not possible, though. It really just depends on how big the file server hard disk is, and how many people need workspace on it. *Some* users may be given 10 Mb, while others may get 2 Gb. The amount of workspace each user is given is down to the network manager and the demands of each individual's job – some will need more space than others – for example, a CAD programmer will need far more than a word processor operator, as CAD drawings generally take up far more space on a hard disk than word processed documents.

Data file processes and file management activities

There are six of these data file processes that you should be sure you can operate over a network.

Retrieve

Make sure you can *open* or *access* files so you can work on them. If you're using Windows then you need to use the File then Open facilities on the menu to display the files available, and then type in the file name you require.

In DOS, find the directory holding the applications software, and type in the name of the .EXE file that runs the applications software. If a user menu system is available in the operating system, select the number you require that corresponds to the software.

Create

If you want to create a new file using Windows applications software, the top left icon which is an open folder is the one to select. Once this is done, you can use the software, and when you have finished, save your work. Alternatively, using the menu at the top of the screen, File, New will create a

new file. To create a file in operating system-based software is usually a similar method.

Amend

If you amend a piece of work, you are simply correcting it. For example, you may have written a letter on your word processor but want to check your spelling. You use the spellchecker facility in the word processor and this highlights a number of errors which you correct – this is amending.

Delete

In order to delete a file you must be in either the operating system or Windows File Manager. In the DOS operating system, if you type in DEL and the file name, including its file extension, the file will be deleted. For example, to delete a file called Work.DOC, we would type DEL Work.DOC and the computer does the rest. In Windows File Manager, we need to select the file to be deleted, using the mouse, and either press the DEL key on the keyboard, or click on FILE and then DELETE. This is shown in Figure 16.4 on page 232.

To delete text or figures within an application you will have to use the facilities offered by the application software.

Save

In DOS based software, to save a new file choose SAVE from the file menu, then key in the name you are giving the file; for an existing file you have only to choose SAVE.

In Windows software, the easiest method for saving is to click on the icon at the top of the screen which shows a disk. This will automatically save the file for you. Alternatively, you need to select FILE from the pull-down menu at the top of the screen and press either SAVE or SAVE AS to save your work. These commands do similar but not identical jobs. The first time you save a document you can select either. The software will ask you to give the document a file name. Once typed in, press the Return key and the file will be saved.

If you are saving work as you go along, use the Save function. The Save As command is used if you want to give a document a new name. The Options key allows the user to select how often they would like their document automatically saved – see Figure 16.5.

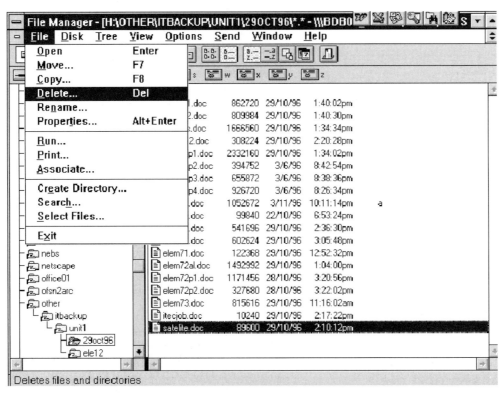

Figure 16.4 Windows screen set to delete the file satelite

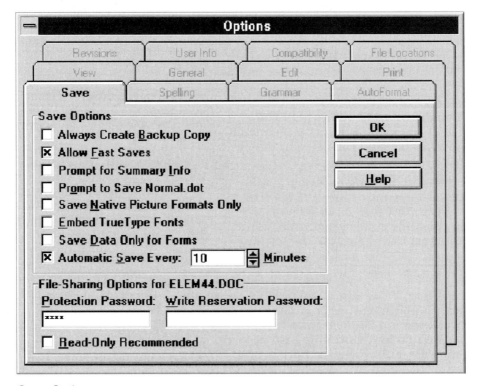

Figure 16.5 Windows Save Options screen

Protect

We have seen how passwords are used to protect user areas on networks. If a shared user area exists, it would be useful to be able to protect individual files so nobody else has access to them. This is made possible by placing a password on files. It can only be done in the Save As function in the pull-down menu in each application. Once this function is accessed, depress the Options button. Clicking on this gives access to another window as illustrated in Figure 16.5 where a password can be set by typing in the proposed password under 'Protection Password'. The password will appear as asterisks. Each time the file is accessed, the user is prompted to type in the password – without it the file is useless.

There's another way of protecting files using the File Manager in Windows. This offers other facilities such as *hiding* files so no one can see they are on a disk (that way they can't be deleted unless someone knows they are there), or making them *read only* files so no one can delete them. This is shown in Figure 16.6. This 'Properties' dialogue box is reached from the file menu. The purpose of 'Archive' is to identify a file that has been modified since it was last backed-up.

Activity

Using any information you can find (contact some companies if necessary), write a short report discussing why an organisation has network computing standards and why they must be upheld. What dangers exist for companies that do not keep up their computer network standards?

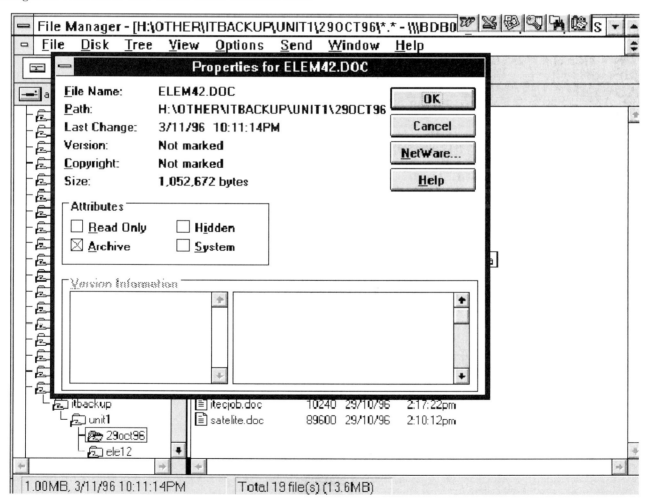

Figure 16.6 Windows Properties screen for protecting files

Let us now consider file management activities. There are nine of these.

Copy

If you wish to copy a file in DOS, type COPY (FILENAME).(FILE EXTENSION) (SPACE = TO) (NEW DIRECTORY OR DISK). For example, if your working directory is on drive C and you want to copy a file called ITADV.DOC from drive C: to drive A: you would type in COPY ITADV.DOC A:

Copying in Windows File Manager is a bit easier! Highlight the file you want to copy, select FILE in the menu options at the top of the screen, and then select COPY. All you have to do then is type in which drive the file is to be copied to – this is shown in Figure 16.7.

Rename

In Windows, open the File menu at the top of the screen and depress the Save As option key. This will give you the opportunity to overtype the existing file name with a new file name.

Under DOS, to rename a file select the name of the file, and from the file menu choose RENAME. The 'Rename File' dialogue box lists the current name. In the 'New Name' box type in the new file name.

Delete

We described the function of deleting a file under *data file processes*, above, and this is illustrated in Figure 16.4.

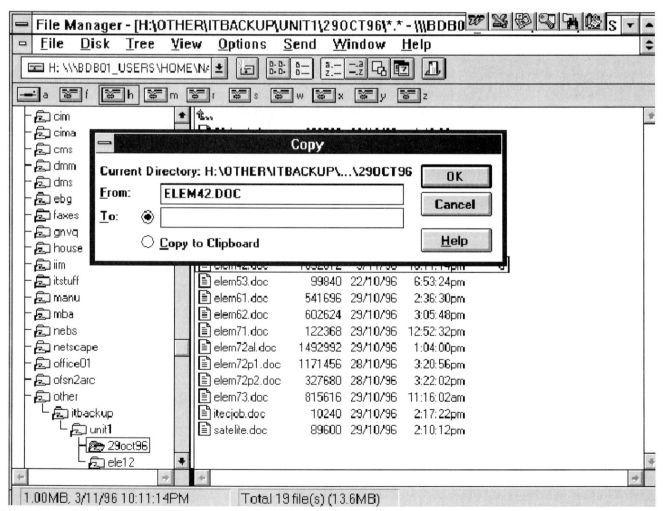

Figure 16.7 Copying a file through Windows File Manager

Move

Moving is the same process as *copying* in DOS – only you have to delete the file once it's been copied to its new destination. In Windows File Manager it's again far simpler as the software does the job for you. First, highlight the file you want to move. Then, in the menu commands at the top of the screen, select FILE and then MOVE. A new window appears and you type in where the file is to be moved to.

Back up

In DOS this is quite easy. Simply tell the software to save and type in the name of the file with .BAC on the end – this makes a backup file. In Windows applications software, select FILE, SAVE As and then select the Options button. You will see a window

appear like the one in Figure 16.5. There are a number of options available that can be selected using the mouse. The top one allows backup copies of files to be made. Remember though that if you use this you will be using up your hard disk space very fast.

List files

In DOS you can type in DIR to see a list of the files on the disk. In Windows File Manager you can see a list of all the files and directories as soon as the software loads.

Create directory structure

In DOS this is done by typing in MD (DIRECTORY NAME). As long as the directory name is no longer

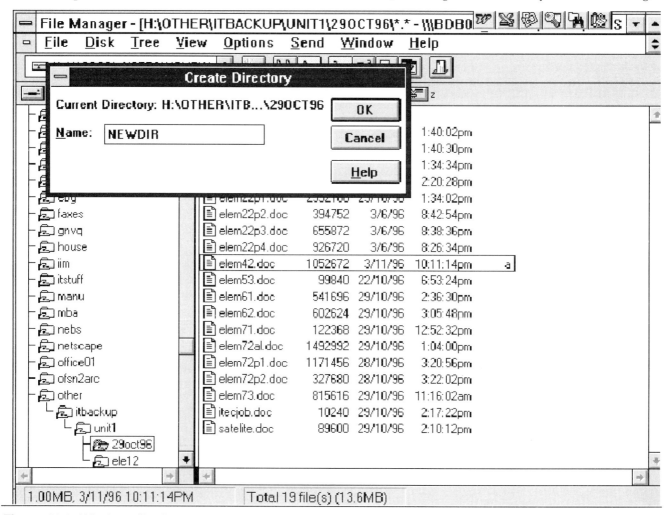

Figure 16.8 Windows file directory

235

than eight characters, the characters you type in will become the name of the directory. In Windows File Manager (see Figure 16.8), select the directory in which you want a sub-directory created, and in the menu at the top of the screen select File and Create Directory. All you have to do then is type in the name you want (again, no more than eight characters long) and the software does the rest.

Modify directory structure

In DOS this involves copying files to new directories and deleting them from their original directories. In Windows, make sure the source and destination are visible, if necessary using the 'Cascade' or 'Tile' command on the Window menu. The destination can be a directory icon, directory window, or drive icon. Then press and hold down 'SHIFT' while you drag the icon for the source file or directory to the destination.

Set rights to directory structure

Most network software provides facilities for protecting files and sub-directories by allowing the owners of them to restrict access for reading, copying, writing to them, or deleting them, by password. Network systems differ in the facilities they offer.

Modify access rights

Whenever rights are set or modified, use is made of the facility most local area networks have to allow users to place restrictions on their files. It was mentioned earlier in this chapter that it is possible to place a password on a file if the file is held in an area on a network that a number of people can access. Files stored in directories that can be accessed by a number of people are known as *group directories* or *public directories* if everyone on the network can use them.

If you are working on a project with just one other person you can ask the network manager to create a 'group' of the two of you, and then give access permission to that group. In that way you could both work on the project data without allowing access to it to anyone else.

As well as placing a password on the file, it's possible to make alterations to its 'properties'. This can be

done in Windows either with *utilities* software or by choosing the 'All Files Detail' command on the 'View' menu. The following properties can be altered:

1 *Read only* so that people can access it but can't make any changes to the data in the file.
2 *Hidden* so that no one can see the file named in a directory. Unless people know that the file is there they will never access it.
3 *Archive,* as mentioned above, under protecting files, identifies a file that has been modified since it was last backed-up.
4 *System* makes a file *seem like a software system file.* If the required file has a .Sys file extension, anyone looking in the directory for a file ending in .Doc will ignore it.

In most network operating systems, access rights to a file *can* be altered: most network software will give the user the ability to allow or deny access to files and directories. Access rights, also called 'privileges', accorded to those allowed access, can be selected:

■ At directory level, typically, a user can be given any or all of the following rights:
  – read any files in a directory
  – write to files in the directory
  – copy a file or the directory
  – delete a file or the directory

Additionally, the user may be allowed to create a directory, or to change attributes to the directory name.

■ At the file level, file attributes can provide further protection which overrides directory level security. For example, if a directory allows a user to delete files within it, one of those files can still be kept safe by marking it 'read only'.
■ Further to these steps, installations can run network accounting systems which keep track of who is using what resource, and for what purpose.

Access network applications

Accessing network applications is just the same as accessing applications on a PC. If the network uses DOS, you simply look for the name of the file you need ending in .EXE. This is the *executable* file that runs the applications software. As a point of interest, if you look at the contents of an .EXE file you will find it looks like garbled rubbish. It's set like this so you can't easily make changes to the software and sell it on, under your own name, as a new product.

The other way to access applications software is to use a *batch file*. This is a command sequence set in one of the fundamental DOS files that runs the computer. If the command is typed in then it automatically runs the software. It's employed for software that is frequently used such as word processors or spreadsheets.

Starting applications software in Windows is easier. Look at Figure 16.9. The Word (word processing) software icon has been selected by either *double clicking* on this icon using the mouse, or by highlighting it and pressing the Return (↵) key on the keyboard for the software to run.

What's the difference between running network Windows or PC-based Windows? Absolutely nothing as far as the user is concerned!

Send and receive electronic mail

Look at Figure 16.10 – this is an example of electronic mail (e-mail) being sent. You can see that the sender is SEAN NAUGHTON and it's being sent to Steve.Almond@Bolton.co.uk.

There may be electronic mail established between the PCs of a single network, with its own special features,

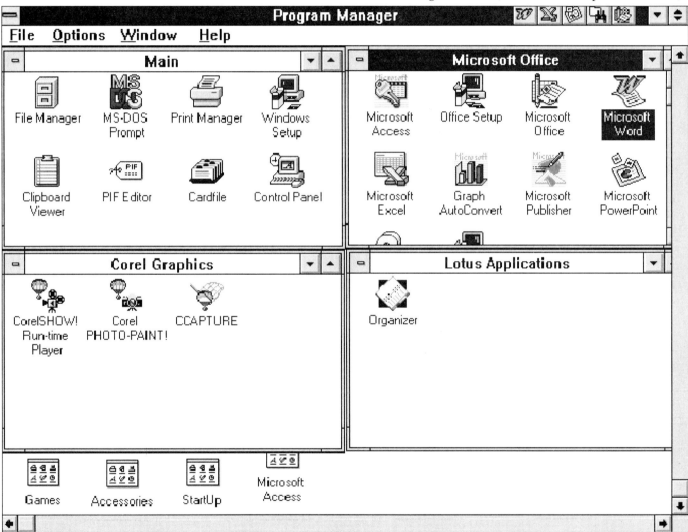

Figure 16.9 Windows applications screen

but for a general wide area E-mail system the procedures are the same for the user of a network and the user of a stand-alone PC linked to the network.

Most people think of the Internet's E-mail service if they need a wide area facility. To use the Internet in this way, the user or the network manager obtains an ID and opens an account with a network service provider such as Compuserve.

There are details regarding the subject and who else is being sent a copy of the message. There are two options here – CC stands for *carbon copy* which sends a copy of the document to the person named in the box. The BC stands for *blind copy*. The purpose of the blind copy is to conceal the fact from the addressee, when someone has been sent a copy.

After these details are inserted, the sender can type in

any message that's required. It's possible to attach files along with messages. Details of any to go should be inserted at the Attach: point near the bottom of the screen. All you have to do is tell the e-mail software which file is to be sent, and the drive it is coming from.

The use of this electronic mail facility is the same for a network as it is for a stand-alone PC running under Windows, as far as the user is concerned.

If you look at Figure 16.11, now, you'll see the In Box for the e-mail. This is the storage area assigned by the service provider for each user's incoming mail which users can read at their convenience. The bottom item in the **In Box** is highlighted. To read it you simply have to press the Return key. An earlier message can be read by selecting it using the keyboard arrows and pressing Return. The opened envelope next to each

Figure 16.10 E-mail screen

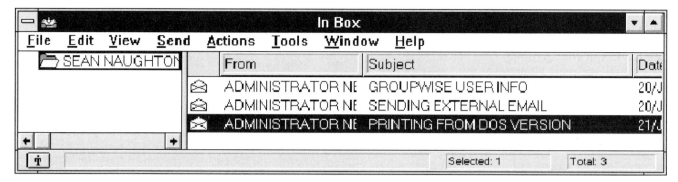

Figure 16.11 Electronic mail In Box

item shows they have been read. An unopened envelope would show an unread e-mail.

Activity

It's possible to find the e-mail address of anyone on the Internet system. Find out and make notes of how this can be done.

Install a new user

When you install a new user on a network, you must ensure that each of the following four points has been covered.

Access server

The new user must be able to access the network file server, and any other shared resources such as printers. This is normally achieved by selecting the Network Option from the opening screen which is displayed after a successful log-on.

Create user name

This is the starting point for accessing a network. The user has to type in a user name: that is, the user's ID. In theory this can be anything, but it's a good idea to make it similar to other user names on the network. For example, you may want to use the first three letters of a user's surname, the first letter of the user's first name and one at the end. Using this method, Michael Schwartz would be given the user name Schm1. The user name should be no more than eight characters in length.

Give initial password

This can be anything at all as long as it's no more than eight characters in length. Users generally change their initial passwords to something more meaningful and easy to remember. Don't make it *too* easy to remember though, as people will guess it. If you happen to be a great fan of George Michael and always talk about him, don't even think of using the word George as your password, as friends (and others!) will try it out before anything else. Use a password nobody is likely to guess and your user area on the network will remain secure.

Set initial access rights (read, write, copy, delete)

Once the user name and password have been set, it's necessary to give each user initial access rights to the network. This means they are given the rights to read their own and public information, write data into their own area of the network file server, and copy and delete their own files on the file server. If these functions aren't set then the user can log on to the network but can't do anything once in.

Evidence indicator project.

This project covers all the evidence indicators related to Chapter 16 (Element 4.4.) It has been designed to be carried out at the end of the element.

Performance criteria: 1–5

Key skills:

	Communication
	Application of number –
	IT 3.1, 3.2, 3.3, 3.4

239

When you feel confident about accessing a computer network and undertaking file management activities on the network, ask your tutor to watch you and talk him or her through what you are doing. You are likely to be undertaking these network activities on the school or college network system so you must ensure you comply with the institution's standards.

As you prepare your demonstration it would be sensible to write notes for yourself of exactly what you plan to do. These notes can go with the tutor's witness statements into your portfolio.

Section 1
First, you must access the network including logging in, displaying files, accessing files, displaying applications and accessing applications.

Section 2
Demonstrate to your tutor that you are able to undertake the following data file processes and file management activities: retrieve, create, amend, delete, save and protect, copy, rename, delete, move, back up, list files, create directory structure, modify directory structure, set rights to directory structure.

Section 3
Show how you have modified the access rights of other users to your files including read, write, copy and delete.

Section 4
Show your tutor an example of an e-mail message which has been sent by yourself and a message which you have received.

Section 5
Show your tutor that you have installed a new user on the network and that you have done the following: accessed the server, created a user name, given an initial password, set initial access rights.

Communications and networking: Unit test 4

1 In order to use electronic mail the minimum requirement is
   a A computer
   b A computer and telephone modem
   c A computer, telephone modem and access to an E-mail or Internet service
   d An integrated computer system

2 The following are examples of conferencing *except*
   a Video conferencing
   b Voice mail conferencing
   c Teleconferencing
   d Tele-video conferencing

3 CCITT...
   a Passes laws relating to telegraph and telephone communication
   b Lobbies MEPs relating to telegraph and telephone communication
   c Discusses quality issues
   d Is a consultative committee making recommendations regarding telegraph and telephone communications

4 The device at the end of a computer communication link is
   a Data Terminal Equipment
   b Data Terminating Equipment
   c Data Transfer Equipment
   d Data Testing Equipment

5 All the following are examples of connectors except
   a XY plug
   b Null Modem
   c Centronics parallel
   d T-piece

6 Information stored in a communications activities log includes
   a Flow control
   b Time taken on line
   c Stop bits
   d Asynchronous modem commands

7 ASCII is
   a A code for characters for data communication
   b An American version of DOS
   c A method of data communication
   d Data transmission theory

8 ASCII stands for
   a American Simple Code for Information Interchange
   b American Standard Code for Information Index
   c American Standard Code for Information Interchange
   d American Science Code for Information Interchange

9 Stop bits are which part of an IT system?
   a Parity
   b Flow control
   c Binary transfer
   d Baud rate

10 Which of the following is *not* a rate of data transmission?
   a Baud rate
   b Baud rate per minute
   c Binary rate of flow
   d Bits per second

11 What is echo?
   a Display of printed pages on screen for checking
   b Display of transmitted characters on the sender's screen
   c A repeat of sound sent over the Internet
   d Double printing

12 Which of the following is a transmission mode?
   a Baud rate
   b Asymmetric duplex
   c Bits per second
   d ASCII

13 Binary transfer is a method of
   a Controlling a network
   b Controlling the movement of blocks of data
   c Transferring data within a computer
   d Sending data from one network user to another

14 System reporting is a function of
   a Network management activities
   b Security
   c System configuration
   d A database

15 Collision avoidance is a function of
  a Reservation
  b Topologies
  c Data flow control methods
  d Network management activities

16 One method for limiting access to a computer system is
  a Contention
  b System reporting
  c Integrated services data network
  d Logical control

17 File management access rights include *all but which* of the following?
  a Read
  b Retrieve
  c Write
  d Copy

18 Which of the following is an example of reservation?
  a Collision avoidance
  b Bridge
  c Gateway
  d Token ring

19 Which of the following is a benefit of using a computer network?
  a Reduced number of users
  b Faster system configuration
  c Resource sharing
  d The use of ISDN

20 Which of the following is a mode of electronic communication?
  a Half duplex
  b Flow control
  c E-mail
  d Video conferencing

21 Duplex is a method of
  a Transmission
  b Half duplex
  c Flow control
  d E-mail

22 The benefits of a computer network include
  a Reservation
  b Share data
  c Check network activity levels
  d Use ISDN

23 A local area network is the
  a Interconnection of computer equipment over a small domain
  b Computers in a local network
  c Medium for data file transfer
  d Minimum requirement for communications activities

24 What is a wide area network?
  a Connections over a local area
  b Interconnection of computer equipment over a large domain
  c Fast
  d Based on the Internet

25 What is a Multiplexer?
  a A device to allow many signals to be sent over one channel
  b Many signals
  c A software command
  d A data communication protocol

26 Which of the following is *not* an example of data transmission media?
  a Air
  b Fibre-optic cable
  c Metal wire
  d CD-ROM

27 Which of the following is *not* a network topology?
  a Star
  b Ring
  c Gate
  d Bus

28 Purging is a method of
  a Improving the effectiveness of a hard disk drive
  b Selecting users for a computer system
  c Checking the effectiveness of a hard disk
  d Creating more useable storage space

29 Which of the following is an example of control arrangements for physical access?
  a Software controls
  b Hardware controls
  c Passwords
  d Identification cards

30 Which of the following data flow processes implies *adding to a file*?
  a Saving
  b Save as
  c Append
  d Delete

The phase in the preparation and implementation of an IT project known as systems analysis is crucial. It normally falls between the completion of a feasibility study and the start of detailed design. The GNVQ specifications regard a feasibility study as falling within systems analysis. There are many different terms used by organisations to describe the process by which planning and economic evaluation move from the recognition of a general need towards the creation of an application system that fulfils a corporate objective. For consistency we assume that systems analysis is followed by system design, then program design, programming, documentation and testing.

This unit covers the principles of systems analysis and specification, and it lets you develop skills in undertaking systems analysis and in producing system specifications on which design can be based.

Chapter 17 (Element 5.1) asks you to investigate processing activities and the associated IT procedures used in implementing them. You will be looking at

feasibility studies and at all the stages of systems analysis; and at the documentation of systems analysis work and at the structure of a systems specification.

Chapter 18 (Element 5.2) lets you learn about and produce a data flow diagram, and consider the purpose of a new system. You will construct a systems analysis report and think about how to review it in the light of responses from users.

Chapter 19 (Element 5.3) takes you through the creation of a complete system specification consisting of statements of the processing, input and output requirements. You will also be reviewing the resource implications of potential new systems.

In addition to the knowledge and skill you can acquire from your tutor you will find many books on systems analysis, and frequently articles in IT journals informative and helpful.

An external test forms part of this unit.

Chapter 17

Investigate principles of systems analysis and specification

This element is devoted to a study of the principles of systems analysis and to the writing of an outline system specification. Organisations can equip themselves only with the IT systems that confer the greatest possible benefits if those systems are founded on analysis that is complete, relevant and accurate. It must also be timely.

Chapter 17 (Element 5.1) builds on the knowledge we have gained from Chapter 1 (Element 1.1) and Chapters 9–12 (Elements 3.1–3.4). It is essential that you understand the material in this element as it is knowledge required for the practical work in Chapter 18 (Element 5.2) and also Chapter 19 (Element 5.3).

After studying this chapter you should be able to:

1 describe *processing activities* and *information technology methods* used to implement them;
2 describe the *user information* needed to initiate a feasibility study;
3 explain the *stages of systems analysis*;
4 describe the *analysis documentation*;
5 describe the *elements of a system specification*.

Special note

There is only one evidence indicator project for this element. It is at the end of the element, on page 254.

Processing activities

What exactly is a processing activity? The last time you spoke to someone you probably performed a processing activity. The last time you thought about anything you underwent a processing activity. There are *four* general types of processing activity. They are *manipulation, calculation, interrogation* and *repetition*. Let's look at them more closely to make sure we understand what they mean.

Manipulation

Whenever we manipulate data, we take it in its basic form, and rearrange it, or use some of it. We do not actually change it. For example, if we took data in a spreadsheet and created a pie chart with it, we have effectively manipulated the data. It hasn't altered,

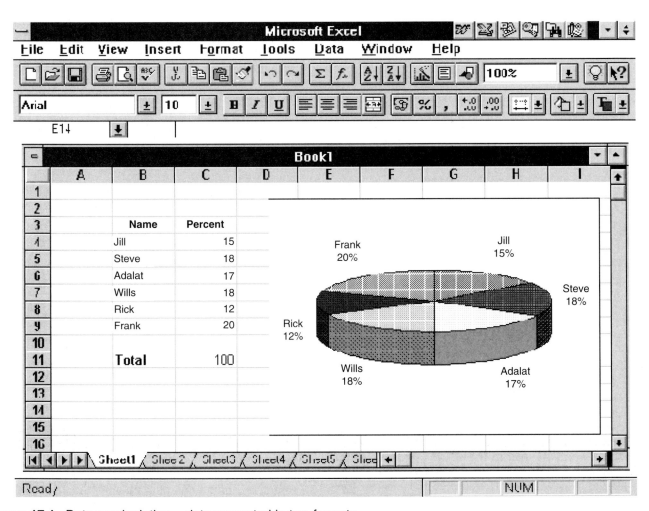

Figure 17.1 Data manipulation – data presented in two formats

but is in a different format. This is illustrated in Figure 17.1. Manipulation includes sorting, selecting, and merging.

Sorting is rearranging, for example, changing the names in a file of students' details from alphabetical order to age order. Selecting is creating a subfile, for example, of the names of students taking GNVQ (Advanced) IT Option Unit 9 as part of the file of all students taking any GNVQ in IT. Merging is the creation of a composite file from two or more existing files, for example there might be a need for a single file on members of staff based at separate sites built up from the files for each site.

We now look at how these manipulations can be performed by PC software.

Sorting

The need to sort data into a particular order is common. Many applications need to process data in more than one order. For example, a car assembly plant may wish to see the list of components arranged by part number within each supplier, and have all the suppliers in alphabetical order; and then, perhaps, have components arranged by model number of the vehicle type in which they would be incorporated. Between meeting these two requirements the data may have to be sorted, depending on how it is stored. For printing in a specified order the data will certainly have to reach the printer in the required order, but for internal processing the likelihood is that no rearrangement of the data on disk will be necessary.

Table 17.1 Makes and prices of mobile phones

Mobile Phone	Price
Nokia Orange	£149
Motorola MR1	£55
Dancall dc1	£75

Table 17.1 shows the names of three mobile phones and the cost of each. If hundreds of makes were to be shown it would possibly be easier to deal with them in alphabetical order. To achieve this order the entries need to be sorted. Figure 17.2 shows the sorting options available in the word processor software package. As the records are to be sorted into alphabetical order on the basis of the characters in the first field alphabetically – the OK button is pressed.

Selecting

In Chapter 10 (Element 3.2) we looked at manipulating information using spreadsheets, word processors and databases by selecting and sorting. For example, in Excel, selecting data may be simple – use the mouse to point to the data you wish to select and click with the left mouse button. If more than one item of contiguous data is to be selected then the mouse should be dragged to the data to be selected, the left mouse button pressed, and without letting go of the button, the mouse should be dragged to the end of the data. The selected data will be highlighted.

More generally, items of data can be selected from a volume of data according to any set of rules or criteria. For instance, from a file of alphabeticallyarranged names and addresses there could be a requirement to select all those with Nottingham post codes. Typically they will be spread throughout the file. We shall see in Chapter 25 (Element 7.3) *how* such selection might be carried out.

Merging

If you look at any examples of modern applications software, the chances are you will find a function that will allow you to bring information from

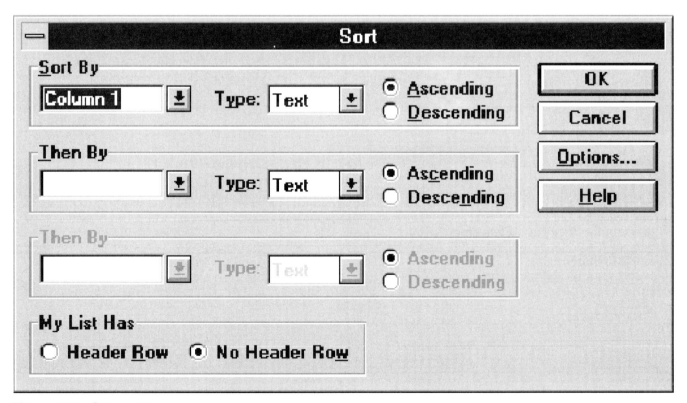

Figure 17.2 Sort options

another file into the document you are working on. An example of this is shown in Figure 17.3 using Word for Windows. The word processor is already showing a page of text, but data from another file is required in the same document. By asking the software to insert the required file, it allows you to bring the data from the two file sources together.

Merging can save a lot of time when reports are being written. If the required data already exists in other files, rather than copy it across by rekeying it, or writing the report from scratch, it is far faster to merge other files into a new one.

Stock control applications need files to be merged whenever product lines not previously held are added to the main product file. Solicitors do merging operations frequently, inserting standard paragraphs into letters to individual clients, a process known as 'boilerplating'.

Activity

Organise a visit to an organisation to view each of the data processing activities discussed in this element. Carefully note the differences between each process so they can be used for examples in your assignments.

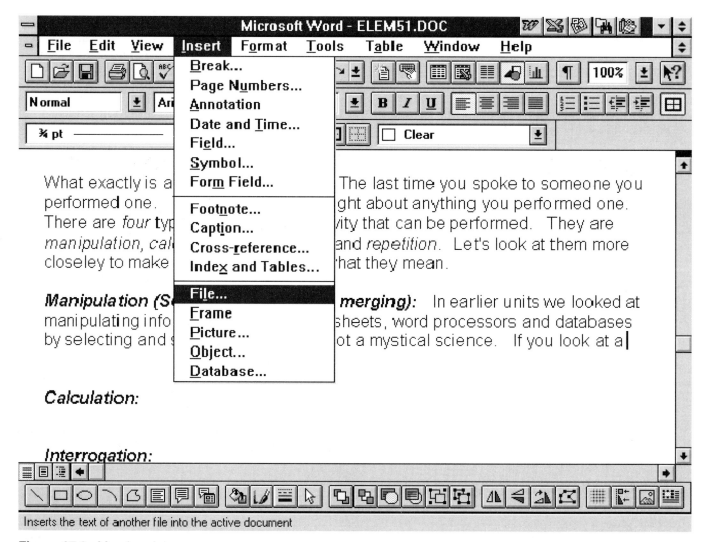

Figure 17.3 Merging data

Calculation

Work out what 2 + 2 = and you have performed a calculation. It's the same for a computer. This is what happens (on a larger scale, though) when BT calculate your telephone bill. Every quarter of a year, the details of all your telephone calls are noted. The computer calculates the cost of each individual telephone call, works out the rental charges and VAT, and adds all the costs together. The bill is printed and sent out to you to be paid.

Computers are particularly adept at making repetitive calculations, either on successive items of data or, in scientific applications, to arrive at progressively converging results. We look at this topic more fully in Chapter 22 (Element 6.3).

Interrogation

Database management software (DBMS) allows *interrogation* of data. Rather than simply show all the available data on the screen and have the user work through it to find the required information, the DBMS allows the user to stipulate what information is needed. Once the DBMs knows this *it* works through its data files to find the data you want, saving much time and effort. Databases are used all the time by organisations of every size. Telephone numbers are stored on databases by BT. If you ring Directory Enquiries and ask for someone's number, the operator types in the name and part of the country he or she lives in, and the computer finds the telephone number. Clubs and societies use databases to store addresses of members. The file of members can be interrogated by specifying what is wanted, exactly, and getting the DBMS to make the search.

Some interrogation needs complicated search criteria. On having the theft of a vehicle reported, the police might want to interrogate their missing vehicles database to see if it included, for instance, an F-registered White Fiesta with alloy wheels and 'go-faster' stripes.

Repetition

Jobs that are done time and time again come under the heading of repetition. We've seen how useful word processors are if the same letter has to be printed several times, and yet be personalised. Database software and spreadsheets also perform repetitive jobs effectively and quickly, without

making the type of mistakes *we* would make. Imagine having to find the names and addresses of a group of club members once a month and writing to them.

Weekly payroll is an example of repetitive processing. Although the data will change from one week to the next, the same rules of processing will be followed every time.

 Activity

Make a list of other activities in organisations that come under these headings of 'processing activities'.

IT methods

There are two ways of exploiting the potential of IT that we shall consider here: *programming languages* and *applications software facilities*. Why are there only two? Simply because we have the choice of either writing programs ourselves or buying software and using it to help us do what is required.

Programming languages

Many businesses, but especially the largest ones, feel the need to write their own programs rather than rely on application packages offered in the market. By writing their programs these organisations are able to carry out business procedures that are distinct from those of their rivals.

In Chapter 2 (Element 1.2), we looked at different types of programming languages and we shall do so again in Chapter 20 (Element 6.1). High-level languages usually have advantages over assembler-level languages in respect of speed of coding, ability to migrate between families of computer, debugging aids and computer-generated documentation. Assembler languages are better able to address operational characteristics of particular kinds of computer, such as the timing subtleties.

Applications software facilities

Applications generators

Applications generators, also called *program generators,* are dealt with fully in Chapter 20 (Element 6.1). One role of applications generators is to provide users with screen graphics. Word 6.0 for Windows has an applications generator offering the user a number of different applications. Figure 17.5 shows two screen dumps from the Word 6.0 for Windows applications generator – in this example, the user asked for a calendar to be created.

Macros

If you find you spend time repeatedly doing the same tasks, you might like to create macros, short for *macro-instructions,* to speed up the job for yourself. Not all software products have the facility, but for those that do, macros are like mini-programming languages that allow the software to be tailored to your use. Using a macro saves keystrokes, saves time and is an aid to accuracy.

As an example, how many times have you word processed a letter and spent time working out where to put the address so it appears correctly through the window in the envelope?

Rather than doing this each time you write a letter, perform the task and have the computer memorise your actions. Give a name to this task (i.e. name the macro), and the next time you need it, simply call up

the macro by name and the computer will set the page out for you. All that's left for you to do is update the address. Macros are further described in Chapter 22 (Element 6.3).

Report generators

If you've spent a while experimenting with databases you may have noticed a facility that creates reports. This is immensely useful. It asks the user to specify what information is needed from the information in the database, and creates a report. Chapter 25 (Element 7.3) discusses the creation of reports from databases.

In a similar way, Microsoft's PowerPoint allows the user to create the slides for a presentation. Its report generator turns this information into word processed format to be handed out to those watching the presentation. It almost does the job for you!

There are also report program generators which create the application programs required to produce a given format of report from specified input data. The user has great freedom to have reports laid out to meet a range of needs. Report program generators are described in Chapter 20 (Element 6.1).

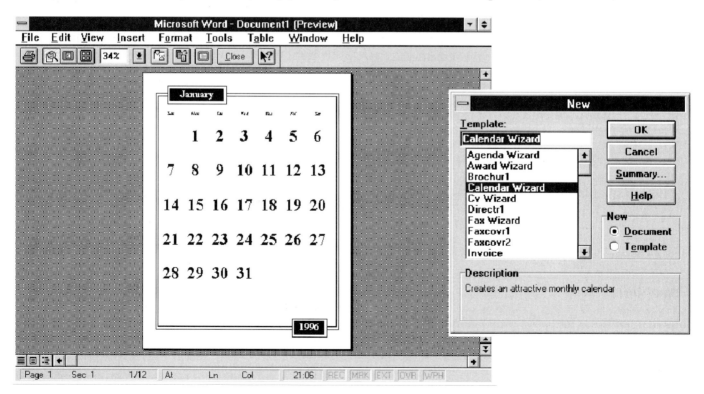

Figure 17.5 Windows applications generator

Data capture

We've looked at the different methods of data capture in Chapter 2 (Element 1.2). How do they relate to applications software facilities? Just about all applications software uses or can use a keyboard and mouse for data capture and input. These are the most common methods used with applications such as word processors, databases, spreadsheets and presentation software.

It's possible to use other methods of data capture. Scanners are used frequently to feed data from paper-based files into databases and word processors. This can be done using OCR software so the computer 'understands' the words it is scanning: that is to say it is able to translate what it reads into ASCII coding. Imagine setting up a database with all the telephone numbers from your local town using only a keyboard. How much faster would it be simply to scan in each page and have the computer do the hard work for you?

CD-ROMs provide another method of data capture. It's possible for a PC to access data on CD-ROM very quickly.

User information needed to initiate a feasibility study

A feasibility study is an investigation to determine whether it is possible and desirable to implement a new computerised system, and to what extent a full analysis and design may be beneficial. We look below, at what a feasibility study usually sets out to do. Let us simply note here that the size, complexity, duration and cost of a feasibility study vary enormously. The scale of the study will always depend on the financial risk in going ahead with a new project, the magnitude of the project itself and the amount of innovation involved.

Most organisations regard a feasibility study as a distinct stage in the evaluation of a prospective new system, treating the feasibility study report, if it is favourable, as the trigger for embarking on systems analysis. Here we are treating the feasibility study as a preliminary activity within systems analysis.

There are a number of different types of user information we need to understand before initiating such a study.

Purpose

Whenever a new system is proposed, whether to replace an existing system or to become a new facility, the purpose must be ascertained. Possible purposes are to

- save cost;
- increase flexibility;
- uncouple a direct relationship between volume and cost;
- improve service to customers or users; and
- improve working conditions.

Unless the purpose of a proposed system is clear there is little prospect of it being designed in such a way that it will be as effective as possible.

Description of present system

The objectives of the present system must be noted so that any changes in the objectives of a proposed new system are apparent.

A full description of the existing system is essential if a new, replacement system is to be accurately conceived. Apart from the objectives, the description should cover the following:

- *Input* Volumes, nature, timing, accuracy; and any trends in respect of any of these attributes.
- *Processing* Files and file volumes, processing operations, file activity, processing speed and performance, accuracy and precision demanded. Equipment used, and its loading.
- *Output* Volumes, quality, timing, location; and any trends in respect of the requirement.
- *Reliability* What level of reliability is needed for the whole system?
- *Security* What level of security is needed for input and output?
- *Perception* What do users feel about the quality of the current service they receive? What improvements or changes do they most want?

Expectations of new system

The user may have wishes about the kind of system that ought to replace the existing system, but those wishes should be disregarded until all the sensible alternatives have been explored.

The purposes of the new system, as seen by the organisation as a whole, are mentioned above. The expectations of users should not be in conflict with those purposes, but they will have a different emphasis. Users' expectations are likely to include:

- Ease of use, and ease of learning to use.
- Tolerance of minor operational errors.
- Convenient, complete documentation of the system.
- Freedom to modify the form of application output.
- Overall robustness, with only small amounts of time taken up by maintenance.
- Spare capacity to allow a margin in meeting production schedules, and for accommodating malfunction and software revisions.

 ## Case study

The Tangerine Entertainment Co. a family-owned organisation, is considering buying a computer to assist in the running of the business. If a computer is to be bought, it must be ordered before 5 April – the end of the tax year. Each member of the family has his or her own expectations of the new system:

- Jim Blanchard (Managing Director) runs an accounts system.
- Lindy Blanchard (Director) runs word processor and database.
- Graham Blanchard runs CD-ROM for game trials.
- Judy Blanchard runs office software.

Accordingly, each family member has a different computer specification requirement to run the software packages they need. Graham has the highest specification machine as CD-ROM games show best results when run on a powerful PC which responds quickly. Jim is less worried about speed and more about accuracy with his company accounts – as long as the system does the job faster than he does it on paper with a calculator, Jim will be happy. Lindy and Judy are less worried about speed and accuracy, and more about the size of the RAM and hard disk to ensure their applications keep working no matter what demands they place on them.

It is possible to meet everyone's requirements, but it will take time and effort to find a machine to do the job.

Constraints

Timescale

Organisations contemplate replacing existing systems by new ones in the expectation, or at least the hope,

of improving overall financial performance. They always want to know as soon as possible whether proposals for replacement systems are, indeed, likely to lead to financial benefits. There is always going to be impatience to learn the judgement of investigation. And, of course, if implementation is decided on, impatience to see if a new system yields the benefits expected of it. If net benefits are to flow from deploying a new system, the sooner it is brought into use the better.

Costs

What is cost-effective, and what is not, is a complicated matter which is different in each case. If a company is 'cash-rich' it may be keen to make a heavy investment now in order to enjoy several years of financial advantage from running a new, better system.

If, in contrast, a business is not in a position to fund investment on a new project whatever the later benefits, it will have to do the best it can within its financial straitjacket.

The outcome of these deliberations is much affected by the way an organisation regards the cost of tying up money in attractive, but nonetheless uncertain, projects.

 ## Activity

Perform a feasibility study in your school or college for replacing the present computer system. Have your tutor check your results. If your findings don't convince your tutor to replace the present system, find out what would.

Stages of systems analysis

Many books have been written about systems analysis – what its aims should be, how it should be structured and what outputs it should generate. There is no agreement on these matters, partly because systems analysis for IT is a young discipline, and partly because of the huge range of types of system that have to be subject to study.

Here we look at six widely accepted stages of systems analysis.

Feasibility

A feasibility study, although it may follow preliminary studies, is usually taken to be the principal mechanism for presenting the issues that have to be weighed in deciding whether or not to proceed with the implementation of a prospective new system. The constituents of a feasiblity study commonly include the following:

■ Statement of the proposed system's functional objectives.
■ Statement of the proposed system's financial objectives.
■ Review of technical options, and the recommendation of one of them.
■ Draft implementation plan.
■ Personnel and training implications.
■ Equipment implications.
■ Effects on other activities.
■ Outline implementation timetable.
■ Proposed allocation of responsibilities.
■ Outline budget.
■ Recommendation.

Problem statement

This is the brief, following consideration of a feasibility study report, given to the manager of the implementation team. It sets out what has to be done, by whom, within what time and cost.

Investigation

Following a *go* decision for a new system, there will be matters to be explored in detail. This is a question of refinement, discussed in Chapter 19 (Element 5.3). Other points will continue to arise as system design proceeds. Typical of such matters are details of software needed, and its method of procurement; likewise for hardware; and discussion with other departments or individuals that may be affected.

Recording

All information found during the investigation stage needs to be recorded for future use. How many times have you understood something a tutor said but when asked about it the next day can't remember a thing about it? If you don't make records (or notes) then you forget most things – this just shows how important record-keeping is. Most organisations have standards to be followed in recording systems analysis work.

Analysis

This is the heart of the analysis phase of implementation, covered in the next chapter, Chapter 18 (Element 5.2).

Reporting

Each organisation will have its own standards for reporting on systems analysis. The principles are that all those concerned directly and indirectly with the introduction of a new system have documentation which sets out clearly the details of the system, the implications for space, procedures and timetables.

Analysis documentation

We have just looked at the stages of systems *analysis*. We have to examine this further, as we need to know what goes into the analysis documentation. It would be a good idea here if you contacted a company using IT, and arranged a visit. If this isn't possible then contact one and ask for detailed examples of analysis documents so you have a good idea of what they use.

So what exactly does go into analysis documentation? There will be amounts of detail appropriate to the different levels from which the system is being viewed. For example, high-level flow diagrams show the flow of information in an organisation. More detailed data flow diagrams show the data flow in a computer system. Let's look at this more closely.

System flow charts

System flow charts display the flow of control, and the main processing and decision events, in a system. Here we are considering an IT system, but flow charts can be drawn for any defined system: and they can be, and often are, drawn for programming. The emphasis is on the control and operation of a system and not on the data structures.

The chart consists of boxes for processes and decisions, and lines, called arcs, to indicate control routes connecting them. The extent to which boxes are annotated depends on local standards. There is an example of a system flow chart in Chapter 8 (Element 2.4); and in Chapter 19, Element 5.3, there is discussion on conventions for drawing flow charts.

Data flow diagrams (DFDs)

DFDs are diagrams which show logical relationships between processes, and the way in which data moves to support these processes.

DFDs can be *logical,* in which case they describe what should take place; or they can be *physical,* in which case they describe the data flow that is actually carried out. DFDs can be drawn to reflect data flow at a high level in a business, or to show in detail what occurs at a lower level. Part of the DFD for a retail business might look like Figure 17.6.

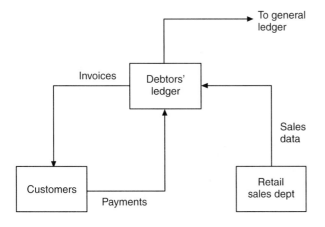

Figure 17.6 A simple DFD

Data model

Entity relationship diagrams

Here we need to establish that an entity is any significant item or class of items which is relevant to a process being considered. For example, in a library application the entities would be the book stock, the borrowers and perhaps a short-loan collection of books. The associated entity relationship diagram would show that there are many borrowers, and that each can borrow up to a given number of books. At a lower level the entities could include acquisition staff, reference books, overdue borrowers and other possibilities.

Activity

You could try to draw the relationships existing between students, courses, modules or units of those courses, lecturers and rooms. Assume one student can take only one course, but that each course has many students; and make similar assumptions for modules, lecturers and rooms.

Relationships are shown by connecting lines between entities. The usual convention is that the line is broken if the relationship is optional or needs to be established, and that where there is more than one instance of an entity, this is shown by a 'crow's foot'.

We look more closely at the development and content of entity relationship diagrams (E-RDs) in Chapter 19 (Element 5.3), in the section on 'Refinement'.

Data dictionary

Chapter 19 (Element 5.3) contains an explanation of a data dictionary. It is a file containing details of all the terms and quantities used in the discussion of a particular system or process to guarantee uniqueness, and to provide a mechanism for promoting accuracy. There is further reference to data dictionaries in Chapters 23 and 25 (Elements 7.1 and 7.3), both of which address the creation and use of databases.

Process specification

A process specification details the different procedures used to define each process in a data flow diagram. When a process is not clearly explained on the diagram, it still has to be defined by a process definition. Decisions in the process specification can be described by decision tables if they are sufficiently complicated to warrant using the technique, described fully in Chapter 19 (Element 5.3). Generally, an overall structure diagram is developed, together with a Structured English report of each subroutine.

A process specification should include the following:

- Structured English.
- Structure diagram.
- Decision tables.
- Flow chart.

Structured English

Purists assert that there is no such things as 'structured English'; only good English, and bad English. None the less the term structured English is in general use in systems analysis to give a name to a further method of specifying a system. It does not use trees or tables, but rather adopts narrative statements to describe a procedure.

Structured English uses three main types of statement to describe a process. They are sequences, decisions, and iterations. All verbs used are imperative, as seen in these shopping examples:

Sequence structure:
- Choose a tin of baked beans.
- Put it in a basket.
- Take basket to checkout.
- Pay for the beans.
- Leave the supermarket.

Decision structure:
- If own-label beans available, *then* take a tin.
- Put it in basket.
- Take basket to check-out.
- Pay for the beans.
- Leave the supermarket.
- *Otherwise:* Leave the supermarket.

Iteration structure:
- Do while inspecting tins.

- Read labels on tins of baked beans.
- If own-label, *then* look at price; if too expensive, return tin; *else* choose it, put tin in basket.
- End *if*.
- *Else* look no further.
- Leave supermarket.

Structured English can be useful, as you can see, for describing conditions and actions clearly. See Chapter 19 (Element 5.3) for more about Structured English, and for descriptions of Structure diagrams, decision tables and flow charts.

Elements of a system specification

Data model in first normal form

The purpose of normalisation is to guide the design of databases so as to ensure correct operation and to reduce to a minimum the occurrence of inconsistencies. First normal form is the simplest form of normalisation. It involves analysing each of the system entities and inspecting each attribute or data element, to make sure it represents only one item of data and that no attribute is repeated. If repeating attributes *do* occur, they are removed by creating a new entity.

The principles and practice of normalisation are further addressed in Chapter 19 (Element 5.3) and Chapter 23 (Element 7.1).

Input specification

This is where the method of data input is specified for the system. The method may be keyboard, mouse, scanner, bar code reader, touch-screen or specialised equipment. The screens used during input specification can be designed to be altered by the user – there may be blanks to fill on a template designed for the task being carried out.

Output specification

What type of output is required for the system? Are the screens to be of a certain size (such as 14 inch – note that monitors aren't yet referred to in metric units!), colour, or black and white? Do they have to conform to radiation emission standards? Are screen guards required?

Are printed reports to be produced by a dot matrix printer, ink-jet printer, or a laser printer? Is colour printing required? Can normal A4 sheets be used, or is continuous paper required? Is speed of printing a major concern? Could a plotter be used?

These are all questions, addressed in Chapter 2 (Element 1.2), that need to be answered for output specifications before a system can be put together.

Process specification

This lays down exactly what processing is to be carried out. There may be different actions to be taken on different classes of data. The specification will say what permanent and temporary storage is to be used, what assumptions are to be made about transaction input from terminals and what the processing performance is to be.

Resources

Are the hardware, software and people capable of the jobs they will be required to do? If not, the hardware and software simply need upgrading until they are suited to the job in hand. The people may have to be recruited and will require training.

Constraints

What system constraints exist? Time is a factor – everyone wants the job done yesterday! In an ideal world, the system will be as fast as technology will allow. However, in time (and not very long by today's standards) all equipment becomes outdated and needs replacing. This is costly.

Some people are unwilling to learn how to use a new system. This is not uncommon as nobody likes *change*. Again though, this is a system constraint that must be overcome.

In summary, constraints usually come down to time and money, though they may initially manifest themselves as problems with lack of skills, restrictive practices, shortage of space, or in any one of many guises.

Evidence indicator project

This project covers all the evidence indicator related to Chapter 17 (Element 5.1.) It has been designed to be carried out at the end of the element.

Performance criteria: 1–5

Key skills:	Communication	3.1, 3.2, 3.3
	Application of number	–
	IT	3.1, 3.2, 3.3

Scenario

The Rayleigh Entertainment Co. is the proud new owner of a small family fun-park in Southport. The company wants to expand its range of amenities and facilities offered at the park, and believes it should look towards computerising parts of its business. In the past all office work at the park has been done manually, and turning the employees into IT experts overnight will not be easy.

In groups of no more than three, making, and stating, and reasonable assumptions write a report for The Rayleigh Entertainment Co. showing

- a description of processing activities they will need and the information technology methods used to implement them;
- a description of user information needed to initiate a feasibility study;
- an explanation of the stages of systems analysis;
- a description of the analysis documentation; and
- a description of the elements of a system specification.

This chapter will help you to assemble your evidence, but you should try to broaden your understanding by seeing how such issues are handled in businesses using IT.

Hand in the report to your tutor in seven days.

Chapter 18

Undertake systems analysis

This element follows naturally from Chapter 17 (Element 5.1). Here you will be using the principles of systems analysis that you studied, to produce a systems analysis report and data flow diagram from information that you will have assembled.

We shall be offering you as a focus for your thinking about systems analysis an example of a simplified commercial application which appears to be due for transfer to computer processing.

After studying this chapter you should be able to:

1 establish the *purpose* of a new system;
2 investigate and record *information*;
3 produce a data flow diagram;
4 produce a *systems analysis report*;
5 review systems analysis in the light of feedback from the user.

Special note

There is only one evidence indicator project for this element. It is at the end of the element, on page 262

Establish the purpose of a new system

The imaginary system we shall be looking at is the sales-order processing operation at an office materials supplier that we shall call 'Diversified Office Goods', or 'DOG' for short.

The managing director of DOG is dissatisfied with the current sales-order processing system. He believes that a properly designed system, making use of computer processing, should provide a better quality of service to customers, faster, at lower cost, with improved efficiency.

We shall take a look at the present manual system, examine the areas where improvements are thought to be possible and in that way establish the purpose of the possible replacement system.

The current sales-order processing system, in outline, works like this:

■ The customer, who has the DOG catalogue,

telephones DOG to place an order.
■ The sales clerk notes the requirement, and rings off.
■ The sales clerk checks the credit position of the customer.
■ The sales clerk checks the availability of the item ordered.
■ The sales clerk confirms to the customer that the item ordered will be delivered, in the quantity requested.
■ The sales clerk arranges for the office to type a multipart invoice, distributing two copies to the accounts department, two to the warehouse, one to the sales clerk and one to the office files.
■ The warehouse sends out the order, accompanied by one copy of the invoice acting as a delivery note.
■ The accounts department sends the customer the top copy of the invoice.
■ The customer pays DOG's invoice after the goods have arrived and been checked, and the invoice checked.

Let us now think about the benefits that the introduction of computer processing might bring.

Improve quality

The new system would provide a much more convenient service to customers. Information on the credit status of a customer and on the availability of stock could be obtained by the sales clerk during the course of the customer's phone call.

Clerical errors made after that original phone call should be virtually eliminated. Information about all orders would be held in a database, accessible to all members of DOG staff. Filing would be simplified, and all queries answered with speed and accuracy. Statistics for management and for publicity purposes should be readily obtained from the new computer-based system.

An important benefit would be an automated stock replacement strategy, sometimes called 'inventory management', providing an improved level of service for a given cost. The 'level of service' is the proportion of customer orders that can be completely satisfied immediately from stock held in DOG's own warehouse.

Increase speed of processing

A notable effect of computer processing would be that the increased speed it would provide should confer great benefits. We have seen how the sales clerk would be able to confirm the fulfilment of the

order during the course of a single telephone conversation. Following that phone call, invoice production could be almost instantaneous, and the accounts department and warehouse could be given the invoice details at once.

The goods could be dispatched and delivered earlier, and the money due in payment of the order collected earlier.

Reduce costs

The new system would be instrumental in reducing costs in several ways. Clerical tasks would be markedly reduced, saving some of the cost of employees; the value of the stock in the warehouse could possibly be reduced, even if the level of service were to be raised; office space would be saved; telephone charges would fall; the costs of correcting errors would be reduced. Conceivably, the better image of DOG stemming from its improved performance would allow less to be spent on product promotion and prestige advertising.

Improve efficiency

The sales-order processing function would become more efficient through the impact of the points made above. In addition, at least some of the tasks carried out in the office would become more congenial, making recruitment for them relatively easy and therefore less expensive. The reputation of DOG's business would be enhanced by the improved customer service, thereby helping to attract new business.

An important advantage of the new system would be to protect these improvements from the effects of swings in the volumes of orders. This is known as the volatility of orders. Typically, with a manual system an increase in the volume of orders has to be matched by a corresponding increase in the number of employees engaged in servicing those orders if the standard of service to customers is to remain unchanged: and a fall in the volume of orders leads to a business having to shed employees. This direct linkage of volume of orders to numbers of clerical staff does not usually occur with a computerised system. In other words, efficiency would have been increased by uncoupling job numbers from the volatility of orders.

Taken together, these four topics constitute the purpose of the proposed new system. We shall return to DOG's sales-order processing system when we look at data flow diagrams later in this chapter.

Did you know?

As projects get larger the magnitude of the task of the systems analyst grows even faster. There are some projects where the analysis requirement is so extensive that it defies the best and most experienced professionals.

The planning and analysis of the Department of Social Security (DSS) benefits system is one. The Public Accounts Committee found out that in the two years to April 1995, £2 billion had been spent trying to iron wrinkles out of the IT system which supported the benefits system. That would have been alarming enough but in working through that huge amount of money the team entrusted with the work actually managed to make matters worse, and increase the scale and cost of errors.

Investigate and record information

A crucial part of the work of a systems analyst is building up a description of an existing system. We consider here methods of investigating the existing system, and recording information about it, that the analyst will have to pursue before setting out to describe it.

First we review aspects of the existing system.

Flow of information

Information technology is the technology of handling information. IT cannot be applied to the creation of a system unless the requirement for the flow of information in the new system is understood, and assuming that the function of the new system is to be the same as that of the existing system, the information flow of the existing system has to be understood and recorded.

Understanding the information flow is close to understanding what the department or business actually does. The information is found or generated in one place, passed to somewhere else for a purpose, processed in some way, passed on again, and stored or distributed. A straightforward example might be in the office of an estate agent. The firm receives instructions to sell a property. It has to find out the details of the property and draft the particulars; then those

particulars have to go to the person looking after marketing; and the marketing person has to get hold of a list of enquirers who might be interested in the property, and send a copy to each name on the list.

Below we shall look at a way of presenting the flow of information in an organisation.

Types of data

In the sales-order processing example above, the data coming in to the system could be alphabetical, consisting of customer name and product description; and numerical, consisting of customer number, account number, quantity ordered, product number and a date.

The data circulating in DOG's departments will be of the same nature, as it will be on the invoices which are typed and distributed. This is true of most commercial and administrative systems. The data can be held in different formats for different purposes such as financial record-keeping, sales and marketing lists, and warehouse stock sheets.

Sources of data

Systems analysis needs to establish where data comes from, because the reliability and speed of arrival of data are related to its source. Most data used by commercial organisations comes from suppliers and customers, but some will come, for example, from trade journals, trade associations, bankers, lawyers, the Inland Revenue, Customs and Excise, and research and educational establishments.

Data collection methods

A business can capture the data it must have in order to operate properly by several means, including post, telephone, fax, electronic mail, broadcast services on TV channels, electronic data interchange (EDI) – also sometimes called 'electronic document interchange' – and by drawing on databases through the Internet or in some other way. If there are no computers in the business its data collection methods would be limited to the first three of these with, possibly, the addition of telex.

Did you know?

Barclays Bank became the first European bank to introduce cross-border EDI in

Europe. BT has redesigned its supplier systems and now has over 80% of its purchase orders passing through its EDI systems. About 50% of the 17,000 British dentists have now adopted EDI.

Documents used

Within a typical commercial business the principal documents used are order forms, invoices, delivery notes, credit notes, files for storing a wide range of data items, ledgers and other accounting documents, and copies of reports, letters and memos.

Personnel

Information on personnel employed by an organisation is likely to include the following: full name, date of birth, address, name and address of next of kin, date joined the organisation, department, appointment or grade, copies of appraisal reports, courses attended and correspondence.

There will probably be less information held for part-time staff, and for contractors' personnel.

Operations

The operations of any organisation are the means by which it achieves its corporate objectives. If an analyst's assignment covers only part of the work of an organisation the operations will be limited to the functioning of that part together with the way it interacts with the rest. The operations may include checking accuracy; calculating discounts, VAT and total costs; maintaining records; moving papers or physical stock; or writing letters.

Decisions

Decision-making is a key management concern in any organisation. The way decisions are taken is influenced by the organisational structure. In Chapter 9 (Element 3.1), we looked at different structures. The responsiveness of organisations to changing circumstances, perhaps in markets or financial constraints, may be crucial. The analyst will be interested in the mechanisms for making decisions.

Within the process itself there will be decisions that are currently taken explicitly that might, in a

computer-based system, be taken automatically. These, which concern the analyst, could include a decision to deny further credit to a customer who has over-run the credit limit, or deciding what size of order to place on a supplier when the amount of a particular product line has fallen below the reorder level.

Processing

The processing steps taken by the existing organisation are probably those that would have to be implemented on computer for a replacement system. During systems analysis they have to be documented fully, with great care, noting the exceptional conditions that arise from time to time.

Storage

Data storage is normally in files holding cards or sheets of paper, possibly kept safely in filing cabinets. Such storage is very vulnerable to becoming untidy, with the contents getting out of order, and to individual papers being lost. It is also bulky. Efficient storage of data is one of the great attractions of transferring an application to computer.

Type of output

The type of output an organisation uses determines the impact the paperwork has on recipients. It is clearly important, where documents are going to customers, lenders of finance and shareholders, that appearance as well as content should be appealing.

The type of output also affects the speed at which it can be produced, the ease of having multiple copies, the means of transmission, its security, the cost of producing it and the noise generated in doing so.

Let us now turn to the question of how a systems analyst can set about acquiring all these kinds of information about an organisation. There are four main approaches.

Interviews

To find out what job someone does, what his or her role is in the system, one can ask that person. However, securing full accurate answers is far from easy. Most people interviewed about their job will try to answer truthfully, to the best of their ability, though there may some reservation or exaggeration if they think their employment may be at risk.

To elicit the whole story needs skill and experience. Practice is needed if the interviewer is to appear warm and interested in the person being interviewed, while at the same time securing all the relevant information. Open questions of the type 'describe for me how you deal with such and such' are often more fruitful than closed questions which can be fully and politely answered with 'Yes' or 'No', though the interviewer must be ready to stop an irrelevant or unduly lengthy answer. The worst habit for the interviewer is to ask leading questions in which it is much easier to supply the answer that appears to be sought. An example of a leading question would be 'When you have checked the credit reference do you simply pass the invoice to Accounts?'

Often it is necessary to hold a second interview with each person seen; this is partly because the interviewer will have gained relevant information from someone else since the first interview which prompts further questions, and partly because both parties are likely to be more relaxed at the second encounter, allowing a fuller picture to emerge.

One technique used by analysts is to draw a chart of the job the person has described and ask if it is right. One way or another the analyst has to make a record of what was learned about the detailed content of jobs, the flow of data, the processing of data and the storage of data.

Questionnaires

As an analyst's tool questionnaires have the advantage of allowing time for reflection in both compilation and response. They do, however, deprive the analyst of the opportunity of picking up indications from the body language and tone of voice of the person being interviewed. They are useful if the person whose replies are wanted is not accessible.

Questionnaires are notoriously hard to design. To have maximum value they must be no longer than is absolutely necessary. If statistics are to be derived from the responses the questions have to be in a multiple-choice form as opposed to free form. The designer has to decide whether the responses can be anonymous or not; there are advantages both ways. And there has to be a decision about the confidentiality of the information on the completed forms.

Document inspection

There is no substitute for seeing examples of the documents with which people operate the existing system work. Their legibility, accuracy and general condition reveals much about the respect with which they are regarded; and the routes they follow through the organisation is confirmation (or rebuttal) of what the analyst has learned by other means.

Observation

As well as seeing the documents it is important for the analyst to watch the process running. Some fresh slant on it is almost sure to emerge. Again there must be a written record made.

Produce a data flow diagram

Business processes, whether manual or computer based, are driven by the data they accept, process, store, and from which they create output.

To understand a system an analyst will want answers to four questions:

1   What processes make up the system?
2   What data is used in each process?
3   What data is stored?
4   What data enters and leaves the system?

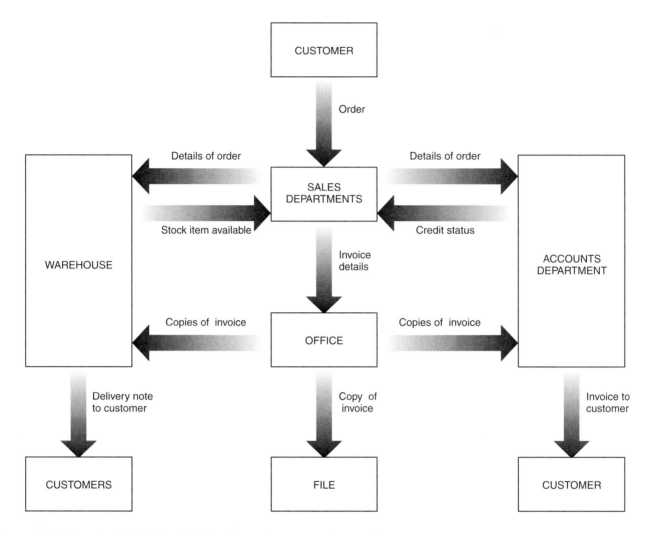

Figure 18.1 Top-level DFD for DOG's sales-order processing system

There is wide agreement that understanding the main data flows in an organisation, or part of an organisation, is the best starting point for constructing a full description of the systems and their processes. If we now return to the functioning of the sales-order processing system of the hypothetical business called Diversified Office Goods, or DOG, we can construct a diagram of the main data flows. This is called a 'data flow diagram', or 'DFD'.

DFDs can describe data flows at any chosen level in the operation. Usually an analyst will first produce a DFD giving an overall view of the data flows, avoiding detail. This would be called a 'top-level DFD' because it shows the main flows of data

throughout the operation. The top-level DFD for DOG's sales-order processing operation is shown in Figure 18.1.

DFDs are of two types, logical and physical. A logical DFD describes the data flows independently of the actual physical implementation of the system. A logical DFD would be drawn for a proposed new system at a stage when the system design had not taken place, and the nature of the processing, storage, input and output equipment had not been decided or the numbers, and tasks of the people working with the system, known.

Figure 18.1 is a physical DFD because it describes an installed system. It does not show processes or equipment because such information would damage the simplicity and clarity of the top-level diagram. In Chapter 19 (Element 5.3), we shall be looking at the way a DFD can be developed to yield more detail, to allow the drafting of a full system specification on which the system design is to be based.

You will notice that in Figure 18.1 the flows of data into and out of the sales department, the accounts department, the warehouse and the office, make it a small step to move forward from the top-level DFD towards a definition of the processing carried out in those places.

For a top-level DFD the symbols used are at the discretion of the analyst. The only criteria are clarity, and completeness appropriate to the level of the diagram. However, in creating a system specification from the results of the systems analysis there are conventions that should be followed consistently.

There is not universal agreement on what notation should be used, but there are several schemes of documentation each of which has its own sets of symbols and rules. The standards in an organisation will lay down exactly which scheme is to be used.

Activity

You might like to think about, and try to construct, a DFD describing the process of registering as a student at a college, even if you do not know anything about how it is done.

Produce a systems analysis report

When an organisation calls for a systems analysis report it may stop short of wanting it to include a system specification for the proposed replacement system. That could come later. The decision of what is to be in the report will ride on the size, complexity, and urgency of the project as a whole; and it may be influenced by the desire of management to obtain some information from the analysis without at that stage being committed to incurring the extra cost of having the specification written.

The report would, in any case, include the following topics.

Feasibility study

In Chapter 17 (Element 5.1), we noted the purpose and composition of a feasibility study. The feasibility study report would always be the starting point for systems analysis, and hence for the systems analysis report.

The feasibility study report will have recommended a strategy for bringing in the new computer-based system. For example, in the case of DOG, it might have rejected the possibility of using an external service in favour of installing a local area network for the sales-order processing operation. Systems analysis would be founded on the pursuit of that strategy.

Problem statement

The problem statement arises directly from the purposes of the proposed replacement system established above, namely to seek improvements in quality, increase in speed of processing, reduction in costs and improvements in efficiency.

To turn the purposes into the problem statement it is necessary to make the requirement specific. This means assigning figures to the volume of transactions and to their frequency and volatility; describing the processing to be carried out; defining the data storage needed, and the type and frequency of updates and interrogations; and giving particulars of the volumes, timing and type of output.

Analysis

A *data flow diagram,* or perhaps more than one, is needed to fulfil the function described above. In all but the most trivial cases there will be a hierarchy of DFDs, with the lowest level giving the detail needed to describe the existing system fully; that is, in the detail required to design the system and the programming. For example, in setting out the detail of a particular paper-based file the analyst would be concerned with the size and content of the records; the growth of the file month by month; the error rates, the frequency of access to the file for updating, reference and deletion; and the relationship with other files and neighbouring processes.

The *resources* expected to be employed in the new system should be restated. They will have been estimated in the feasibility study report, but their role will be more fully understood following the systems analysis.

Costs, too, were forecast in the feasibility study report, but again they should be reaffirmed or modified.

Constraints imposed by shortages of suitably trained professional staff, equipment, software or space, and

261

any pressures arising since the feasibility study on the delivery schedule for the new system, or on details of its specification, or on its budget, must be reported.

Expectation of the new system can now be made more specific than before, in the light of knowledge gained during systems analysis. This expectation can therefore be updated and fleshed out. The analysis should have something to say about the operational characteristics of the new system, including:

- the function of the system itself;
- the pattern of use;
- the number of individuals needed to run the system;
- the skills and training needed to use the system effectively;
- the technical and user support to be available;
- the reliability, and the fall-back provision;
- the security issues; and
- the running and maintenance costs.

Did you know?

Any kind of service offered to the public has to be carefully planned and checked before launch to try to make sure that there are no disasters when it goes live.

IBM and American Express have just launched a travel smart card that provides identification for the passenger

holding it, and authorises the boarding of planes and the booking of hotel rooms. The prospect of inadequate analysis for such a system is truly awful.

Review systems analysis in the light of feedback from users

We shall be looking in Chapter 26–28 at the importance of the development team, the 'Implementer', keeping in close touch with the user, the 'Customer'. Systems analysis is one phase of the total development process, and the principle applies here as in other phases. Making the systems analysis report available to the Customer for comment is essential.

Adequate time for the various people making up the Customer to read, deliberate on and comment on the report must be allowed. The comments should be on paper except for the very smallest systems. Those comments then have to be discussed with the Implementer.

Each paragraph of the systems analysis report should be subjected to scrutiny by the Customer. This process will take time, and may appear wasteful, but it has invariably been shown that the greater the involvement by the Customer at this stage the greater the likelihood of the completed system meeting the Customer's wishes and expectations.

We ought to emphasise that no matter how fully and carefully the proposed system is defined and described there will always be matters of detail that may seem insignificant to the Implementer but that do cause concern to the Customer. Such questions can be, and should be, resolved before further investment is made in the system; the risk of disappointment and nasty surprises when the system is presented for acceptance are thereby much reduced.

Evidence indicator project

This project covers all the evidence indicators related to Chapter 18 (Element 5.2). It has been designed to be carried out at the end of the element.

Performance criteria: 1–5

Key skills: Communication   3.1, 3.2,
                                                    3.3, 3.4
              Application of number   –
              IT   –

To meet the evidence requirements of this element you will have to have a system to analyse. It could be provided by your tutor or, if agreed, identified by yourself; or it could be based on the simple sales-order processing used as an example above.

You have to produce your own data flow diagram. If it is based on the Diversified Office Goods example it must, of course, be at a lower level than the diagram in Figure 18.1.

You must also provide notes, covering the range, showing that you have

1 established the purpose of a new system;
2 investigated it, and recorded information about it;
3 reviewed your systems analysis in the light of feedback from someone playing the part of the users of the new system.

Produce a system specification

A system specification is a document that marks a stage in the realisation of a new system. It contains the information derived from systems analysis that is needed by a system designer to move implementation forward into program design and programming. The specification may consist of some or all of

- data definitions
- process specifications
- input specifications
- output specifications
- resource requirements.

Knowing what a system specification is, we need to consider the aspects concerned in creating one.

After studying this chapter you should be able to:

1 refine the data flow diagram to produce *data definitions*;
2 produce *process specification*;
3 produce *input specification*;
4 produce *output specification*;
5 identify *resource implications*.

Special note

There is only one evidence indicator project for this element. It is at the end of the element, on page 269.

Refine the data flow diagram to produce data definitions

Data flow diagrams show the basic processes a system is expected to perform. As the information in data flow diagrams is not sufficient for a system designer we need to extend that information to produce definitions of the data being used in a system. The resulting data model must include all the data needed in each of the processes in the data flow diagram. And that data must be in first normal form, which is the first step in a technique called normalisation that will be covered in detail in Chapter 23 (Element 7.1). First normal form (1NF) is achieved when all repeating groups are removed. An

effect of this is to make all records of fixed length. Separate files, or *relations,* are built to contain the repeating elements.

Relations

We can illustrate this point more effectively through the use of an example; rather than simply state 'Company details' and expect a computer programmer to understand what is required, we must show exactly what company details are needed. If we state 'Person's name', the programmer will need to know what these fields should include:

1 *Title* – Mr, Mrs, Miss, Ms, Dr, Reverend, etc.
2 *First name*
3 *Second name(s)* or *initials*
4 *Surname*

The data model should also show clearly the format in which each set of details is required in the computer. For example, a person's title is placed into a *character* field and not a *numeric* one as a name consists of letters of the alphabet and not numbers. A standard number of characters will be set for any title – it is unlikely that a title will run into 30 letters. Therefore the programmer can be told that the field length (the total space required to fill in details regarding the title) will be no more than, say, 12 characters long.

Although this may seem an irksome way in which to do the job, it is necessary to ensure accuracy and consistency. Ensuring accuracy at the start of a job will make the task easier throughout. Every element to be used in the program must be detailed in this way.

Entity

We now need to consider the term 'entity'. An entity is any person, place, thing or event of interest to the designers of a system and about which data items are captured, stored or processed. The relationship between entities is crucial to the analysis of a system.

Refinement

The word 'refinement' applies to system design, program design, and programming. It is the process of developing successively representations of systems or programs that are more detailed, or more specific, than those used up to that point. It is a progression from the abstract, and the high level, towards the concrete and the low level. This refinement cannot be defined with greater exactness; it does, though, have the property of preserving at every stage the integrity of the specification of the system or program being depicted.

Refined data flow diagrams are diagrams which provide refinement, in the sense just described, of the previous version of the data flow diagrams. There is a degree of refinement which develops data flow diagrams into a form known as entity relationship diagrams (E-RD), which are usually drawn using *rounded* boxes. An example would be:

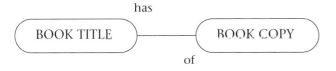

The boxes are connected by a series of lines that help to show the relationship between them.

To start with, we look at what is known as a *one-to-one* or 1:1 relationship – individual symbols are connected together by a single line. Note that there are no arrows showing any connection.

This is unfinished, though, as we must place wording beside the rounded boxes to illustrate the relationship more fully:

This diagram tells us that a book title has an associated copy of the book, and that the book itself has a title.

The 1:1 relationship will not correctly reflect the situation if there is more than one copy of the book. A slight alteration to the theme will allow us to show a *one-to-many* (or *1:M*) link, as illustrated below, again representing book details in a library:

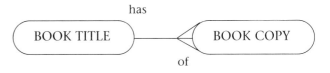

The addition of the 'crowsfoot' shows there are many copies of the book with that title in the library.

Although there are more relationships that could be shown, we shall deal with only one more here – *many-to-many* (*M:N*) or (*M:M*):

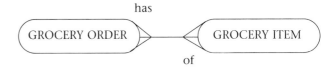

In this example the E-RD means that every grocery order contains one or more grocery items, and that every grocery item appears on one or more orders.

If a relationship is optional, it is illustrated through the use of a broken or dotted line. For example, the relationship between course and student could be

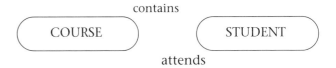

showing that a course may have no student, but all students must be on a course.

Data dictionary

To be effective, the results of this refinement are held in a data dictionary. This is a catalogue of all the data attributes that make up the system.

An *attribute* is a single property of an entity, such as the name of the publisher of a book in a library application. An attribute normally corresponds to a particular field in the record which describes an entity. An attribute must be *atomic;* that is to say, it must consist of a single piece of data. The data dictionary normally shows the *name* of the data items, the *types* of data items, their *size, description,* the entity in which they occur, *names of entities* and a *description of entities.* It is easy to see that the data dictionary allows us to use precise definitions and ensures completeness and consistency. If data definitions are inaccurate they will be misunderstood by others on the project team and this in turn will lead to further problems and mistakes being made. The data dictionary is dealt with in more detail in Chapter 23 (Element 7.1).

As a rule of thumb, the following items appear in data dictionaries, although more could be added if required:

- *Fields* – how they are to be used, how long they are to be, and the format they are to be in.
- *Data attributes* – giving a description of the text used, and a description of how and where the text is to be used.
- *Data relationships* – giving a description of the text used and any entity relationships that exist.
- *Entities* – detailing a text description, any primary or foreign keys (explained in Chapter 23, Element 7.1) being used, an estimated use and growth rate, and the types of entity being used.
- *External entities* – providing a text description, and the recipient and originator of data.
- *Data stores* and *data flow* – detailing their contents.
- Data inputs and outputs.

We can now move forward and consider how these details can be used to create a process specification.

Process specification

The process specification details the different procedures used to define each of the processes represented in a data flow diagram. When processes are not clearly displayed on the diagram, they still have to be defined. Generally, an overall structure diagram is developed, together with a structured English explanation of each subroutine.

A process specification should include the following.

Structured English

We mentioned Structured English in Chapter 17, (Element 5.1). Here we develop the topic.

Structured English is purely a contracted version of the English language, working for the process specification in much the same way that shorthand works for a secretary. Certain basic (but not explicit) rules apply:

1 Only basic build-words are used such as *SEQ* (sequence) and *ITR* (iteration). We shall deal with such build-words when we look at 'structure diagrams' below.

2 Terms appearing in data flow diagrams or anywhere else in the process specification can be used.

3 Only imperative verbs such as *compare, add, subtract, multiply* and *divide* are used.

You may have your own version of structured English – if you write an assignment plan, you no doubt eliminate unnecessary words and include those that are the standard 'lingo' for the subject you are studying.

Structure diagram

A structure diagram, also known as a *structure chart,* is the part of the process specification which displays the relationships between processing modules. It shows which modules within the system interact, and it can show the nature of the data passing between modules. As with other graphical descriptive techniques, there is no completely agreed way of presenting a structure diagram.

A structure diagram is a device used by a system designer to illustrate the points noted above. It is not a way of expressing procedural logic or the physical boundaries of parts of the system. It may, nonetheless, be prepared by the systems analyst.

There are three distinct types of relationships between processing modules that can be conveniently represented in structure diagrams. The commonly used notation is shown in Figure 19.1. This means that module A calls and executes B, then calls and executes C.

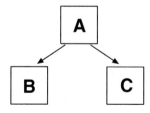

Figure 19.1 Sequence

In Figure 19.2 (selection), A can call either B or C, as circumstances require, without affecting any subsequent choice.

Figure 19.3 (iteration) means that module B can be called and executed as many times as necessary to fulfil the processing task.

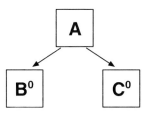

Figure 19.2 Selection

Naturally, in depicting a whole system there will be many modules linked in accordance with these principles.

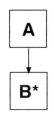

Figure 19.3 Iteration

Decision tables

Decision tables were introduced in Chapter 17 (Element 5.1). We now look more fully at the technique.

Decision tables are tools used by systems analysts to describe the choice of actions that flow from certain conditions. There are other ways in which analysts can display and describe the same issues, but sometimes a decision table is both the most compact and the most intelligible way.

A decision table is made up of four sections (Table 19.1). The role of each box is best explained by an example. Let us consider a situation in which prompt payment by a customer, or the placing of a large order, can earn the customer a discount. The decision table might look like Table 19.2.

Table 9.1 A decision table

Condition statements	Condition entries
Action statements	Action entries

Table 9.2 A customer discount decision table

Conditions	Rules			
Invoice paid within 14 days	Y	N	Y	N
Value of order more than £10,000	Y	Y	N	N
Discount of 5%	X	–	–	–
Discount of 3%	–	X	X	–
No discount	–	–	–	X

This is a very simple, self-explanatory table. Some sets of circumstances require much larger tables. Large tables have to be constructed with care to ensure situations that are not valid are excluded.

Software products called 'Decision Table Processors' exist to convert decision tables into executable program code.

Flow chart

Flow charts have been discussed in Chapter 8 (Element 2.4) and Chapter 17 (Element 5.1). A systems analyst uses flow charts at a level that describes to the system designer the main flow of control through the system.

Organisations often have their own standards for drawing flow charts covering such matters as the symbols to be used, the amount that can be presented on one page and the use to be made of off-page connectors. Symbols that are universally used are shown in Figure 19.4.

There are variations amongst users in the extent of the labelling of the symbols and the lines connecting

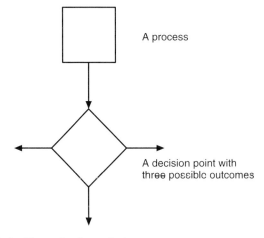

Figure 19.4 Flow chart symbols

267

them. What is important is that the chart should be clear and accurate, and should contain only the information needed for design to proceed.

Input specification

The input specification is essential for a complete system specification. We consider the input specification under five headings.

Data source

The source of the input data needs to be stated because it will have a bearing on reliability and its maximum rate of arrival. Possible sources are keyboard entry of data on documents; words spoken into a microphone; electronic transfer from data storage devices; or scanned information from drawings.

Data capture methods

Data capture methods were reviewed in Chapter 2 (Element 1.2). The equipment used for capturing data includes keyboard, bar code reader, magnetic strip reader, magnetic ink character reader (MICR), optical character reader (OCR), optical mark reader (OMR), special-purpose keyboard and touch screen, digitiser and mouse.

Screen layout

System designers have wide discretion over the layout of screens and users can also customise the layout to a small degree. The layout design criteria are

- conformity with local practice;
- clarity, and freedom from congestion;
- minimum data entry by the user; and
- colour and arrangement to avoid tiring users unnecessarily.

Validation

See Chapter 11 (Element 3.3). As the analyst knows, in detail, the characteristics of the input data, he or she can stipulate what checks should be imposed within the process to check its validity. Data is invalid if the process has not been written to handle it. An example of invalid data would be a person's name containing a numerical or special character apart perhaps, from hyphen or apostrophe.

Verification

See Chapter 11 (Element 3.3). This is a facility made available to users for them to check that some or all of the data that appears to the system to be valid is actually correct.

Output specification

We need to consider the two most widely used types of output.

Output on screen

The analyst may have to make compromises between the various attributes of computer screens. Large screens are likely to be easier to read, but they are more expensive than smaller ones. The output may have to be clear on a monochrome screen, on a laptop machine and may have to be in colour. Where screen output is extensive the user should have the option of printing it.

Output on printer

Again the analyst can make choices. As we saw in Chapter 2 (Element 1.2), the issues are

- speed of printing
- quality
- cost
- noise.

There are further subsidiary choices between printing in colour, the use of multipart continuous stationery and the use of thermal printing technology. Types of printing equipment are reviewed in Chapter 4 (Element 1.4).

There are other forms of output (not considered here) including computer output on microfilm (COM), output on to a digital plotter, output to TV and special-purpose printing, for example on cheques.

Resource implications

Let us examine four aspects of resource implications. Points to consider are as follows:

Hardware
- compatibility with other systems
- communications capability
- processing power
- secondary storage capacity
- manufacturer support
- potential for expansion
- contract terms
- cost

Software
- functional specification
- reputation of supplier
- contract and licence terms
- availability and cost

People
- job specifications
- experience, skill, knowledge
- selection criteria, potential
- availability, timing
- cost

Constraints
- timescale:
  - deadlines and penalties
  - reviews, and revisions of system specification

- costs:
  - budget responsibilities
  - spending profile
  - reviews, and revisions of budget
  - contingencies.

Evidence indicator project

This project covers all the evidence indicators related to Chapter 19 (Element 5.3) It has been designed to be carried out at the end of the element.

Performance criteria: 1–5

Key skills:	Communication	3.2, 3.3, 3.4
	Application of number	–
	IT	3.1, 3.2, 3.3

Scenario

As the newly appointed member of the design team at Einstein Designs, you have been asked to produce a system specification for a new stock control system.

You may make any reasonable assumptions about the number of types of items in stock, the frequency of issues from stock, the frequency of receipts of new or replacement stock and reorder levels. Keep it simple.

Produce a system specification for the new stock control system which includes the following:

1 A refined data flow diagram.
2 Data definitions; entity relationship diagram in first normal form; data dictionary.
3 Process specifications, covering three of the following: Structured English, structure diagram, decision tables, flow chart.
4 Input specification, covering the following: data source, data capture methods, screen layout, validation, verification.
5 Output specification: screen reports, printed reports.
6 An identification of the resources you would use, including hardware, software, people; and refer to the constraints (timescale, costs).

Write your report to the manager of the design department at Einstein Designs. At the start of your report, state clearly any assumptions you make.

Systems analysis: Unit test 5

1 Sorting is a process of
 a Manipulation
 b Calculation
 c Interrogation
 d Repetition

2 Selecting is a process of
 a Manipulation
 b Calculation
 c Interrogation
 d Repetition

3 Which of the following is an element of a system specification?
 a Data model in first normal form
 b System flow chart
 c Feasibility study
 d Problem statement

4 What type of IT system can be interrogated?
 a A spread sheet
 b A word processor
 c DOS
 d A database

5 A report generator is most likely to be found on which type of software?
 a A database management system
 b A word processor
 c DOS
 d A spread sheet

6 Database software that creates different reports uses
 a Programming languages
 b Macros
 c Word processing facilities
 d Applications generators

7 Human resources form essential
 a Costs of all systems
 b Components of data manipulation
 c Elements of systems specifications
 d Quality aspects of all systems

8 What is the purpose of a feasibility study?
 a to see how effective a computer is
 b to check how a system works

 c to see if it is desirable to put in a new computerised system
 d to see if it is possible to use data on a new system

9 Recording is important in systems analysis because
 a It's easy to forget details
 b It's a legal requirement
 c Memos need to be sent
 d Company legislation says so

10 Which of the following is *not* user information for systems analysis?
 a Purpose
 b Description of the present system
 c Feasibility
 d New system expectations

11 Process specifications can include *all but which* of the following?
 a Data dictionary
 b Structured English
 c Decision tables
 d Flow charts

12 Database models must include
 a Data dictionary
 b Diagrams
 c Relationships
 d Reports

13 A system constraint is imposed by
 a The speed data can be entered into a system
 b The method used to enter data into a system
 c The type of system output used
 d The type of system input used

14 Which is *not* an essential element of information?
 a Sources of data
 b Costs
 c Personnel
 d Security

15 The flow of information and data collected are
 a Contents of a data dictionary
 b Elements of information
 c The purpose of a system
 d Resource implications

16 A feasibility study and problem statement are
    a Part of a system quality study
    b Part of a data dictionary
    c Part of a structured English definition
    d Resource information

17 Input specifications for a data handling system include
    a Hardware
    b Data capture methods
    c Software
    d Constraints

18 What is important in systems analysis?
    a The diagramming notation used
    b Personal details of the systems analyst
    c Data accuracy
    d Screen layout

19 An organisation with many PCs must consider which of the following resource implications?
    a People
    b A feasibility study
    c Types of data being utilised
    d Data collection

20 A CD-ROM is an example of
    a A hard disk drive
    b A permanent storage facility
    c EPROM
    d Programmable memory

21 The contents of any data dictionary may include
    a Entity relationship diagram in first normal form
    b Data descriptions
    c Software
    d Data capture methods

22 Examples of legal and statutory bodies include *all but*
    a Health and Safety Executive
    b Inland Revenue
    c Customs and Excise
    d The Home Office

23 Screen layout refers to
    a Where the monitor is placed relative to the computer
    b The layout of data items on the screen
    c Where data is placed on the screen relative to where it will be printed
    d The design of software

24 Structured English is often used in
    a A feasibility study report
    b A process specification
    c A data source
    d Resource implications

25 Creating a directory can be done either in File Manager software or in
    a The diskette
    b A CD-ROM
    c The operating system
    d The hard disk

26 A device driver is run by
    a A printer
    b A scanner
    c A computer
    d A keyboard

27 Serial and parallel output cards are examples of
    a Output devices
    b Hardware controls
    c Electronic data control
    d Calculating devices

28 A systems analysis report will contain *all but* which of the following?
    a Error report
    b Analysis of resources
    c A feasibility study
    d A problem statement

29 Process specifications may be easier to understand if
    a Only headings are used
    b Information flows easily
    c Decision tables are used
    d A feasibility study is performed

30 Systems analysis will *not* include which of the following?
    a Feasibility study
    b Problem statement
    c Examples of the type of data to be used
    d Constraint analysis

271

Applications software is the mainspring of IT. Equipment and systems software are acquired and brought into use purely so that applications programs can run. Without systems software no application can run, and computing equipment is incapable of doing useful work. This unit is concerned with software in its entirety.

You will develop an understanding of software, how it is constructed, and what its purposes are.

Chapter 20 (Element 6.1) identifies categories of software: applications software, and others which are collectively often called systems software. You will learn about the roles of applications programs, the features of programs, and modes of operation of software.

Chapter 21 (Element 6.2) looks at programming environments and features of program execution. The term program constructs is explored, and you will be learning about data types and data structures.

Chapter 22 (Element 6.3) investigates automated procedures. You will study the advantages of specifying, creating and using automated procedures; and also the way to evaluate their usefulness.

You will probably be able to use software which allows you to experiment with the features discussed in the unit, and gain skill in undertaking the practical tasks; and you will be able to acquire knowledge from textbooks, which are plentiful, as well as from your tutor.

Opportunities for students to write and test programs are provided in the optional and additional units of this GNVQ.

An external test forms part of this unit

Chapter 20

Investigate software

In this element we look at the wide variety of software that is available for us to use, building on the knowledge we gained in Chapter 2 (Element 1.2), and studying the subject in greater detail. Do use the software you have available to you to put the theory in the book into practice. This way you will acquire a practical and thorough understanding.

Software is the term used to embrace all computer programs. For example, a word processor package comes under the term of software, as does a bespoke application program, a database management system and an operating system. No particular brand or package is mentioned – they all come under the same heading of software.

After studying this chapter you should be able to:

1 describe *categories of software* and their purposes;
2 explain the *purposes of applications software packages*;
3 explain *features of computer programs*;
4 describe different *modes of operation* of software.

Special note

There is only one evidence indicator project for this element. It is at the end of the element, on page 281.

Categories of software

Applications software

Applications software is software that directly provides the processing that users want to have performed. Applications software can be *generic,* meaning that it has relevance to every type of user organisation; or *specific* to meet the needs of particular industries or kinds of business.

Generic applications software enjoys a large market and is therefore commonly sold as packages. Examples of such packages are listed in Table 20.1.

Table 20.1 Generic applications software

Spreadsheets	Desk-top publishing
Lotus 123	Aldus Pagemaker
Excell	Corel Ventura
Quattro	GST Pressworks

Word processors	Accounts packages
WordPerfect	Quicken 4
Word	Sage Instant Accounting
Lotus Ami Pro	Intuit Quickinvoice
Accent Express	Sage Sterling

Specific applications software, sometimes called 'vertical application software', may be sold as packages or built to meet the requirements of a user or group of users. Examples of vertical application packages are those for firms of solicitors, hotels, estate agents and local councils.

Applications software built by users to meet their own needs, known also as 'bespoke software', is found in most large companies, as discussed in Chapter 2 (Element 1.2).

Operating systems

Again, we looked at operating systems in Chapter 2 (Element 1.2). Here is a restatement of the tasks of most operating systems.

A computer's operating system, which may amount to a substantial amount of code, possibly hundreds of thousands of instructions, has many duties. The main ones are as follows:

- Scheduling and loading jobs, and controlling their execution. Making the computer conform to the user's priority allocation. Keeping the machine busy while there is any work that needs to be done.
- Monitoring the computer's behaviour, assessing any indications of malfunction, trying to recover from malfunction, and reporting failures.
- Managing storage so that primary and secondary memory are used equably and efficiently by active jobs, and that access to stored data is restricted to authorised programs and individuals.
- Selecting and controlling input and output devices.
- Offering responsive communication with the user or, on large systems, with the computer operator.
- Keeping records of the activity of all system resources.
- Providing users, on demand, with 'help' information, and reports of system activity.

From this list it will be seen that for a computer system to service applications software effectively the operating system has important functions to fulfil.

Examples of operating systems include MS-DOS, UNIX and Windows '95. Generally only one operating system is used on a computer but it is possible to use alternatives providing only one is used at a time. The Apple computer Power Mac is an exception to this as some versions use two processors to run the MAC operating system and DOS operating system at the same time. This is to allow the emulation of an IBM-compatible processor on the Apple machine to run as fast as possible, protected from the need to execute functions of the MAC operating system.

Utilities

There are times when computer users have to carry out maintenance tasks. This used to be done in the operating system. It has not always proved itself to be an easy task as it requires the computer user to understand and be able to use whichever operating system the computer is running. To simplify the process, utilities software exists. Rather than having to instruct the computer in the operating system language, a pull-down menu system gives the user the options available to perform the maintenance tasks necessary. Examples include File Sort and Delete File operations.

Utilities, like user interface software, languages, program generators and database management systems, are sometimes classed as components of systems software but are more usually referred to by these names with the implicit understanding that they are not themselves applications software but that they support the running of applications software.

Activity

If you use Windows, try deleting a file using the File Manager utility software. Now try the same thing in DOS. Which method is easier?

User interface software

As we've already seen, the operating system is the interface between the user, the hardware and the applications software. We also know that it may not be particularly user-friendly. This is where graphical user-interface software can assist us. Rather than have the user load software from the operating system, it is made simpler by having all software products on the computer illustrated on a graphical-user interface screen by pictures, or icons. When the user wants to run software, the relevant icon is simply selected by using the mouse.

Languages

We looked at programming languages in Chapter 2 (Element 1.2), but need to look at them now in more detail. In order to create new software, programmers must be able to use tools to help them interface with computers. The recognition of this need led to the emergence of high-level languages which offer the opportunity to define the processing steps required in English-like statements. The software which translates the programmer's statements into machine code are called language processors. The languages that are used most widely, and the nature of the translation process, are covered in Chapter 21 (Element 6.2). There are two categories of language software we need to know about.

Assembly languages

Assembly languages are machine-specific but are easier to learn and safer to use than machine code, as they are written using symbols. Assembly languages help the programmer by allowing symbolic names to be substituted for addresses and for constant and variable quantities, and by the use of mnemonic codes for instructions. The actual codes used for instructions vary from one assembly language to another, so assembly language translators, called *assemblers,* are specific to each type of computer.

The virtue of assembly language programming is that it gives the programmer close control over the operation of particular features of the computer. The main drawback is the inability to move the code directly from one machine type to another.

An assembly language is a *low-level language* – closer to machine code in format and structure than high-level languages.

There is further reference to assembly languages in Chapter 21 (Element 6.2).

High-level languages

These programming languages have a syntax and a large vocabulary of words that the programmer can use for writing program statements. As high-level languages are closer to English than assembler code, they improve the work rate of the programmer, allow programs to be written and used on different types of computers, make testing and correcting problems faster, and make programs easier to understand. The limitation of high-level languages is their inability to exploit the hardware features of particular types or makes of computer. Examples of high-level languages include Pascal, BASIC, Cobol and Fortran, which are studied in Chapter 21 (Element 6.2).

These high-level languages are called *procedural* languages, because the programmer using any of them has to take account not only of what is to be done, but also of how it is to be done. Some languages which have emerged more recently under the general heading of *fourth-generation languages,* are called *non-procedural* languages require the programmer to specify only what is to be done; the language translator, or compiler, works out how the objective is to be met. Prolog is an example of such a language. Program generators discussed below process fourth-generation, non-procedural, languages.

When high-level languages were first developed and made available they were for use on mainframe computers, feeding the source code in job by job in succession, usually through a card reader. Later they were used by programmers with multiaccess facilities, that is, terminals, so that as machines became faster concurrent operation would enable efficient use to be made of the extra processing capacity. Now, as you will have seen, language compilers for many languages are available for PCs.

Did you know?

In the early days of using high-level languages, until about 1975, most programmers had to put their jobs in a physical queue of decks of punched cards. Often they had to wait hours for their work to be processed.

Program generators

These are also known as *application generators.* They are themselves fourth-generation programs capable of creating a range of application programs in domains, or areas, which include simulation, process control and user interface software.

The aim of program generators is to allow users who are not trained programmers to develop applications. Users describe what is wanted in terms of application requirement, not in terms of processing steps.

Perhaps the most popular use of program generators is for the creation of reports. *Report program generators* (RPGs) provide a language in which a user can define the format of a report and provide a description of the file structure; the RPG constructs a program to read the file, extract the desired information, and format it as required. The best-known RPG is the product RPG II.

Database management systems

Also known as DBMS. This is software that builds, handles and allows access to, structured data in databases. It insulates the user from the demands of handling the physical storage medium and the problems of addressing items of data in a database. Chapters 23–25 (Elements 7.1–7.3), on database developments, consider DBMS more fully. A DBMS offers the user the following facilities:

1 Accept the *schema* which defines the logical view of the database.
2 Reorder a database running under the DBMS, for optimal operation.
3 Identify any associations and cross-references that exist between data elements.
4 Allow new information to be entered into an old database.
5 Make changes to information stored in a database, or delete it.
6 Interrogate a database.
7 Maintain the data dictionary.
8 Accept new procedures to process data in a database.
9 Communicate with the user.

Purposes of categories of software

There are a number of reasons for developing and using software.

Use for common data processing tasks

Software is written for tasks that are too complex or too expensive to accomplish manually, or that are to be performed a number of times. This broad statement applies to almost all kinds of software.

System control

Any computer system must have comprehensive and precise control procedures. Without them the system will be prone to problems. The most obvious and the most comprehensive type of system control is an operating system. Not only does an operating system control the application software, and the memory, storage systems and other hardware inside a

computer, but it also controls all peripheral devices such as printers and monitors. Operating systems are discussed above and in Chapter 2 (Element 1.2).

Simplification of user interface

The graphical-user interface (GUI) provided by Windows and MAC operating system software has been designed to simplify as far as possible the interaction between user and machine. Certainly it is a marked advance on any previous command-based interface.

A GUI makes use of input devices in addition to the keyboard, and visual presentation techniques. GUIs provide windows, icons, menus and pointing indicators. The windows can contain control objects such as tool bars, slider bars, click boxes and other textual and graphical information.

The objects forming the interface display can be readily moved, and changed in shape.

Software production

Software production has been dealt with in Chapter 2 (Element 1.2). It is important to realise that it is the end user's needs that have to be accommodated by the software author, no matter how or in what language the software is written. If it fails to satisfy the end user, the software is of little use.

Creation and conversion of code

Software is written in a form that the software author can understand, but must ultimately be converted into machine code for the computer to handle and execute. In order to create the code, software developers use software that allows programs to be written in readable textual formats and then be converted into machine code. This is achieved by the use of language processors or assemblers.

Management of shared data

Multiaccess mainframe computers allowed many people to use a powerful computer at the same time. This takes the form of not only shared operating system access but also of shared application software and data.

The management of shared data became even more necessary when PCs began sharing information in a network. It is apparent that PCs in the network have to share the same operating system and work files, but it is important to ensure that certain files are given restricted access rights. This is particularly important when a work file is being edited. It is not effective to allow only one user to work on a file at a time. Therefore, computers have to manage data files between users and ensure they are saved correctly, in their entirety at the end of the editing process.

Purposes of applications software packages

Let us look at four principal purposes.

Processing

The software acts as a processing engine to convert the data and text we input into a computer into binary number format for the computer to 'understand' and process. In the same way, all data the computer holds is converted by the processing software into a form that we can either read or else use directly in some manner. Different applications software packages process different sorts of information. For example, documents can be processed by word processors or desk-top publishers; numerical data by spreadsheets mathematical routines, and databases; and *graphical* data by spreadsheets, CAD, desk-top publishers, and drawing software. Structured data, in which items of data are expected by the application program to be of a defined form and to appear in defined places on the screen, is used to increase handling speed and to safeguard accuracy.

Software vendors have realised that some of their products are used in conjunction with one another. Rather than sell the software packages separately, they offer *software suites,* or *integrated packages,* that included such titles as word processors, spreadsheets, databases and personal organisers. Lotus Smartsuite is one such example.

Modelling

Data modelling was covered fully in Chapter 7 (Element 2.3). Models of proposed artefacts, before commitment to the cost and risk of creating the artefacts themselves, are used to help make analysis and introduce refinements. We have referred to models built on CAD earlier, in Chapter 7 (Element

2.3). It's cheaper to create a model to see what it looks like, and whether or not it is suitable for the job, than to build the real thing only to find it is unsuitable and has to be demolished. Cars are modelled by computer before being built so that the engineers can see how they look, and how they can be serviced and repaired. Architects use CAD software to model houses they design. This gives them the opportunity to move around the virtual building, and see it from different angles, before it is built.

Controlling

Any software that manages a piece of hardware or a process is controlling it, or making it run effectively. In Chapter 8 (Element 2.4), we studied control systems. We noted that mass-produced domestic pieces of equipment, known as *white goods,* have control procedures embedded in single micro-chips. Even though the processes might be complicated the software built into the chips would be standard and fixed; it would not allow modification by the user of the equipment. Washing machines are an excellent example; modern machines weigh the clothes in a load and calculate how much water will be required to complete the job. Video cassette recorders are controlled by software. The internal processor can be set to record a programme at a precise time. Digital alarm clocks work on the same principle. The processor has a time programmed into it for the alarm to go off. At the required moment the software electronically activates the alarm sound. Most industrial processes are controlled by computers, as we saw in Chapter 8 (Element 2.4).

Expert systems

We met expert systems in Chapter 2 (Element 1.2). You will recall that an expert system is an application that allows the user to take advantage of the knowledge of a human expert. The knowledge is built into the system as a set of decision-making rules and can be accessed by the user asking the system questions. Why do we have expert systems? Because it is cheaper and easier to carry a computer around or have one sited at a job to provide the answers to questions than it is to have the human expert present all the time. For example, there may be only one person who is expert enough to give advice over drilling for oil in the North Sea. He or she may not be available when needed by the drilling company. It's easier (and cheaper) to have an expert system replace the human expert. The expert probably prefers it too as it means not having to go out on the North Sea in bad weather conditions!

There is a limitation to an expert system, though. It is limited to the knowledge base originally entered; it might become out of date, or wrong. Fortunately, expert systems can be updated and improved by simply adding more knowledge or better decision-making rules. Nonetheless, we all have to remember that expert systems are for providing advice, not for taking decisions.

The features of computer programs

Code

Computer programs consist of sets of instructions that the computer can obey. When these instructions are read and obeyed by the computer, it performs the operations in the sequence prescribed by the program itself. These instructions are known as the program code. The program statements or instructions written by the programmer are known as the *source code*; the binary executable program which has been generated by the language processor or assembler from its translation process is called the *object code*. Source code in a high-level language is mainly or wholly machine-independent, though that is not necessarily the same as manufacturer dependent. If two makes of PC are both IBM-compatible a piece of object code that runs on one should run on the other.

Program structures

Computer programs tend to be written in certain structures in a similar way to essays being structured through the use of sentences and paragraphs. The overall form of a program has to recognise the main components and inter-relationships. A well-structured program will have followed some accepted methodology or set of principles when being designed. It will use appropriate data structures, and may itself have a structure which at least partly corresponds to the data structures it uses.

Data types

These are the characteristics of the programmed data. In any computer program, words and expressions are used by the programmer as representations to tell the computer to perform certain tasks. This may include

- *characters* such as a, b, c, d, e, f, g;
- *numbers* both real and integer, defined in Chapter 21 (Element 6.2);
- *graphics;*
- *logic statements,* known as Boolean expressions, and discussed in Chapters 7 and 21 (Elements 2.3 and 6.2).

It should be noted that *data types* is not a formal, unique name for these four examples, which are required for this GNVQ unit.

Data structures

Data structures are arrangements of individual items of data. They come in a number of different forms.

Arrays

If we were to write a computer program that allows us to load 100 names, one method is to tell the program to have 100 areas put to one side in the computer memory for the names to be stored. This works well, but is not effective in terms of memory use. It would be better to have an area for information to be stored in the computer memory *if and when it is needed.* This is what an array allows us to do. Rather than inform the program that 100 names may be entered and they are to be stored under the data types a, b, c, d, e, etc, an array is created telling the computer to make space for the names only when needed. As one space is filled, another is developed. Arrays are defined more formally in Chapter 21 (Element 6.2).

Lists

If you write a shopping list or a list of jobs you have to do, you are working in much the same way as a computer when it produces lists. Ideally, new individual items of data are placed at the bottom, or *tail*, of the list and dealt with in turn as they reach the top, or *head*, of the list. This may not always be possible, though. We may find that there is a logical order for items in a list to be dealt with rather than following the physical order in which they have been placed.

Records

Individual paper records consist of details relating to the same person or task in hand. Large volumes of information from paper records can be loaded into a computer and called up at a later date. To ensure each item of data relating to each record is accurate, it is possible to link them all together by denoting a corresponding field within each record to act as a reference point for the computer.

Queues

If you stand in queue in a shop, you join the end of it and wait your turn until you get to the front of the

Figure 20.1 A queue in a shop is similar to a queue in a computer

queue. This is very similar to queues in computers. Data is entered to one end of a queue and deleted from the other. A queue is sometimes called a *push-up list*. It is a *first in, first out* (FIFO) organisation of data.

Stacks

Consider the laundry basket! You stack clothes on top of one another until the basket is full. You then take the basket to the washing machine and lift the clothes out and place them in it – in reverse order from the one in which they were placed in the basket. This is the same for a computer stack. Data is entered into the stack and dealt with by taking items individually off the top. A stack is *a last in, first out* (LIFO) organisation of data.

Strings

A string is simply a set of characters placed together. For example, if we wrote a program that required someone to type his or her name in to the computer, we would set aside an area in the computer memory to store this information. A name consists of a string of letters (such as 'Peter Dysan' which has 11 characters – 5 for Peter, 5 for Dysan and one for the space between the two words) that must be kept together in the sequence in which they were typed – a string (see Chapter 21 (Element 6.2) for more discussion of strings).

Tables

Tables are ordered arrangements of records, and are described in Chapter 21 (Element 6.2).

Trees

Trees, or *rooted trees,* are probably the most commonly used data structure. Each node of data has a predecessor but can have two or more successors. Each node therefore needs data and links to its successors. If a tree is drawn it looks similar to a family tree with nodes and branches. (see Figure 20.2).

Method of translation

All computer code written by software engineers or programmers has to be converted into binary for the computer to "understand" it. This conversion is

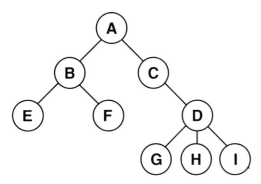

Figure 20.2 Graph of a tree structure

accomplished by a translator in the program software package. There are three common types of convertor – *interpreters, compilers* and *assemblers*. These are dealt with fully in Chapter 21 (Element 6.2).

Interpreters

Interpreters take the program code and convert it into machine code line by line as and when it is needed. It tends to be slower than its compiler equivalent.

Compilers

Pascal is an example of programming software that uses a compiler to translate the source code into object code. The compiler translates the entire Pascal program into machine code, stores it in memory and then, if required, sets it to run.

Assemblers

Assemblers take in source code and convert it into object code ready for execution. The object code can be in *relocatable* form, in which case the operating system will adjust all addresses in the code to allow correct execution wherever the program is placed in memory.

Constructs

The constructs of sequence, repetition and selection are looked at in Chapter 21 (Element 6.2).

Different modes of software operation

Commands

Most software packages invite the user to make selections from pre-determined application functions in order to get the most out of the package. These functions are known as commands. In modern Windows software, they are found through the use of the menu system at the top of the screen (as illustrated for Word for Windows in Figure 20.3). They can, however, be accessed through other means including the use of the *function keys* at the top of the keyboard (F1 to F12); *character keys* and *multiple key combinations*. For example, if we want to open a new file in Word for Windows as in Figure 20.3, we can call up the File option in the menu system and select New. However, without using the menu screens, it is possible to open a new file by pressing the 'Alt' and 'N' keys together or by depressing the 'new file' icon at the top of the screen.

Function keys

Function keys are generally the grey ones at the top of the keyboard that are numbered F1 to F12. They are assigned special functions within any software that needs to use them. An example can be seen in the WordPerfect word processor software. The F10 key saves work. If the Shift key is pressed at the same time as F10 data is retrieved from a disk. This shows how *multiple key combinations* can exist and work together with function keys.

There are additional keys which can be used for prescribed functions, including Escape, Print Screen, Insert, Delete, End, Page Down, Control and Tabulate. These keys and their functions are standard on all IBM-compatible keyboards.

Character keys

Character keys are all the keys that show a character on the screen when pressed, and are generally used for entering data. They have two shifts, so that the letters can take the form of lower case or upper case; and there is a choice of digits and special characters such as !, $, & and +.

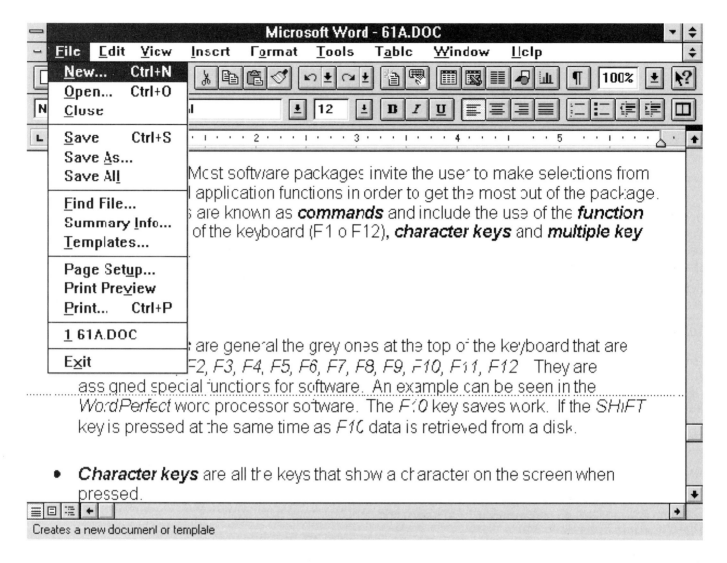

Figure 20.3 Command options in Microsoft Word

Multiple key combinations

Multiple key combinations can be used by software to increase the range of the function keys. For example, each function key could be depressed in conjunction with the Shift, or the Control, or the alternate keys or, of course, on its own. This gives four operations that can be triggered by each function key, or 48 by using all 12.

Menu

We use menus on computer software all the time. There are two ways of using such a menu system. First, through the use of the arrow keys on the keyboard. When the down arrow is pressed the highlighted bar moves down the options. Secondly, through the use of the mouse. The arrow cursor is moved to the required point, the mouse is clicked, and the selection made.

Did you know?

The author of the *Hitch Hiker's Guide to the Galaxy* – Douglas Adams – has started an electronic publishing and production company called the Digital Village. It's intended to be a company that takes creative and imaginative ideas and puts them to commercial use. The company will be creating a Web site on the Internet soon. The Digital Village is not in multimedia company – it's a multiple media company, producing television, CD-ROM and virtual reality material. The latest specific projects include a new work of fiction that will make its first appearance on CD-ROM called *Starship Titanic*. This will be followed by a TV series, a documentary on evolution and a TV drama science fiction series.

Graphic interface or graphical-user interface (GUI)

This is the use of the computer screen to make it easier to use the software. Figure 20.3 is a good example of a graphic interface as the software (Microsoft Word for Windows), in this case, uses pictures as well as menus to help the user select the function wanted. For example, if the user wants to draw an arc, all he or she has to do is use the mouse to 'click' on to the arc icon and then drag the cursor along the line needed. The software will then construct a smooth arc approximating to the line indicated.

Evidence indicator project

This project covers all the evidence indicators related to Chapter 20 (Element 6.1). It has been designed to be carried out at the end of the element.

Performance criteria: 1–4

Key skills:	Communication	3.1, 3.2, 3.4
	Application of number	–
	IT	3.1, 3.2, 3.3, 3.4

Scenario

The Worldwide Animation Company have been making animated cartoons for many years. They have decided that now is the time to start to use computers to help them make their films, as other well-known animation companies are doing. They have a problem, though – they don't know the first thing about computers, and need the whole concept of computer software explained to them.

Your task is to prepare a report covering the following:

1 A description of the categories of software and the purposes of each category.
2 An explanation of the purpose of applications software packages to The Worldwide Animation Company.
3 An explanation of the features of two computer programs of your choice. Your tutor will provide you with two simple computer programs for commercial applications, e.g. stock control or payroll programs.
4 A description of different modes of software operation.

Your report should be supported by a short talk and a question-and-answer session.

Examine software production

In Chapter 20 (Element 6.1) we investigated software generally. Now we have to examine software production. This process is dependent upon the design and creation of software to implement processes that meet user needs. In this element we look at the process of writing software.

After studying this chapter you should be able to:

1 describe types of *programming environments* and give examples;
2 describe *features of program* execution;
3 explain what is meant by *program constructs* and give examples;
4 describe *types of data* and *data structures* and give examples;
5 describe the *expressions and operators* used in software production and give examples.

Special note

There is only one evidence indicator project for this element. It is at the end of the element, on page 289.

Programming environments

The different types of program environment can be broken down as follows.

Program language

A programming language is a formally defined language, whose syntax is recognised by language processor software. This software translates the program source code, written in the programming language, into binary object code equivalent. There are many programming languages including BASIC, Pascal, Cobol, Fortran and C. We looked at some in Chapter 2 (Element 1.2); and we shall look at them again in Chapters 17 and 20 (Elements 5.1 and 6.1).

The five languages listed here are those most extensively used, both in UK and elsewhere, as programming is a wholly international activity. Each has characteristics which suit it for certain types of application.

There are other languages, some of which you may encounter. PL/1 is an IBM language intended to address commercial and scientific applications with equal capability. Ada is a language developed for the US Department of Defense to replace the large number of programming languages then in use by defence contractors and suppliers. Its name commemorates Augusta Ada King, Countess of Lovelace, who helped Charles Babbage and who has some claim on being the world's first programmer. Ada was first published in 1983 and was adopted as a standard by the International Standards Organisation (ISO) in 1987. There have been several releases of Ada, the latest being called Ada 95.

BASIC

BASIC stands for 'Beginners' All-purpose Symbolic Instruction Code' and was developed in the mid-1960s for use in education. Its aim was to introduce the possibility, novel at the time, of remote use of a computer from a terminal.

The language can be learned quickly. It contains a simple program editor to protect the user from the complexities of the computer operating system. An ISO standard was granted, but nonetheless a large number of incompatible dialects appeared.

Recent developments include Microsoft's Quick Basic and Visual Basic. The latter is used for the rapid modification of Microsoft Windows applications.

Pascal

Pascal was designed as a tool to help the teaching of programming as a formal discipline. It embodies the control structures, or *constructs,* of structured programming which are introduced later in this chapter.

Standard Pascal was accepted by the ISO in 1982, but Turbo Pascal (which is widely used) has departed from the standard.

Cobol

Cobol, which stands for 'Common Business-Orientated Language', has become the *de facto* standard for commercial data processing. The language was first used in 1960. Since then many revisions have been developed, notably Cobol 68 and Cobol 74. The latest version is Cobol 85. Forecasts that Cobol would be superseded and subsequently die have been frequently made but never fulfilled. There are in existing commercial systems hundreds of millions of lines of Cobol code.

The language is verbose – deliberately – in the founders' expectation that it would be self-documenting.

Fortran

Fortran is an acronym for 'Formula Translation'. The first version was issued by IBM in 1956. It was called Fortran I, and was quickly followed by Fortran II, Fortran IV, Fortran 66 and Fortran 77. The most recent version is Fortran 90. The Fortran language was intended for scientific and mathematical computation and, like Cobol, it has enjoyed a long life. It is still used extensively in scientific and academic establishments.

The C Language

The C programming language was designed to implement the UNIX operating system mentioned in Chapter 20 (Element 6.1). A close relationship between UNIX and C has been maintained, so C is widely used on PCs which employ UNIX. C combines features of high-level languages with the capability of addressing PC hardware in the intimate style of assembler languages.

A well-known derivative of C is the C++ language. This claims to combine the power of object-oriented programming with the efficiency of C. C++ is widely used for implementing applications to run under Windows.

Do your best to experiment with languages available to you so that you can make your own mind up as to what's best for what job.

Translators

A translator is a program, usually called a *language processor*, that converts one program written in a given language – the *source language* – into a corresponding program written in another language – the *target language*. A translator's use which most IT people are familiar with is to provide conversion of a

program from a high-level language into an *object code* equivalent (in binary) that can be executed by a computer.

There are three types of translator. They are known as *compilers, interpreters* and *assemblers*. We touched on the reasons for using translators in Chapter 20 (Element 6.1). Let us now consider, in outline, how they work.

Compilers

Compilers take in the source program, written in the source language, check its syntax, generate diagnostic comments, build tables necessary internally for execution, and construct the object code equivalent of the source text, ready for execution. If the object program is to be run on a different type of computer compatibility details may need to be addressed.

Interpreters

Interpreters translate the source program line by line, executing the derived instructions as they go. This process is slower than compilation, but it can allow the programmer to intervene at chosen points. Some programming languages are designed for interpretive translation. BASIC is one example.

Assemblers

Assemblers translate programs written in assembly language. As explained in Chapter 20 (Element 6.1), *assembly language* is a notation for representing machine-code programs in readable terms. It allows the programmer to make use of mnemonic operation codes; symbolic names for variables, constants, and addresses; and labels for lines of program text.

Special programming languages

These languages are not general-purpose programming languages. They exist to fulfil particular roles, such as interrogating databases or simulating processes that might include transfer lines and conveyor systems used in manufacturing. One of the most popular types of special programming languages at the moment comes in the form of Lotus Notes. This is a communications software package, but it is possible to create special documents and standardised company forms and procedures for use within the software itself. Special programming

languages are characterised as being aimed (in each instance) at a particular purpose. They therefore lack the features necessary for providing the generality of use of general-purpose languages.

Automated applications software routines

Chapter 22 (Element 6.3) looks at the production of automated procedures. Here we shall consider the purpose of three types of user facilities: macros, styles and templates.

Macros

This word is an abbreviation of *macro-instructions*. A macro can be an instruction in a programming language, or a command issued by key depressions on the keyboard, which invokes a sequence of instructions that were coded prior to compilation or assembly. The purposes of using macros are to save time and to safeguard accuracy whenever there is a frequent requirement for the same code to be executed. An example would be a standard salutation or the closing words on correspondence.

Styles

This is a feature of word processing. It allows an author to maintain the same appearance throughout a whole document. For example, you could create a style which laid down the treatment of indents, the page numbering, the heading sizes, weights and positions, and you could give that style the name of, say, 'Text'. Whenever you set that style the appearance would conform to the rules you gave earlier.

Templates

The word 'template' is often employed by users of PCs to mean a framework of boxes and lines on the screen where the user can insert variable data. The template acts as a prompter to help the user provide the necessary details of, for example, a motor insurance policy. More generally, a template is any pattern that specifies the form of a structure. The term is a convenient one for differentiating between the specification of a structure and the details of the structure itself.

Did you know?

Software is easy to copy; and copying software is inexpensive, and hard to detect. Software piracy is commonplace. For each user who acquires a software product without paying the proper price, the owner of the copyright in the software and the vendor are losers.

Microsoft believe that the annual cost of software piracy in Europe now stands at £4 billion. More than half of all UK businesses are trying to improve their reputation and image by claiming that they are eradicating software theft!

The features of program execution

When a program is executed you must be aware of two features.

Run-time system

This is a collection of procedures that supports the execution of a program written in a high-level language, at the instant that its object code is on the point of executing. The run-time system provides the software environment in which the application programs are to run. It provides functions such as storage allocation and input/output facilities.

Executable file

Within your directory you will have files containing data, programs, commands and systems code. You need to be able to run the applications that are stored in those files. The files that hold executable program code are called program files. If the files hold user applications the file extension will be `.EXE`.

The `.EXE` extension tells the operating system that there is a program in the file to which control may be passed, and which will then run. While executing, the program in the `.EXE` file will be able to call data from other files to which linkages will have been set up by the operating system.

Program constructs

Large computer programs may have more than a million lines of code, and a computer will have to execute them in the correct order to obtain the required results. Such programs can be planned, written correctly, checked and understood by others only if they have a recognisable structure.

There are three 'constructs', as they are called, which give names to, and formalise, three common characteristics of program design. These are *sequence*, *repetition* and *selection*, which were described in outline in Chapter 19 (Element 5.3).

Sequence

It is accepted that computer programs are executed in the order dictated by the flow of the program logic. If a number of processing steps have always to be taken in the same order those steps form sequences. For example, in a payroll program there would be a sequence which calculates:

- gross wage,
- tax, and
- net wage.

Those three calculations would form a sequence because they could not be undertaken in any other order.

Repetition

Often in executing a program the computer will have to apply the same sections of code in succession to different data. If we take the payroll case again but think of it at a higher level, we can see that the program segment working out the pay of one employee is applied successively to all employees. It is repeated until the roll of employees is exhausted. That segment is thus called a repetition.

Selection

By having independent program modules built into a program, it is possible to have these modules run in different orders, as and when they are required. This is known as selecting; if a program is made up of a number of subprograms that can be executed in whatever order the data requires, we have selection. In an inventory management application the transactions fed to the application could be an unsorted mixture of

- add new product line;
- add stock to existing stock; and
- issue stock from existing stock.

The program would have to direct control to whichever of the modules, or subprograms was appropriate for the transaction type.

Types of data

Let's just remind ourselves of what exactly data is. One definition is that it is information in a form that can be stored on and processed by a computer. With this in mind, what types of data do you think exist?

Integer

An integer is a whole number, positive, zero, or negative. Any computer system has to place a limit on the magnitude of the integers it can handle. For example, if a PC allows two bytes for holding integers, those 16 bits can accommodate $(2^{16} - 1)$, or 65,535 possible values. But if one of the bit positions is to hold a bit to denote the plus or minus value for the integer, only 15 bits are available to hold data, giving a ceiling of 32,767 possible signed integer values, or $(2^{15} - 1)$.

Real number

A real number is also called a 'floating-point number'. It is held in computer storage as a number raised to the power of another number, such as a^b meaning a to the power b. In this example a is called the mantissa, and b the exponent. In the computer the mantissa and the exponent are stored separately, usually taking up four bytes. By using this arrangement of a signed mantissa and a signed exponent the number can take up a very much greater range of values than integers occupying the same space of four bytes, and the real number can be expressed to many decimal places, allowing considerable precision in results.

Character

We have already looked in Chapter 13 (Element 4.1) at how character data is represented in a computer. For transmission, 7-bit ASCII, which allows 128 possible characters, is generally used. For storage within a computer an 8-bit byte offers 256 possibilities. You will realise that not all these arrangements of bits result in characters that can be printed. 'Blank' and 'sound bell' are examples of non-printing characters.

Did you know?

The police now use special computerised cameras that can tell when a car is speeding. They are placed at the side of the road, and slightly in front of them in the *middle* of the road are dotted white lines. If the camera detects that the time the car was over the first white line was so short that there was a probability that it was exceeding the speed limit it takes a photograph of the car's registration plate. It then takes another picture as the car passes the last white line. The computer calculates the speed by taking the two times away from each other (that is, the time when the car passed the first white line and the time the car passed the last). If not enough time has passed then the car is going too quickly and the driver will have notice demanding the payment of a fine

sent to his or her home – possibly with a photograph of the crime being committed! This is just another example of how IT is being used to make the roads safer for everyone.

String

This is the term used to describe a group of characters. We looked at strings in Chapter 20 (Element 6.1) and we discuss strings further under data structures, below.

Boolean

We introduced Boolean data parameters in Chapter 7 (Element 2.3.) We now look at Boolean data a little more formally. It is named after the English mathematician George Boole (1815–64), who invented mathematical symbolism to express logical relations.

There are only two values for data in Boolean logic. These are *true* and *false*. There are three *operators* which are used to operate with these values: *or*, which is referred to as 'disjunction'; *and*, referred to as 'conjunction'; and *not*, referred to as 'negation'.

We shall study these operators below, but mean while note that a typical use of a Boolean variable is as a flag, used to record the outcome of a process, which is to be saved. For example, if a search of a database finds that a particular item is present, that fact could be recorded by setting the flag.

Constant

A data 'constant' is one that is not changed during the execution of a program that holds and refers to it. A constant can be numeric or alphabetic. Examples are interest rates which, although they change from time to time, stay fixed throughout one cycle of operations, perhaps calculating interest due from borrowers on a single day, or the name of the current managing director of a company.

Variable

A data variable is really the name assigned to the storage location that holds a type of data that is expected to change during the execution of a program. For example, there could be a field called 'quantity' in an invoicing application. Each time an invoice is to be prepared for printing the field 'quantity' will be loaded with the relevant number for each line. In scientific applications a result that is repeatedly refined by successive processing steps would be a variable.

Data structures

Strings

We looked at 'strings' in Chapter 20 (Element 6.1). We observed that a string is a sequence of characters. The characters do not have to be alphanumeric, there is a need for binary strings in some applications.

A data area has to be assigned to hold a string, though the area may not be filled. The program making use of the string, for example by using the characters in the string to act as indices which point to other data entities, will work its way along until it detects a void (Figure 21.1).

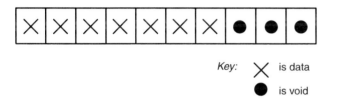

Key: ✕ is data
● is void

Figure 21.1 A string

Arrays

You can think of an array as a rectangular grid of cells each of which can hold a data item, although within the computer and its storage devices the array would be held as a string (Figure 21.2).

1	101
2	107
3	119
4	131
5	142
6	160
7	177
8	184

Figure 21.2 An array. All elements are numeric

The two key properties of arrays are that they are made up of a fixed number of cells, or elements, in any one case, and all the elements must contain data of the same type. There is a resemblance between arrays and spreadsheets. The marks scored by a number of candidates in a number of subjects could be displayed on a spreadsheet; they would be processed by the spreadsheet program as an array.

Records

Records are structures for holding groups of data items that are associated with one another. Unlike arrays, data stored in records need not be all of the same type.

Take as an example a company personnel file. There will be one record assigned to hold the data on each employee. Each record will have the same structure, with fields, let us say, for

- surname
- first name
- date of birth
- date joined company
- grade.

All the corresponding fields would be the same size in every record so a program which handled one record correctly would automatically handle all the personnel records correctly. To this extent the layout of records is similar to that of arrays, with each record corresponding to a row in an array.

Most database management systems operate or, at least, operate more efficiently, on fixed-length records such as those described above.

Tables

A frequently used data structure is a table, which is a series of related records. Look at the example in Figure 21.3.

1	SW24	Corinne Leon	23 Apr 54
2	SA23	Alan Smith	12 Feb 65
3	KP35	Ken Shaw	23 May 35
4	NSJ27	Milanda Tetrada	3 Apr 72
5	SM18	Sandy Meir	28 Jul 69

Figure 21.3 A table

287

Each entry in a table is referred to as a row. In Figure 21.3 we can see that the table is made up of five rows and four columns.

As we saw in Chapter 20 (Element 6.1), fourth-generation languages (4GLs) are high-level languages designed to allow IT staff and users who are not trained as programmers to develop applications. These languages are usually *non-procedural* languages in which the desired output is defined in terms directly related to the application, and not through a description of the process required to create it. Tables are often used for output definition in 4GLs. They are addressed through the use of *fields* and an index structure. The index structure works on *primary keys* which identify each record, or row, uniquely. Its data structure is important because individual items in the table can be picked out by referring to rows and columns. We shall be looking at primary keys and other aspects of database organisation in Chapter 23 (Element 7.1).

The expressions and operators used in software production

Chapters 7 and 11 (Elements 2.3 and 3.3) provided a survey of expressions and operators. We review them again here, with different examples.

There are arithmetic expressions, and relational and logical operators; and a data handling process known as concatenation. These terms have been raised in Chapters 7 and 11, but are now addressed as a group.

Arithmetic

The arithmetic expressions include + (add), − (subtract), / (divide), * (multiply). We use these expressions in spreadsheets. One example might be:

```
=sum(D4+(H2/100)*25)-123
```

The value is worked out by applying the operators in the order given by the acronym BODMAS:

Brackets	( )
Division	/
Multiplication	*
Addition	+
Subtraction	−

This stipulates that the expression above has to be performed as follows:

- First evaluate H2/100.
- Then multiply that result by 25.
- Add that result to D4.
- Finally, subtract 123.

The same result would be achieved by omitting the internal parentheses, and simply writing

$$= (D4 + H2/100 \times 25 - 123)$$

because the division would be carried out before the multiplication, with the addition and subtraction following.

Relational

These operators are

=	equals
>	greater than
<	less than
<>	greater than or less than
<=	less than or equal to
>=	greater than or equal to

A relational operator represents or defines a comparison between two operands. The result of the comparison is either *true* or *false*. For example:

$$2 > 4$$

is always false, a Boolean value.

$$x > 4$$

is true if and only if the value of x is an integer and at the time the comparison is made is 5 or more.

You should note that the relational operator 'equals' (=), is used to make a comparison, like the other relational operators. This is in contrast to the use of = in a high-level language, as in

$$x = 4$$

which means set the value of x to be 4.

Logical

Logical expressions are those that can build up logical positions in programs using the *NOT, AND, OR* statements as we saw above when looking at Boolean data and processes. They *can* be used in some spreadsheets, databases and programs. We assume that the programmer wants the flow of the program to be governed by the relationships that are found between groups of variables. Let's look at a few examples where the temporary values of variables have been used:

If 4*5–5 <= (3*5) AND (2+2) > (1+1)
then go to line 20 in the program

In this case, the outcome would be that the computer would jump to line 20 in the program as both outcomes are true.

If 4*5–5 >= (3*5) OR (2+3) < (1*1)
then go to line 20 in the program

In this case, the outcome would be that the computer would jump to line 20 in the program as the first sum is correct.

The NOT expression essentially starts the logical argument in a negative perspective:

NOT 5+4 > 10 then go to line 20

In this case, the argument is saying 'if 5+4 is not greater than 10 then go to line 20 in the program', so again control is transferred to the statement at line 20.

The decision on whether or not to jump to line 20 in each of these three examples is a binary outcome to the application of the logical operators and so can be seen as a Boolean result.

Activity

Calculate the following:

1 2(5+3) >= 2(1+4+9)–28   *answer* = false
2 a(b+c) <= (ba+ac)   *answer* = true
3 NOT 8(2+4) > 3(5–4)
then read this page again!

Concatenation

This is the linking or sequencing of strings to produce longer strings. For example, if a string contains the data 1, 2, 3 and another string holds the data 4, 5, 6, when they are concatenated the new string becomes 1, 2, 3, 4, 5, 6 (or, of course, 4, 5, 6, 1, 2, 3, depending on the instruction given).

Although concatenation may seem an obscure process for which there would be little need, there are occasions in working with databases when it is useful. For example, linking together two parts of a name so that the concatenated name can be used for sorting and selecting may be the best way to obtain a particular result. The writers of systems software also make use of concatenation.

Evidence indicator project

This project covers all the evidence indicators related to Chapter 21 (Element 6.2). It has been designed to be carried out at the end of the element.

Performance criteria: 1–4

Key skills:	Communication	3.2, 3.4
	Application of number	3.2, 3.3
	IT	3.2, 3.3, 3.4

Prepare a presentation, and a report for submission, to include the following:

1 A description of the types of programming environments that exist, with two examples of each.
2 A description of the features of program execution.
3 An explanation of what is meant by program constructs with at least one example of each.
4 A description of data types and structures with at least one example of each.
5 A description of expressions and operators used in the production of software, with one example each of an arithmetic expression, relational and logical operators.

Investigate the production of automated procedures

One of the principal motivations for an organisation to embrace IT is to take advantage of the efficiency with which computers can carry out tasks repetitively, reliably, accurately and inexpensively. A high proportion of commercial and administrative applications need steps to be repeated frequently, as do some scientific ones; examples of commercial appplications which rely extensively on repetitive processing are payroll, stock control and order processing. In a sense the IT solutions for these applications either are, or contain, automated procedures. It is the execution of the same portion of code a large number of times that furnishes the user with important benefits; but the scope of this element is somewhat narrower.

Here we shall be studying procedures which are developed by users to meet specific needs for automatic treatment within application programs.

After studying this chapter you should be able to:

1 describe the *purposes* of using *automated procedures* and give examples;
2 describe *facilities* available for creating *automated procedures*;
3 produce a *specification* for *automated procedures*;
4 create *automated procedures* to meet the specification;
5 *evaluate automated procedures.*

Special note

There is only one evidence indicator project for this element. It is at the end of the element, on page 293.

Purposes

There are four main reasons why users may wish to employ automated procedures.

Reduce input error

Any input process, particularly one requiring input through the keyboard, is vulnerable to error. The input may be to issue commands to the system, or to an application program, or to carry out some operation on data. Any action that can reduce the total amount of input for a given job reduces the opportunities for error. Automated procedures serve the user in this way. For example, if an automated procedure cut down the number of keystrokes from 50 to five, and the procedure were to be invoked 100 times during the course of a day in running a series of jobs, the 4,500 keystrokes no longer needed would represent a notable reduction in the opportunities for making errors.

Speed up processing

A reduction in the volume of input must reduce the amount of time devoted to handling the input, and thus to the time needed for the overall processing task. To make use of the example immediately above, the 4,500 keystrokes not needed would save at least half an hour a day, and probably more than an hour.

Standardise procedures

Standardisation has merits in most walks of life, and particularly so in IT. Standardisation justifies the effort of identifying the best practice, and of insisting that the practice is followed where appropriate; it simplifies training and reduces its cost, and it helps management in several ways. The design and use of automated procedures can be standardised throughout an organisation.

Convenience

In the paragraphs below we shall look at the range of facilities available for producing automated procedures. One of the criteria for picking a particular approach is the degree of added convenience which the procedure will provide. For example, if the user often wants to be able to change the way in which a procedure is linked to another processing activity, that may guide him or her to one course of action.

Automated procedures

We now look at five sets of requirements in which automated procedures have a role to play. We shall then move on to consider what facilities are able to satisfy these needs.

Repetitive routines

Data processing is full of repetitive routines. Those are routines which accept different data values each time they run, but which carry out the same processes on the data. Some repetitive routines can use the values of the data they encounter to modify the processes they are performing. For example, in a billing application for a utility, if a negative quantity for the consumption of, say, gas should reach the routine, the routine would depart from its usual path and switch control into another routine which handles out-of-line situations.

Templates

The word template has many uses, especially in engineering. It means a pattern that specifies some physical characteristics of a structure. In IT it means a

skeleton of boxes, lines and possibly prompts which can be brought up on to a user's screen to help the input process. Templates are useful for businesses providing services such as insurance or hotel bookings where there are likely to be many telephone enquiries. The template helps the employee capture as quickly as possible the facts needed to respond efficiently to each enquiry. For example, if you wanted to get a quotation over the telephone for insurance cover for your car the underwriting clerk to whom you spoke would use a template to record the essential facts about you and your car.

Calculations

Most applications have calculations built into their programs, but a user may want to introduce extra calculations, perhaps to derive statistics which are not normally part of the output. In mathematical and scientific work there is often a need for calculations. Some will be dealt with by standard *function subprograms*, also called simply *functions*, which handle frequently needed calculations such as trignometrical relations, exponentiation and logarithms. For example, a user could write

$$X1=sqrt(x)$$

to replace X1 with the value of the positive square root of a variable x, rather than write code to work out the square root, because this standard square root routine is sure to be held in the function library of, say, a Fortran compiler.

Did you know

Geographical information systems (GIS) are finding favour with many types of user. One of the most recent purchasers has been Monmouthshire County Council who have acquired Windows-based GIS to share information between highways, planning, and housing departments.

A GIS consists of a relational database with a special-purpose database management system which is tuned to provide answers to queries about locations, such as how many hospitals are there in Wales.

File management activities

Some pathways and command sequences that have to be presented to an operating system are long and not intuitively clear. Whenever such input has to be used frequently there could be advantage in automating it.

Similarly, procedures for saving information or moving files that occur frequently could be automated.

User menus

Most users are familiar with the drop-down and pop-up menus offered by Windows. Some applications provide similar facilities. Toolbars and function bars are also menus. Users can make their selections directly from these menus, or they can write automated procedures to make regularly wanted selections for them. Menu-driven systems are now commonplace. ATMs at banks and building societies use automated procedures based on menus available to the program which activates each machine.

Facilities for creating automated procedures

There are three sorts of facility that can be used for creating automated procedures.

Macros

The word macro is short for *macroinstruction*, disclosing its role of substituting one instruction for many. We have just seen the advantages in employing macros. They can be applied to assembler languages or to high-level languages. A macro call in the source code is expanded by language processing software to exist as the full code, ready to accept parameters and process them at execution time.

Examples of tasks for user-written macros are the presentation of printed pages according to a certain style, or defining calculations. Software products contain macros. Word processing features, such as spellchecking or merging pieces of text, are based on macros embedded in the software. The manuals that accompany software products give details of the macro facilities. The DOS Users' Guide has detailed information on creating and running macros.

Batch files

The word *batch* is overworked in IT. Batch totals were commonly used to verify that batches of input had not been corrupted. Batch processing, discussed in Chapter 10 (Element 3.2), relates to the running of a

processing activity without intervention, possibly overnight. We are concerned here with batch files, which are files containing one or more commands to the operating system. Like macros, batch files need only one command to provoke the execution of several. In DOS there are eight commands specially designed for use in batch programs, one of which allows the batch program to call another batch program.

You may have come across the AUTOEXEC.BAT file which is a batch file in DOS defining the characteristics of each device connected to your system. The file can also include any DOS commands you want to execute when you start up your system; for instance, to lay down the timing at which keystrokes repeat, or to change the default settings for port allocation.

Did you know

A home banking system launched by Abbey National has a voice response facility based on 1,000 words. When the system has interpreted the telephoned message from a customer it constructs an appropriate response. The application was built to be able to cope with a wide range of regional accents, and was tested with the voices of 5,000 callers spread from west Scotland to Cornwall.

Programs

Automated procedures for application programs can be constructed directly, as an alternative to using macros, by using high-level languages. In this case the procedure code is compiled and added to the compiled code of the program. The procedure code you have added in this way is treated by the compiler as a subroutine or module that can be entered many times.

Specification

In Chapter 19 (Element 5.3), we looked carefully at the contents of a system specification. The drafting of specifications for automated procedures is not different in principle:

- *Purpose* We looked at possible purposes at the start of this chapter.
- *Facility to be used* The choice of facility will be governed by the purpose. The considerations are explored above.

- *Type of automated procedure* In the same way, the type of procedure will be dictated by the purpose.
- *Types of data* The type of data that initially has to be handled by the procedure will be plain from the purpose. Flexibility to be able to cope with other types might be desirable.
- *Structures* The majority of automated procedures hardly need a structure, but if it involves more than a few keystrokes or events an explicit design structure is essential to allow straightforward modification and maintenance.
- *Program constructs* The same considerations apply. If the procedure is big enough or complicated enough to warrant formal design then the accepted constructs of sequence, repetition and selection covered in Chapter 21 (Element 6.2), should be incorporated.
- *Expressions and operators* These were explored thoroughly in Chapters 7, 11 and 21 (Elements 2.3, 3.3, and 6.2). Their use in automated procedures, if the design warrants it, is not inhibited.

Create automated procedures

Following our discussion in Chapter 19 (Element 5.3) and above in this chapter, you should be able to write a simple specification and create an automated procedure to satisfy it.

You may want to draw on the experience of your tutor to work on an existing specification that has been shown to have a suitable level of complexity.

Evaluate automated procedures

We are involved in evaluation only if we are considering substantial automated procedures. If such is the case we are facing a conventional system development project which calls for the scrutiny discussed in Chapter 17 (Element 5.1). Let us look at the main headings again.

Costs

There will always be a direct cost of assigning people and other resources to any project, and there will probably be opportunity costs and other indirect costs as well. Naturally, if a procedure has not been fully tested the possibility of faulty operation constitutes a risk which could be expressed in financial terms.

Benefits

Potential benefits were discussed at the start of this chapter. As part of the evaluation process the benefits actually realised should be measured and compared with those that were expected.

Fitness for purpose

To gauge the extent to which the procedure is fit for its purpose it is desirable to obtain the views of users. How easy do they find it to use? Does it do everything that the specification requires? How much training is needed to prepare new users to run the procedure?

Possible improvements

The potential for improvements is again largely in the hands of users. If the procedure is extensive there are likely to be opportunities for making it faster, or more convenient, or more cost-effective.

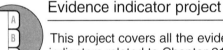 Evidence indicator project

This project covers all the evidence indicators related to Chapter 21 (Element 6.2). It has been designed to be carried out at the end of the element.

Performance criteria: 1–4

Key skills:	Communication	3.2, 3.4
	Application of number	–
	IT	3.1, 3.2, 3.3, 3.4

Making use of guidance from your tutor, you need to do the following to accumulate and present the evidence for this element:

1 Write specifications for two automated procedures, each of which uses a different facility and which together cover the specification range.
2 Write two automated procedures to meet the requirements of specifications provided by your tutor.
3 Write notes on.
  - the full range of purposes of using automated procedures, with an example of each;
  - the full range of facilities available for creating automated procedures; and
  - the evaluation of two automated procedures.

Software: Unit test 6

1 What does an operating system do?
   a It's a programming language
   b It allows the user to interact with the computer
   c It provides the environment that the applications software works in
   d It works like Windows

2 Which of the following is an example of applications software?
   a BASIC
   b PASCAL
   c Word for Windows
   d Windows

3 Utilities software enables the user to perform tasks that can also be performed in
   a Windows
   b The operating system
   c Applications software
   d Programming software

4 User interface software is intended to
   a Make it easier for users to interact with the system
   b Replace DOS
   c Make programming easier
   d Replace applications software

5 What job do language processors do?
   a Write computer programming languages
   b Create reports in applications software such as databases
   c Help the user by expanding statements into code
   d Help the user by expanding pictures into code

6 A DBMS is used in
   a Spread sheet development
   b Handling large volumes of data in a database
   c Handling large volumes of data between a database and a spread sheet
   d Word processor links to spread sheets

7 An expert system is a
   a Program used by experts in particular fields
   b High volume database
   c Software application allowing users to benefit from knowledge of experts
   d Type of programming software

8 Which of the following is not a data type?
   a Character
   b Number
   c Real
   d List

9 What is different between machine code and source program code?
   a Machine code is easier to understand
   b Source code is in 0's and 1's
   c Machine code is in 0's and 1's
   d Machine code is faster to use

10 All of the following are examples of program translators *except*
   a A compiler
   b A comterpreter
   c An interpreter
   d An assembler

11 An example of a graphical user interface is
   a DOS
   b Applications software
   c Windows 3.1
   d A database in DOS

12 Which of the following is a method of processing?
   a Interpreting
   b Compiling
   c Assembling
   d Batch

13 A translator performs which of the following tasks?
   a Converts speech into text on a computer screen
   b Converts one kind of machine code into another
   c Converts program statements into machine code
   d Converts machine code into programs

14 A macro is a facility provided by an
   a Automated software instruction
   b Automated applications software routine
   c Automated word processor
   d Automated database

15 A computer executing code in a set order is said to be doing so in
  a Repetition
  b Sequence
  c Selection
  d String format

16 What does the symbol * signify in a formula?
  a Add
  b Multiply
  c Subtract
  d Divide

17 Which of the following is *not* a program construct?
  a Sequence
  b Selection
  c Automated routines
  d Repetition

18 Which of the following tools available to a programmer is a data structure?
  a Boolean
  b Variable
  c Array
  d Character

19 A record is a type of
  a File
  b Boolean expression
  c Data structure
  d Program construct

20 Which of the following is *not* a logical expression?
  a NOT
  b =
  c OR
  d AND

21 Which of the following is *not* a type of data?
  a Constant
  b Variable
  c Character
  d Table

22 Which of the following is *not* used in automated routines?
  a Sub routines
  b Input error reduction
  c Calculations
  d Macros

23 One benefit of using an automated procedure is
  a To improve operations such as printing
  b To teach people to use the system more effectively
  c To eliminate the need for some repetitive actions
  d To reduce the amount of hardware in the system

24 What is a macro?
  a A program to report errors
  b A software report
  c A way of automating keystrokes/events
  d A program written in a high level language

25 A batch file is
  a Part of DOS
  b An operating system program file
  c A temporary file created in Windows
  d An operating system file like a .EXE file

26 Which of the following is a specification?
  a The speed of processing
  b Facility to be used in translation
  c Repetitive routines
  d The ways in which a computer program is to operate

27 File management activities in Windows are examples of
  a Windows GUI
  b Copying files from one directory to another
  c Automated procedures
  d Macros

28 Which of the following is a logical operator?
  a WHEN
  b AND
  c >
  d =

29 Which of the following is a relational operator?
  a >=
  b NOT
  c OR
  d +

30 Which of the following is a real number?
  a A+B=C
  b 280769A
  c 280769.1
  d 2907691

The role of databases in the use of IT by organisations is becoming ever more prominent. As the cost of secondary storage falls and the capability of database management software increases there is a trend in organisations of every type to design applications which are built around their databases.

These databases have to contain data that is current, complete and accurate if they are to fulfil their objectives; and they must be easy to update and maintain. This unit, which follows naturally from the data-handling techniques discussed in Unit 3, and the systems analysis issues covered in Unit 5, extends your understanding of the specification, creation and use of a database system.

Chapter 23 (Element 7.1) lets you build a data model diagram to meet a given specification, and it returns to the concept of normalisation so that you can produce relational database structures to suit the model.

Chapter 24 (Element 7.2) gives you experience and practice in creating and modifying database input forms on your screen, making sure that you satisfy the needs of the specification.

Chapter 25 (Element 7.3) requires you to design database report layouts and to interrogate the database using different types of queries in order to produce the desired reports.

There are many textbooks which address the design and development of databases, and suppliers of database management software often provide examples of the use of the software. Tutors may be able to offer case studies of database use.

An external test forms part of this unit.

Chapter 23

Create relational database structures for a given specification

After studying this chapter you should be able to:

1 create a *data model* diagram to meet the specification;
2 refine the *data model* using *normalisation* procedures;
3 produce *relational database structures* to suit the data model.

Special note

There is only one evidence indicator project for this element. It is at the end of the element, on page 302.

Introduction

Chapters 23, 24 and 25 (Elements 7.1, 7.2 and 7.3) deal with relational databases. Let us first explore the term *relational,* and then introduce ourselves to some of the specialist words used in any discussion on databases.

A *database* is, strictly, information held on some computer storage medium that is using the facilities of a *database management system* (DBMS). The database itself is simply inert recorded data: the DBMS makes it useful.

The database can be viewed in different ways through different approaches adopted by users. The three recognised types of database systems by which users interact with their databases are called *hierarchical, network* and *relational* systems. Since about 1970 relational systems have come to be regarded as superior, and most DBMS software since that time has supported relational systems. A relational system is one in which

- the data in the database is seen by the user as tables, and nothing but tables; and
- the software tools, used for example to extract data from the database, generate new tables for old.

Supporters of hierarchical and network models claim that these two systems correspond more closely than relational approaches to the real world. The advantage of relational systems is that they are simpler to use. All the data seems to be immediately accessible to the user, and it can be changed, deleted and incremented in consistent, straightforward ways.

Before looking at the requirements for the first performance criterion, we should remind ourselves of the components of a database system. They are data, hardware, software and users:

- The *data* may exist for a single-user system, or it may have to be shared by a number of users.

A major objective of the DBMS on systems that might have users sharing the data is that each user can enjoy the illusion that he or she is the only user. In general, the data in a database will be an accumulation of several distinct data files.

- The *hardware* must comprise a storage capacity that is big enough to hold the database, and a processor powerful enough to give users acceptable performance.
- The *software* has two main components: the DBMS and the application programs that make use of it. There are supporting items of software, as a rule, including language processors, utilities and program generators.
- The *users* also fall into two categories. There are the programmers who create the application code which interfaces with the DBMS; and there are the end-users who use the applications to attain their goals. Figure 23.1 illustrates these ways the parties relate to one another.

Did you know?

Desktop PCs have had an advantage in data storage capacity over laptop and notebook computers. But now Toshiba have announced a CD-ROM drive for their notebook machine that runs at ten times the speed of a domestic CD.

When thinking about the data in a database you should distinguish it from input data and output data. The database contents are sometimes called permanent data, even though they may not be truly permanent, in contrast to transient, or ephemeral, data associated with input and output operation.

Data independence is an important characteristic of DBMSs, and an objective of all DBMS design. Data independence is defined formally as immunity of applications to change in either data storage structure or access technique. This means that once an application is running successfully it need never be changed just because new users are added or because of changes made within the DBMS affecting the physical storage arrangements.

Did you know?

Every time you use a supermarket loyalty card, or settle your supermarket bill with a plastic card, the store is potentially able to note your name, your card number, the date and time of your visit, how much you spent and what you spent it on.

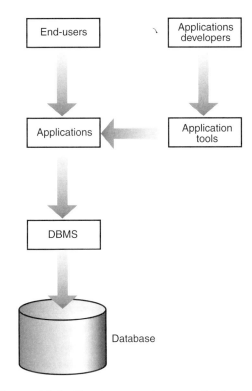

Figure 23.1 Database system architecture

Imagine the vast amount of detail that the head office could accumulate about the buying behaviour of their customers – possibly many millions of them – by location, by time of day, by day of the week, by date of the month, and by product lines chosen. The business needs just to obtain the age of each customer to be able to build an uncomfortably complete profile of every one. All this information could be used to guide market research and merchandising policy.

For reasons such as these, companies are for ever wanting to hold more and more data, and to have DBMS software that makes access to selected portions of it convenient and fast.

Creating a data model diagram

Entity relationship diagram

A data model is an abstract model of some real-world situation about which information is to be held in a database. Let us look first at terms that are used in discussing entity relationship diagrams (E-RDs). These terms are *entities, attributes, relationships, tuples* and *keys*.

297

There is nothing mysterious or magical about databases. They are part of the solution to an application problem. Some databases are huge, such as those needed by the Department of Social Security, Department for Education and Employment and, of course, some are small; but the same principles apply to all.

A relational data model is a model that views the information in a database as a collection of distinctly named tables. Each table represents a relation, and is made up of rows of records, or *tuples,* that have the same field structure as each other. Each column of corresponding fields is named and defines a particular *attribute* of the tuples within the table.

Each tuple is an entity *instance,* or occurrence. No two tuples, or rows, may be identical, but the tuples may be arranged in any order in a table. The attribute columns may also be arranged in any order. Every attribute column in a table has a heading.

All the items of data in a table have to be atomic. In other words, each item has to consist of a single item of data – not a group of data items. It could, for example, consist of a surname and first name as one item, but not a name and an address.

One further feature of relational database tables is that of *keys*. One field, or attribute, in each table must be unique for each tuple. Some DBMSs require it to be the first, or left-most, field; but most do not. As an example, consider the parts list used by a manufacturing business (Figure 23.2).

Part no.	Description	Supplier	Weight (gm)	Colour
771	Shield	ABC	1,200	Black
772	Washer	BCD	75	Grey
773	Clip	CDE	75	Grey

Figure 23.2 Keys

The part number is allocated to each type of part, and is not duplicated. The part number is thus suitable to be a key. The description is *dependent* on the key. This key is sometimes known as the *primary key* because, as we shall see later in this chapter, there are other kinds of key. On large tables the tuples are likely to be numbered so that an index can be created. These record numbers could be the primary keys provided that there is no duplication of numbers, as could the part numbers, though the convention is usually to put the key field on the left (Figure 23.3).

Record no.	Part no.
1	771
2	772
3	773

Figure 23.3 Record numbers

Most DBMSs can make use of indices to speed up processing.

A data model diagram has no set form. In every case it should consist of whatever ingredients provide the most lucid and complete illustration of the real-world situation concerned. The diagram will probably include an entity relationship diagram (E-RD), and a data dictionary.

Before a data model can be created, it is necessary to ask the people who will use the database what real-world details it will have to handle. This information is collated and assimilated together by the database designer and is known as a *requirement analysis*. From this a database specification, described below, can be built up.

As a result of this analysis, a data model (Figure 23.4) is created that shows the model in conceptualised form. This will be the foundation from which the database will be logically or rationally designed and then, later, physically built.

The specification is the full set of details needed by a database designer to design a database system to meet user requirements. It is likely to contain the relevant data model, the requirements analysis, resource requirements, and input, processing and output specifications.

Activity

Think about going on a package holiday. Think about it from the travel agent's point of view. In a group of two or three, list the entities which the travel agent will see as the most important ones in making your holiday booking, and produce a diagram showing the principal data flows between the entities. Is this a data-flow diagram for the booking system, or do you need more information?

We looked at E-RDs and data dictionaries in Chapter 19 (Element 5.3). To refresh your memory, an entity is any distinguishable object that is of significance to the situation reflected in the database. For example,

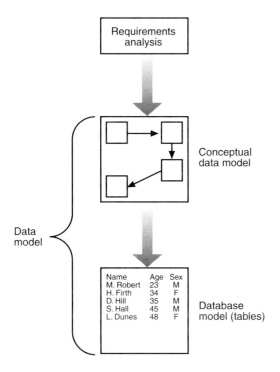

Figure 23.4 Data model

in a hospital application, entities might include patients, nurses, doctors and wards. *Relationships* link entities one to another, and disclose information about the interaction between them. Thus there will be a relationship between patients and wards saying that a given patient can be in exactly one ward at any instant, and that any one ward can contain nil, or one, or more than one patient. We showed in Chapter 19 (Element 5.3) how to illustrate this one-to-many relationship, and other relationships, graphically. In the example above, the E-RD would contain the relationships as shown in Figure 23.5, meaning each patient has to be in a ward, but each ward may or may not contain patients. The E-RD is thus part of a conceptual data model, as shown in Figure 23.4.

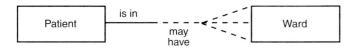

Figure 23.5 The relationships between patient and ward

Data dictionary

A data dictionary is a collection of all the definitions needed to allow fully complete database applications to be created. It will include field names, synonyms, data types, field lengths, possibly descriptions of the data and the name of each relevant table. It will include cross-reference information showing which applications use which items of data and which users need particular reports. The data dictionary fulfils the crucial role of maintaining the uniqueness of data names.

We have noted above that DBMSs protect users from the labour of dealing with the operation of the physical storage devices used to hold a database, and they allow a high degree of data independence. DBMSs provide comprehensive facilities for the organisation and management of a body of data required for groups of applications. They will give users a database language in which user views of the data, and the requirements for using it, can be specified. Other facilities of DBMSs include

- handling the data dictionary;
- safeguarding security and the integrity of data;
- servicing DBMS input which is in database language; and
- attempting to recover from database malfunction and data inconsistency.

Normalisation procedures

Let us assume that we have now created a relational data model to meet a specification. The relations, or tables, now need to be scrutinised and changed to the extent necessary to ensure that the relational operations work properly, and to reduce to a minimum the inconsistencies that may lie within the tables.

This process of improving the quality of the data in the tables is called normalisation. We touched on normalisation in Chapter 19 (Element 5.3). We now look at the process a little more closely.

Normalisation is a process of ensuring that redundant elements are removed and that the database has complete consistency. Every data item has to be determined by the *primary key* item for its *tuple*. For example, on the assumption that the NI number, the key, is unique, the table in Figure 23.6 needs to be normalised because Name is dependent on NI number, but Address is not, as Assenheim

National Insurance no.	Name	Address
LW978180A	Assenheim, P	17 Railway Cutting Reading

Figure 23.6 Normalisation

could move house. The table therefore needs to be replaced by two tables which both have the necessary dependency (Figure 23.7).

The effect of carrying out normalisation on a table is often to replace it with two or more tables. Normalisation is thus a 'bottom-up' process of refinement, in contrast to the production of E-RDs which is a 'top-down' process starting at the highest level, working from the general to the particular.

National Insurance no.	Name
LW978180A	Assenheim, P

and

Name	Address
Assenheim, P	17 Railway Cutting Reading

Figure 23.7 Dependency

To summarise, the normalisation process is based on the concept of functional dependency, meaning that in a row, or table, every one of the data items is determined by the key data item.

The normalisation process is broken into levels that have to be applied successively to achieve full normalisation. The first level, known as first normal form, requires that the data items are atomic (as described above), contain no duplicates and within each tuple are determined by the key.

Activity

Suppose you have to hold on a database details of a group of your fellow students. Choose a purpose for this database, then consider what attributes would be needed. Lay out a table of the items of data as preparation for entry to your database. Now study the data and decide if it is already normalised or if you have to rearrange it to get it into first normal form.

We do not need to look further than first normal form (1NF); the formal definitions of second and third normal forms (2NF and 3NF) are stated for interest. The strong mathematical basis of relational databases and normalisation has led to the concept of fourth and fifth normal forms, though they are rarely used. The larger and more complicated a database is the more benefit will be obtained from carrying out higher levels of normalisation.

A relation is in second normal form if it has a single attribute that can serve as a key or, if having a compound key (see below), all other attributes are functionally dependent on the whole of the key and not just on part of it. A relation is in third normal form if it contains no functional dependencies among its attributes that are not themselves keys.

We have defined primary keys. Two other terms in use are *compound* keys and *foreign* keys. Compound keys make use of the data items in two or more attribute columns, or domains, to create a single unique key in circumstances where no unique key could be supplied from any one attribute domain. For instance, it could be held that postcode and name taken together would constitute a valid compound key.

A foreign key is an attribute of one entity that has a value that is the primary key value for another entity. In the example relation below, the members' names are foreign keys. The term *secondary* key, though used informally, appears to have no rigorous definition. Certainly none appears in any of the better known sources of database specialist terms, although an index that is built on any attribute other than the key attribute is sometimes called a *secondary index*.

Let us carry out a first normal form normalisation on a table representing a page from the membership records of a sailing club. In its unnormalised form it looks like Figure 23.8.

All data items can be seen to be atomic. Membership numbers are unique; the same number is not issued to more than one member. Name is therefore functionally dependent on Membership no. Name determines the attribute address, at least until a member moves house. However, address and the fields to the right of it are not directly related to the Membership no. though they are dependent on Name.

Membership no.	Name of member	Address	Date of birth	Year of joining
77	Halyard, P	19 Slipway	11 Jan 43	1976
78	Clew, J	6 Mariners Ave	10 Feb 44	1976
79	Tiller, R	3a Captain's Walk	9 Mar 29	1977
80	Keel, P	The Moorings	8 Apr 51	1977
81	Cockpit, D	22 Anchors Way	7 May 38	1977
82	Deck, F	2 Rope Alley	6 Jun 60	1977

Figure 23.8 Unnormalised table

To carry out normalisation we therefore need to decompose the table into two tables (Figure 23.9). The particulars of members table could, of course, be rearranged so that the tuples fell into alphabetical order of members' surnames. We can see that no further work is required to achieve normalisation to 1NF, because in using the member name as the key for each tuple we note that each attribute is dependent on the key and on no other attribute.

Register of members

Member no.	Name
77	Halyard, P
78	Clew, J
79	Tiller, R
80	Keel, P
81	Cockpit, D
82	Deck, F

Particulars of members

Name	Address	Date of birth	Year of joining
Halyard, P	19 Slipway	11 Jan 43	1976
Clew, J	6 Mariners Ave	10 Feb 44	1976
Tiller, R	3a Captain Walk	9 Mar 29	1976
Keel, P	The Moorings	8 Apr 51	1977
Cockpit, D	22 Anchors Way	7 May 38	1977
Deck, F	2 Rope Alley	6 Jun 60	1977

Figure 23.9 Normalisation

Did you know?

Following the publication of the Cullen Report into the Dunblane massacre the Government is to set up three new databases. One will contain a register of all firearms, which will have to be centrally registered. One will hold the national register of adults working with children in voluntary groups; parents are being advised to use the database to check that the organisers of such groups have been vetted and cleared. The third database is to consist of the records of all known or suspected paedophiles.

Producing relational database structures

You now have enough knowledge to be able to construct a database structure. If you have not already been given, or have not developed, a data model, you could create one from the scenario at the end of this section.

To help you with your reading in textbooks, may we introduce you to the word *schema*? Schema is short for *logical schema* which is the name given to the encoding of a data model in the relevant database language. It provides a specification of how the data relationships and rules will be mapped on to the physical storage scheme. The facilities offered by DBMSs to support the development and processing of schemas vary greatly between DBMSs. Details will be given for the DBMS you use in the DBMS manual.

Relational database structures are built in the way that is most helpful to the reader, from relationships, tables, indices and keys, all of which have been discussed above.

Sample specification

Construct a data model and create normalised relationships to first normal form for this situation, which is to be handled by a database system:

- A school library has 1,000 books.
- The books consist of one or more copies of 600 titles.
- All pupils in the school are allowed to borrow up to four books at a time.
- Books can be taken out of the library, on loan, only following signature of the librarian.
- Books must be returned within four weeks or they accumulate liability to fines at the rate of 2p per book per day overdue.

Evidence indicator project

This project has been designed to cover all the evidence indicators related to Chapter 23 (Element 7.1). It has been designed to be carried out at the end of the element.

Performance criteria: 1–3

Key skills:	Communication	3.2, 3.3, 3.4
	Application of number	–
	IT	3.1, 3.3

When you have been given a specification by your tutor, you are to

- construct the corresponding data model diagram;
- draw up an appropriate relational database structure; and
- write notes describing how you used normalisation procedures to refine the data model.

Create data input forms for a database

In Chapter 23 (Element 7.1) we looked at the design of relational databases. In Chapter 25 (Element 7.3) we shall be looking at ways of creating reports from the data held on a database. In this chapter we consider the design and use of data input forms. The forms are representations on the screen of a PC or terminal of a conventional form drawn on paper.

There are many database products that run on PCs, including Microsoft Access, Borland Paradox, dBASE IV and its derivatives, and Approach, as well as PC versions of DBMS software, originally implemented on larger machines, such as Oracle and Ingres. The principles of using these packages are similar, as, indeed, are the reports required from the DBMS. The examples used in this chapter to illustrate the design and use of input forms are based on Access.

We need to remember that although input forms are created by many software packages, the system designer can overrule the software and substitute a local form design or, alternatively, modify the design that was generated automatically.

The appearance and layout of an entry form, as seen by the user on a screen, are important. Some organisations enter large numbers of sets of data every day. The forms acting as the doorway for this data must be as ergonomically efficient as possible.

After studying this chapter you should be able to:

1 create *screen input forms* to enable data entry;
2 modify *form fields* to enable accurate input of data;
3 ensure that data entry fields comply with the *data dictionary*;
4 create and use *special fields* to meet specification.

Special note

There is only one evidence indicator project for this element. It is at the end of the element, on page 309.

Creating screen input forms

The objectives of the design of screen input forms are as follows. To

■ relate the layout of the form to the layout of the raw data with which the users will be most familiar;
■ choose colours and shapes that do not irritate the users, and preferably ones that are restful and avoid unnecessary text;
■ follow a form design that bears a family resemblance to other form designs used, or to be used, in the organisation or department; and
■ provide users with prompts and exit routes.

We saw in Chapter 23 (Element 7.1), that attributes can appear in more than one table. It follows that although data items will sometimes be wanted for loading into just one table, the general case is for them to be targeted at two or more tables. We distinguish between these two possibilities by referring to *single data* entry forms and *multiple data* entry forms.

Throughout this chapter we shall be basing our consideration of input forms on a library application. For completeness we start by establishing the library database. In Access we select New Database from the File option on the opening window. This action gives a new window, as illustrated in Figure 24.1. The software also lists all the other files or databases that exist when creating a new one. Here we insert a file name for the database being created. As with other

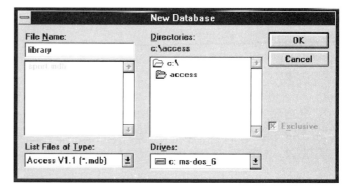

Figure 24.1 Establishing a new database

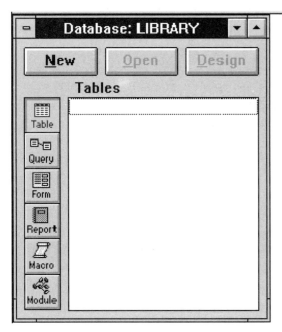

Figure 24.2 Structure of the empty database

file names (except in the case of software to be run under Windows 95) a maximum of eight characters only can be used. When OK is selected we progress to Figure 24.2.

In Figure 24.2 we see the Access opening screen again, but a new window now exists showing the database LIBRARY. At the moment there is no data stored in the database; this is recognisable from the fact that the area below Tables is empty. We need to take an important step here and create a set of tables in the database LIBRARY. This is done by selecting the option New.

By selecting New, a window is created (illustrated in Figure 24.3) which always allows space for Field Name, Data Type and Description. Under Field Name we have inserted *ID, ISBN* (which will act as the primary key for the database), *Title, Author/s, Publisher, Publication Date* and *Edition*.

This information is amplified in the next column – Data Type. It is here that we stipulate the type of data for each field that the Field Name is to hold. Note that several different data types are being utilised in our BOOKS table. The entries under 'Data Type' provide checks that data entered into the table 'Books' is of the correct form.

■ 'Counter' holds the sequence number of the next record to be entered, and is therefore numeric. It

is void in the table definition screen because no data has been entered.

■ 'Number' is also a numeric field because an ISBN consists only of decimal digits and blanks. 'Edition' will also be numeric.

■ 'Text' will accept letters and special characters. Numerals do not normally appear in book titles, authors' names, or publishers' names, although there may occasionally be exceptions in which case the Data Type entry could be left empty.

■ 'Date/Time' will have the format adopted as standard by the organisation. It is likely to contain alphanumeric characters, that is to say letters, numbers, and one or two kinds of special characters.

A final column allows us to add a Description to each Field Name. This gives us the opportunity to make brief notes as to the way in whch the database has been set up, some or all of which can be incorporated into the data dictionary.

Figure 24.4 shows the machine-created form for data entry to be used in loading the table BOOKS. You should note that this table will contain the data items of an entity. Other tables will hold items for relations. The process of loading a table is sometimes known colloquially as populating it.

Activity

In the first Activity in Chapter 23 you were thinking about a travel agent's booking system. Now, in the same group, list the items of information that the travel agent will have to feed into the system in order to book your holiday, noting the type of data for each item, and the maximum number of characters that would be needed to cover the entries for most holiday-makers. Then design a screen layout that would be as helpful as possible to the travel agent employee making the booking.

Modifying form fields

The fields on a data entry form are known as form fields. There are four main types of field:

■ Data entry fields.
■ Title field, normally just one.
■ Heading fields, for columns.
■ Instruction fields, addressing the DBMS.

Each field has a maximum length specified by the analyst who drew up the input specification. There

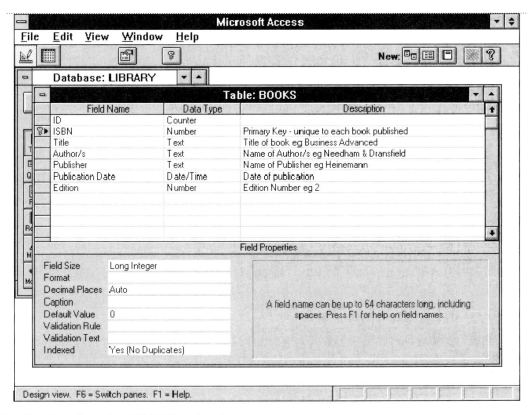

Figure 24.3 Creating the table BOOKS in the database

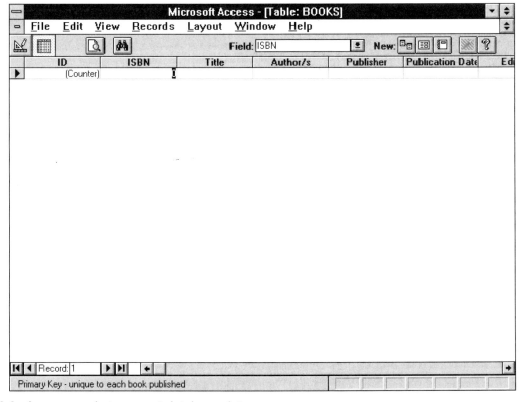

Figure 24.4 Access ready to accept database data

305

will also be validation checks that the analyst suggested and the user accepted. The field length, and the nature of the validation checks, are unlikely to be displayed explicitly because they would conflict with the objective of keeping the screen uncluttered.

Modifying form fields will probably be essential if the views of several users, and perhaps a manager or two, have to be taken into account. Changes can include the following:

- Increasing or decreasing the lengths of individual fields.
- Adding or deleting fields.
- Altering headings; adding or deleting headings.
- Rearranging the form layout.
- Picking different colours.

This process of modification is usually called *editing*. This editing can be carried out at any time.

Rather than have data entry fields in the format we have looked at so far (i.e. so each entry can be seen on the screen), it is possible to create alternative entry screens that allow only one record at a time to be viewed. We have illustrated such a screen in Figure 24.5. Microsoft Access does most of the work. The user *is* in the position to create such a screen manually, but is more likely to have the software do most of the work and then make alterations to it.

The screen layout can be altered using a mouse and *click-and-drag* techniques. The toolbar in the right side of the screen dump. The toolbar offers the user extra facilities when it comes to creating the best screen for the job. Two options from this toolbar have been used – the click-spots. By selecting and clicking with a mouse they allow the user to build in fast (generally yes or no) responses to the screen. Let us now revert to the loading of the table BOOKS in our

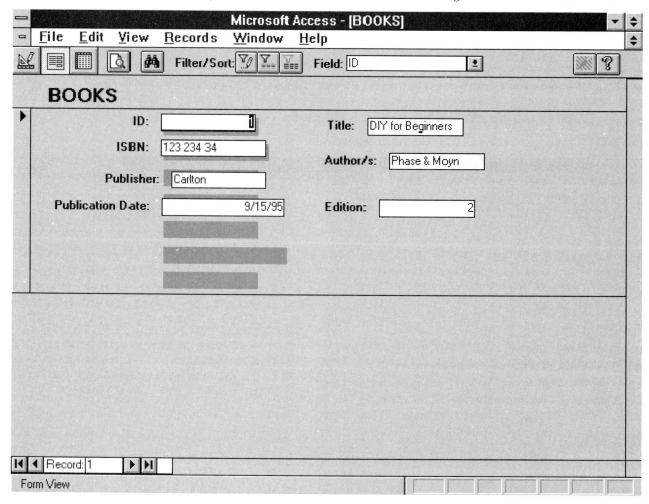

Figure 24.5 Alternative entry screen for data input

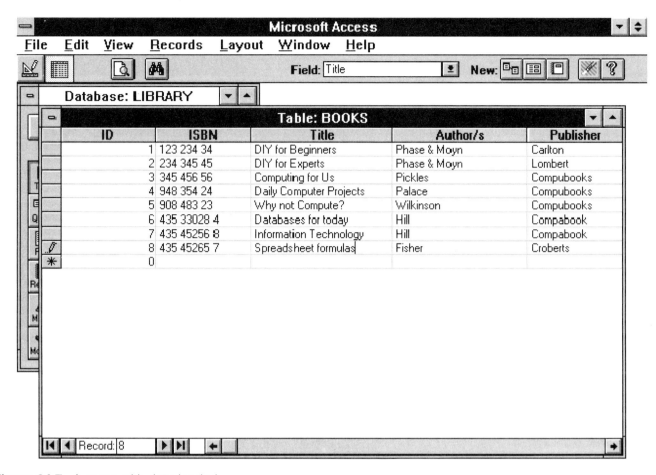

Figure 24.7 A ccess with data loaded

LIBRARY database. As we are still in Table Creation mode, we need to close the window. The software prompts and requests a file name for the table. Furthermore, if a primary key has not been assigned it prompts a response. If necessary the software assigns a primary key itself – this is likely to be the ID number in this case.

Figure 24.7 illustrates Microsoft Access the Table: BOOKS with data loaded.

In Figure 24.8 we can see that the database table has had data entered. However, the listed items of data entered is incorrect and does not comply with the database set-up requirements. Microsoft Access therefore shows a small window informing the user of the problem.

Did you know?

Until a few years ago, databases could be only used by computer programmers. This was because interaction with a database could be conducted only through the DBMS language. Although such databases are still available, they tend to be used for professional purposes as software companies have created easy-to-use databases such as Microsoft Access. This has brought the use of databases within the capacity of the average PC owner.

Did you know?

The Department of Social Security (DSS) is introducing legislation to allow it to have the right to access databases at the Inland Revenue and at Customs and Excise. One of the main

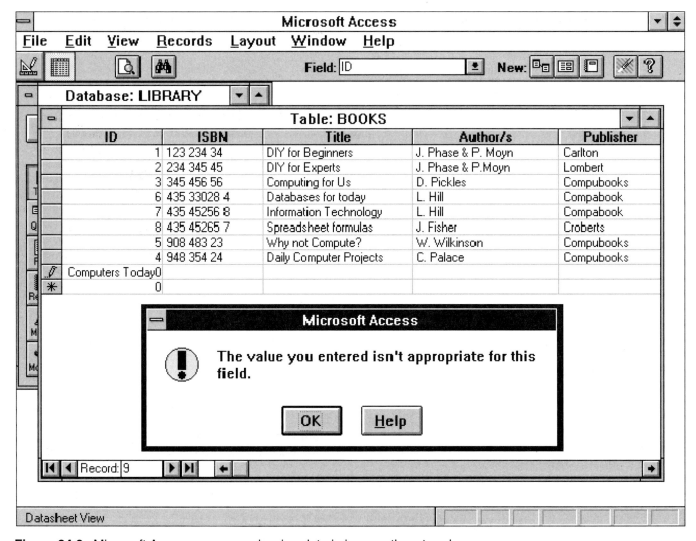

Figure 24.8 Microsoft Access message showing data is incorrectly entered

aims of the Data Protection Act, 1984, was to prohibit the aggregation of data about individuals across databases held for different purposes; but the DSS drive against fraud is so important that an exception is about to be made in this case.

Ensuring the data entry fields comply with the data dictionary

We have discussed the purpose and contents of a data dictionary in Chapter 19 (Element 5.3), and in Chapter 23 (Element 7.1). As a reminder, the items in a data dictionary are likely to include:

- field names;
- synonyms;
- data types (such as numeric, character, date and logical features);
- formats (currency, standard format for date and time, etc.);
- a description of the fields;
- field length; and
- table name.

Data dictionaries have evolved since the 1960s from being no more than an aid to program maintenance. Now, for large-scale and complex systems, the data dictionary is a vital tool for the central control of the syntax and semantics of the systems. One definition of a data dictionary is 'an automated repository of all definitive information about an organisation's data resources' (*Data Dictionary: Implementation, Use and Maintenance,* Rom Narayan, Prentice-Hall, 1988). The data dictionary should be the ultimate authority for the details it holds. Analysts and designers have to take care that their work is always in line with the contents of the data dictionary. DBMSs contribute in different ways to the automatic generation of data dictionaries.

Did you know?

Data warehousing is the name given to the concentration of databases within an organisation, no matter where or how they are held, into a single facility. The aim is to allow searches to be made across a wider body of data than was previously possible. Building and operating data warehouses has been a growing trend which is set to continue.

A benefit of introducing data warehousing is that consistency across the data from a variety of sources can be introduced. One example of this is in the National Health Service where managers have had difficulty in the past in establishing unique reference numbers for patients.

Special fields

A field is designated a special field if its purpose is to contain data that is required to be in a particular format, and to serve a specific purpose. Examples are as follows:

- Date field, where any date has to be entered in a standard way. Word processing packages offer their users a choice of data format such as 13 Feb 99, 13/2/99, 2/13/99 (which is the US version of the same date), 13–02–99. There are many other possibilities for the same purpose.
- Time field can be presented in a variety of ways including 2359 hrs, 11.59 p.m., and eleven fifty-nine p.m.
- Results fields of many kinds. These can hold totals of columns of numeric data, or page numbers that are continually incremented, or the results of calculations of any kind.

Special fields help to reduce errors of data input by drawing attention to the local rules for entering the kinds of data to which they relate.

Evidence indicator project

This project has been designed to cover all the evidence indicators related to Chapter 24 (Element 7.2). It has been designed to be carried out at the end of the element.

Performance criteria: 1–4

Key skills:	Communication	3.2, 3.4
	Application of number	–
	IT	3.1, 3.3

Brandon Photography is a small firm of photographers specialising in providing pictures to the advertising industry. Until recently, the company partners were happy indexing each photograph they took on a paper-based system. They now believe that this is inefficient as they hold up to 50,000 photographs at any one time – any one of which could be requested by an advertiser. As a database designer, you have been contracted by Brandon Photography to develop a computerised database system for them, to improve their efficiency.

1 Construct screen input forms that allow the user to make data entry as easy as possible. Produce *screen dumps* to show what you have done. Each form must illustrate the following – index number of photograph, short description or name of photograph, name of the photographer, date of photograph, and details of advertisements in which it has been used.
2 Show how changes can be made to the form fields in the original input forms. It should be possible to input data easily and accurately once the changes have been made. Use screen dumps here again to help.
3 Ensure the data entry fields conform to the data dictionary, for which you can make any reasonable assumption.
4 Construct and apply special fields to meet the specification.

Create database reports

In Chapter 24 (Element 7.2) we created database input forms. Now we will create reports so that the information put into the database can be used and manipulated to show us what we want to know.

We assume that the specification you produced in Chapter 19 (Element 5.3), or in Chapter 24 (Element 7.2), is still available to you. If it is not you will need to obtain a process specification based on an entity relationship diagram in first normal form, and the associated output specification. As before, we shall be using Microsoft Access as the basis for our examples.

After studying this chapter you should be able to:

1 design database *report layouts* which meet the *specification* and *data model*;
2 interrogate the database according to the *specification*;
3 use *queries* and produce reports according to the *specification*;
4 ensure reports meet the *specification*.

Special note

There is only one evidence indicator project for this element. It is at the end of the element, on page 321.

Introduction

Before looking at the creation of database reports in detail, we shall take note of the principles and usage of SQL. The initials SQL were originally the acronym for *Structured Query Language,* and often pronounced SEQUEL. The language name has now been formally changed to SQL, and the language definition has been given international recognition by standardisation bodies.

SQL is the language in which a user communicates with a relational database. Although mainly employed in specifying and obtaining output from databases, SQL has been developed to offer facilities for data definition, data manipulation and data administration, in addition to those required for data retrieval. Data retrieval operations are often called

queries and, as we shall see below, are expressed by the keyword SELECT. The word *interrogation,* also widely used, strictly means the act of making queries.

Two more terms are associated with SQL. A user often wants to see database output based on two or more tables. This output is called a *view* of the data obtained by executing a *join* operation. The join operation gives SQL and the relational model much of their power and flexibility. When you join two tables the system behaves as if you had actually combined them for the duration of the query.

Did you know?

A program called Microcosm Plus has been written to help users who do not have much knowledge of databases. They can easily extract the knowledge they need, according to Peter McManus, director of Microcosm, who is quoted as saying that anyone who could use a word processor could use Microcosm Plus. The program is said to run 'using pen-driven software' which allows engineers working on the shop-floor to retrieve technical details by simply pointing at the appropriate screen.

Designing database report layouts

We shall continue using the database model we built up in Chapter 24 (Element 7.2) whilst designing our report layouts. Remember that the data is in first normal form as a result of this, and we therefore don't have to perform any further normalisation procedure. We are still using Microsoft Access, although other database application software is available and can do the job equally well.

Before taking this element any further, it is important to understand what the term *report layout* means. This is the way in which a database report is set out both on the screen and on paper when printed (*generally*, the database report you see on the screen is a *print preview* of the report).

When you come to your own report layouts, you should keep the following points in mind.

Screen

The screen layout is important – if a screen is difficult to read, it takes longer to use and wastes the operator's time. Ensure you set everything out in the report in an easy-to-read way, as mentioned in the context of input screens in Chapter 24 (Element 7.2).

Printed

In the world of business, reports are printed on paper. They are rarely e-mailed or communicated orally. As they tend to be working documents it is important that they are easy to read and are well spaced out on the page. If a given report layout is to be used by certain people very frequently the declarative content (headings and explanatory notes) which quickly seem unnecessary should be kept to a minimum. The designer of the layout always has to strike a balance between complete clarity for the reader unfamiliar with it, and minimum redundant material for the reader who knows it well.

Pagination

If you were to look at a page full of text without any text breaks, it would be very difficult to read. Bearing this in mind, in planning the production of a report you must be sure to number each page, and perhaps supply enough detail on each sheet so that if one sheet becomes separated from others it can quickly and correctly be reinstated. The numbering of pages is called pagination; it will be carried out by the software, as it can be by word processing packages.

Headers and footers

These terms have the same meaning as they do in word processing. A document header is the zone at the top of a page, before the first line of text, and a document footer is the zone at the bottom of the page after the last line. Headers and footers can contain the pagination particulars and whatever else is needed, such as the name of the report's author and the date.

Data grouping

This will dictate how report details are to be presented. For example, a car dealer might want a list of vehicles for sale arranged by engine size, within body type, within year of manufacture, within make. Data grouping provides the facility we discussed in Chapter 20 (Element 6.1), under report program generators.

Totals and calculations

Databases can hold numerical data. Rather than having it in a database file just as items of data, it's possible to have it used in calculations as a mathematical entity, as in a spread sheet, by framing queries to provide exactly what is wanted.

Interrogating the database

Order

In what order does the user require the data to be presented – from the top of the file in the way it was input, in alphabetical order or in some other order that makes it as useful as possible?

Fields

We dealt with database fields in previous chapters. When it comes to database reports, though, what fields do you want to include? The person specifying the contents of a report has complete discretion over the fields to be displayed, whether they lie in one table or in more than one.

Field positions

It's possible to choose where to place fields in a database report. Using modern Windows database applications software, drag and drop facilities make this a simple task.

Spacing and layout

How much space is available for the database report? As we know from other applications, it's better to space work out to make it easier to read rather than to squash it up in a small space, subject, of course, to limiting the physical bulk of a long report! The output specification should also include details of the layout, as discussed above.

Interrogation and queries

These two words, used interchangeably, have much the same meaning. Interrogation is the quest for a response to a specific question posed to a DBMS, normally through SQL. A query is also intended to provide information that satisfies retrieval criteria from a database.

Did you know?

The commentators for the London Marathon have databases holding details of all the runners. When a runner goes past a camera, the commentator types into the database the number on his or her vest and the computer provides all the information we could wish to know!

In the 1996 marathon, all runners were given the option of wearing a special computerised tag on their shoe laces that linked into the race timing computer. At any point, the commentators or race officials could check to see how fast a runner wearing a tag was going.

Data model

We need not say anything further about the data model that underlies our specification except that you should always bear its existence in mind and, from time to time, check that it is accurate and at the right level of detail for the work you are doing on your database. In your work in Chapter 23 (Element 7.1), you will have developed a data model with a normalised entity relationship diagram, and you will have built up a data dictionary.

Interrogation

With these points in mind, we shall now consider interrogating our LIBRARY database to provide reports that meet the specification dealt with in Chapter 24 (Element 7.2).

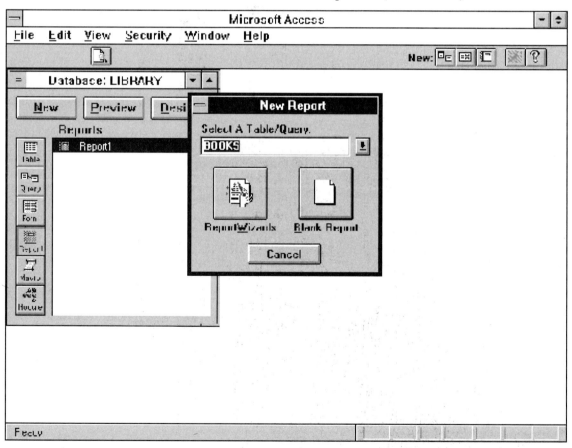

Figure 25.1 Selection of BOOKS table

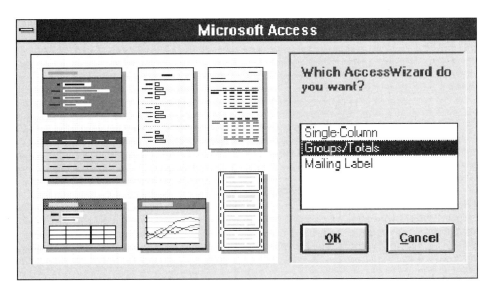

Figure 25.2 Choice of type of report

The report is being created using Microsoft Access ReportWizard. This is a utility built into the database application software that does much of the work for the user. However, it requires the user to know exactly what is to be included in the report. We shall consider one step at a time.

In Figure 25.1 we are presented with the Access standard LIBRARY options screen, from which New Report has been selected. A small window appears and requests the table or query on which the report is to be based. In this instance, we are using the BOOKS table created earlier.

In Figure 25.2 the user is invited to select the type of report the database is required to produce. An Access facility called Wizard which is an example of query by example (QBE) at this stage is to be used to specify the report – a simpler process than using SQL itself.

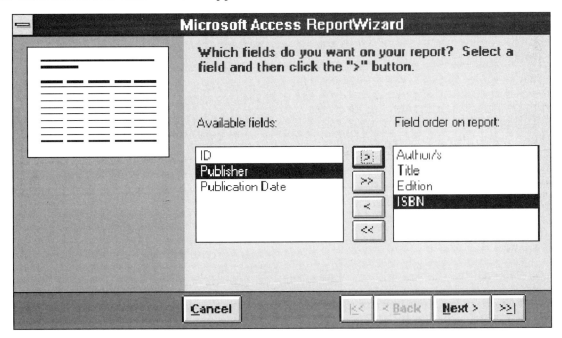

Figure 25.3 Selection of fields for report

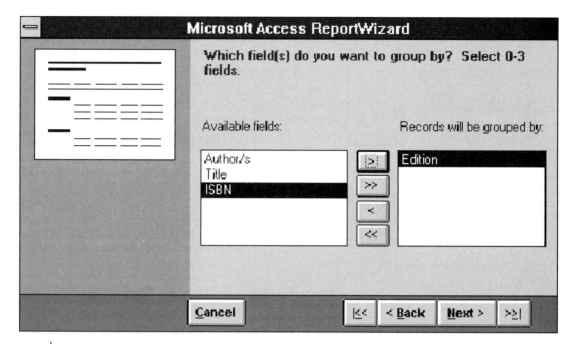

Figure 25.4 Selection of Edition for grouping

If you look back at the BOOKS table in Chapter 24 (Element 7.2), you will see that it contains seven fields of data. The window in Figure 25.3 presents us with each of these fields and requests the user to select from the fields present, which are to be included in the report. In this example, only four are needed – Author/s, Title, Edition and ISBN. They are selected by the user in the order they are required in the final report. The remaining fields are left in the left-hand box and will not be used in the report.

Now that the fields required in the report have been selected, we are in a position to stipulate which of them we wish to be grouped in the final report. This is similar to a sorting process. In this instance, the grouping is required only according to the book Edition, as illustrated in Figure 25.4. The remaining fields will not be used in the grouping operation, and remain in the left-hand box.

We are now dealing only with the book Edition field, and must stipulate how the data in this field is to be grouped. Figure 25.5 shows that normal has been selected – this ensures that all the same book editions will be printed in the report together, for example all second editions, followed by all third editions, and so on. The numbers in the right-hand window could be used for a field where there was a large range of numbers which could be conveniently grouped in value bands 1–10, 11–20, 21–30 ... and likewise for wider bands.

Did you know?

Operators of large databases have been constrained by the speed of the 32-bit technology that until now has been the fastest available to them. Recently five major manufacturers have agreed to collaborate in marketing brand-new 64-bit DBMS software, called VLM64. The use of the wider data path is claimed to bring about sensational increases in the speed of searching databases. One US user says that under test VLM64 performed 200 times faster than any previous 32-bit platform.

We must state which of the remaining three fields we wish to sort the database by, in order to produce the report. In Figure 25.6 it has been decided that the report should be sorted according to the Author/s. The remaining fields (title and ISBN) will not be used in the sorting process and remain in the left-hand box.

User input for the report is now complete – in terms of the database operations, the software has all the information it requires to produce its report. The user is finally asked to state what type of presentation format is required for the report. This is shown in Figure 25.7.

At this point the report is complete. It can be given a title, and the user has the option of either previewing it on the screen, modifying it or printing it (see Figure 25.8).

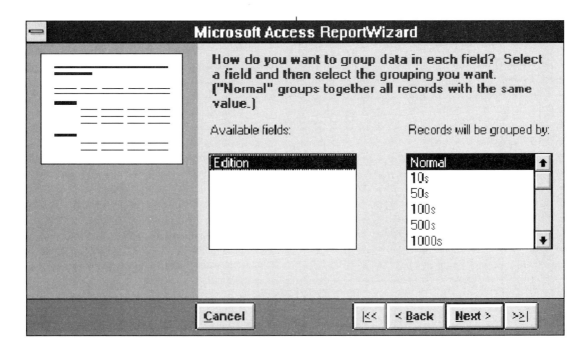

Figure 25.5 Lay down type of grouping

Finally, Figure 25.9 on page 317 shows the report in print preview mode. It illustrates primarily each of the editions, and then the relevant details such as the Author/s, Title and ISBN that follow.

Although this is only a small database, the report has effectively ordered the required details. Should the database contain 10,000 records, it would do exactly the same task.

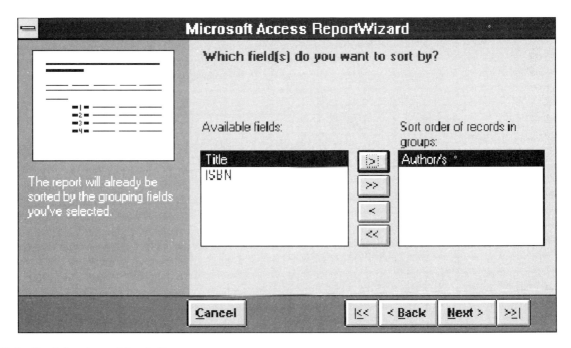

Figure 25.6 Decision to sort by Authors

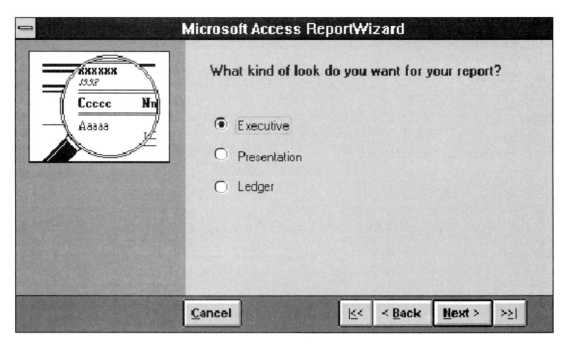

Figure 25.7 Choosing report format

Using queries

We have considered database reports so far, but have not yet considered a database *query*. Queries can be applied to single or multiple tables. We look at the ways open to a user to frame a query to obtain information from a database.

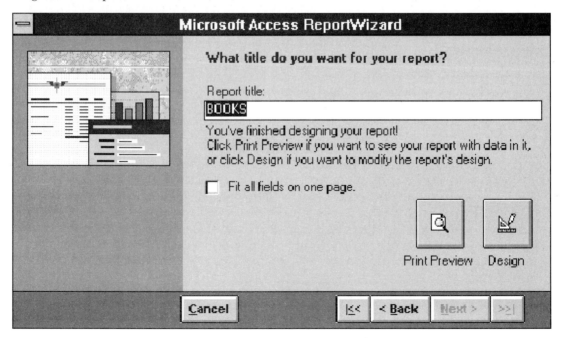

Figure 25.8 Option to preview the report

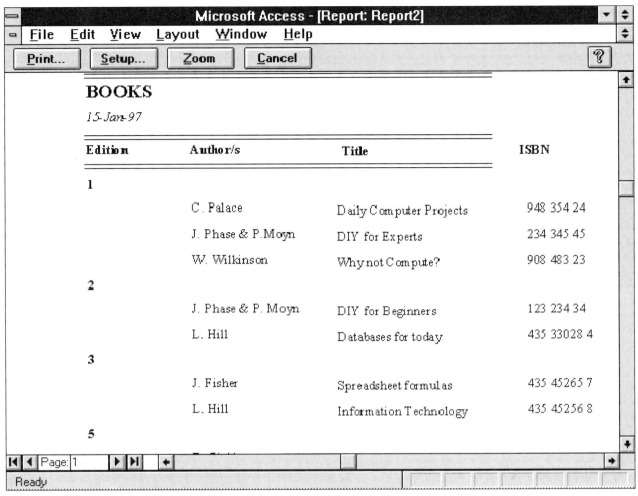

Figure 25.9 Report in print preview mode

SQL

At the beginning of this chapter we introduced SQL. To use SQL for any task beyond the trivial, training is needed. The task is even more forbidding than already implied because although there are standards for SQL, standards necessarily lag far behind practice which is itself constantly evolving. There are therefore as many dialects of SQL as there are vendors offering it. The example of an SQL query given in Figure 25.10 is purely for illustration, to give you an idea of the language. You will see the pivotal position of the word SELECT, which initiates all query operations.

QBE

QBE stands for 'query by example'. It's an uncomplicated way of entering SQL queries. It can be used either through a menu command system (look at the top of most modern software for examples of a query command menu) or by keystroke (possibly invoking a macro) sequences that the PC converts into an SQL command. We shall be using QBE-type query with Microsoft Access in the examples that follow.

xBase commands

This is the easiest term to understand. It is used to refer to any of the widespread relational database applications software and command languages that exist.

317

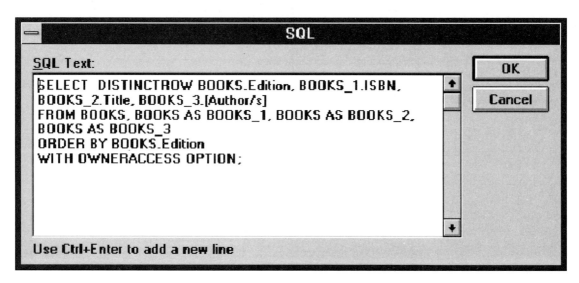

```
SQL

SQL Text:                                          [  OK  ]

SELECT  DISTINCTROW BOOKS.Edition, BOOKS_1.ISBN,   [ Cancel ]
BOOKS_2.Title, BOOKS_3.[Author/s]
FROM BOOKS, BOOKS AS BOOKS_1, BOOKS AS BOOKS_2,
BOOKS AS BOOKS_3
ORDER BY BOOKS.Edition
WITH OWNERACCESS OPTION;


Use Ctrl+Enter to add a new line
```

Figure 25.10 Example of an SQL search definition

Producing reports

We are now in a position to use the specification and database we have been dealing with so far and put queries to it. We will illustrate the operations in each of the stages Microsoft Access goes through.

Having instructed Microsoft Access that we wish to create a new query, we must add a table in order to start the operation. This is illustrated in Figure 25.11, where Microsoft Access prompts the user to select a table or tables on which the query is to be run.

Microsoft Access presents us with the fields present in the BOOKS table. To produce a query it is essential that the relevant fields are selected and placed in the correct format. Figure 25.12 illustrates how the BOOKS fields are illustrated by Microsoft Access, and where the selections will be placed.

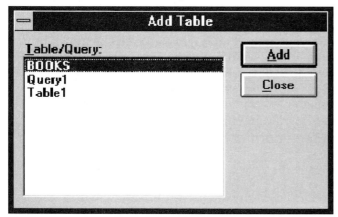

```
Add Table

Table/Query:                    [  Add  ]
BOOKS
Query1                          [ Close ]
Table1
```

Figure 25.11 Add Table

Rather than simply using one field from the BOOKS table, it is possible and highly likely that a number of fields will be selected and used in conjunction with one another in formulating the query. Figure 25.13 illustrates more than one table as the same table may be selected several times to run a query, and details some of the means by which the data can be sorted – in this case it is requested the EDITION be sorted in *ascending* order.

It should be noted that in this instance the query is being viewed in Query Design viewing mode – the Microsoft Access version of QBE (illustrated in Figure 25.14). As with so many other types of database applications software, Microsoft Access is capable of dealing with database queries in SQL. As users we tend not to use SQL as it is more difficult to work with than QBE.

By using a keystroke sequence QBE can be automatically converted into an SQL command – in this case it is an option available under the View menu. The Query requirements or specification has now been entered into Microsoft Access, and we are ready to proceed. The software must be instructed to *Run* the Query in order for us to see any results (Figure 25.15).

Activity

Activities in Chapters 23 and 24 invited you to consider the booking functions of a travel agent. Working in the same small group, imagine that you are the manager of the travel agent. You are interested in the volume and value of the package holiday bookings your branch is transacting, month by month. Compile a list of the totals you would like to see presented in a report at the end of each

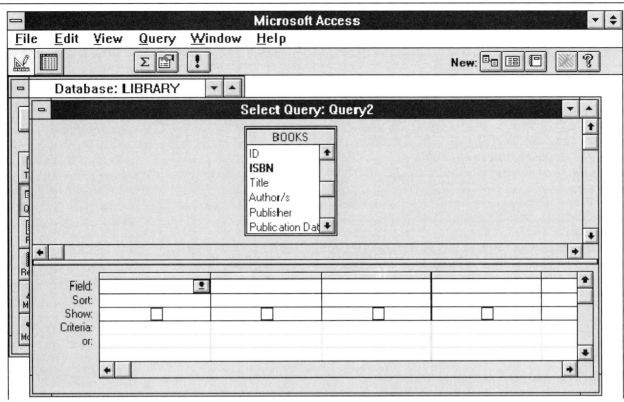

Figure 25.12 BOOKS fields

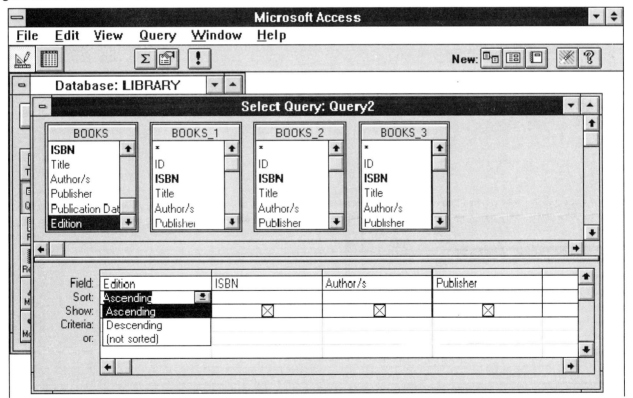

Figure 25.13 Sorting in ascerting order

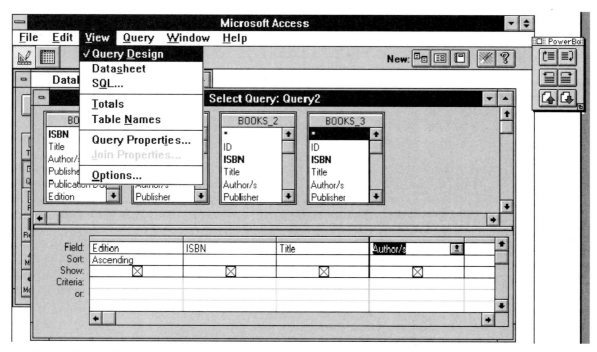

Figure 25.14 Query Design viewing mode

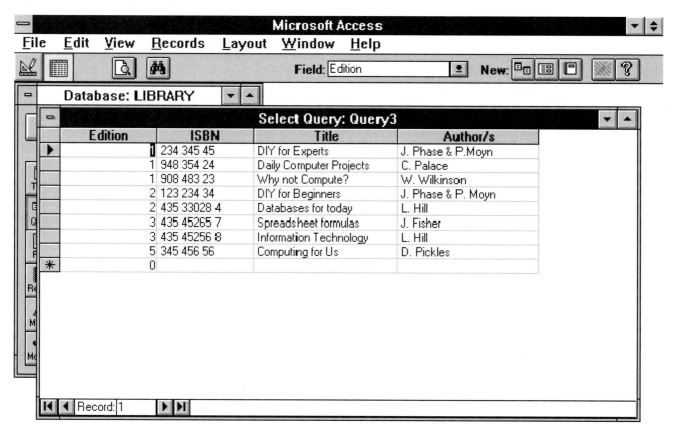

Figure 25.13 The output on screen from the Query

month. Make sure you include the facts that, as manager, you most want to see in your monthly report; but keep the content as simple, and therefore as easy to read, as possible. Design the report layout.

Ensuring reports meet the specification

There are several ways in which you could have inadvertently introduced errors into your work while specifying and producing your database reports. It is vital that you check very carefully that every aspect of every report is exactly as you intended. Wherever you spot a difference between what you wanted and what actually appeared you must go back, find the cause of the discrepancy and correct your data or your procedures as necessary.

Evidence indicator project

This project covers all the evidence indicators related to Chapter 25 (Element 7.3). It has been designed to be carried out at the end of the element.

Performance criteria: 1–4

Key skills:

	Communication	3.2, 3.4
	Application of number	3.3
	IT	3.2, 3.3, 3.4

Your tutor will have issued you with a database that you have worked with throughout Chapters 23 and 24 (Elements 7.1 and 7.2). Using the same database, you have to create reports according to an output specification. If your tutor has not issued you with a specification, you must create one yourself. If, for example, your database contains personnel details relating to all the employees working for an organisation, a report specification you may develop yourself could involve detailing all employees over 25 years old with birthdays in December. Alternatively, you may stipulate the report should include the names, addresses and pay-scale grades of all personnel.

In order to satisfy the criteria, you must demonstrate you can

■ design a database report layout;
■ interrogate a database according to the specification;
■ use at least two types of query, showing the database can produce reports; and
■ show that the reports meet the requirements of the specification.

Database developments: Unit test 7

1 A data model diagram includes
   a Data to be input
   b The DBMS
   c Entities
   d Indexes

2 An entity is
   a An element in a relational database
   b Invoice
   c A object of the real world, relevant to an information system
   d Part of the normalisation technique

3 What is an attribute in a database?
   a A link to other software
   b The nature of the data
   c The data type
   d An item of data representing an individual property of the entity

4 A data dictionary is a
   a File containing database relationships
   b File containing references to all the data items in a database
   c File containing the thesaurus dictionary in a word processor
   d File containing words used in spell checking in a word processor

5 A data dictionary can include *all but which* of the following?
   a Element size
   b Data type
   c Entity descriptions
   d Entity relationship diagram

6 Normalisation is the process of
   a Converting an invalid data model into a valid one
   b Converting a valid data model into an invalid one
   c Swapping data in a data model
   d Deleting old data from a data model

7 A relational database is one where the data is
   a Organised randomly
   b Related to the output structure
   c Connected through user-created links
   d Held in a number of related tables

8 In a database, a key is an
   a Attribute of a relation
   b A software lock
   c A distinctive attribute of an entity
   d Ideal method of securing the data from non-system users

9 An identifying attribute is also known as
   a A primary key
   b A normalising key
   c A specification
   d A data dictionary

10 What is a screen input form?
   a A menu system for a database
   b Part of a database
   c A form allowing data to be input to a computer
   d The field where data is entered

11 What is a multiple table entry form?
   a A form allowing data to be entered once to form part of a number of tables
   b A form in Windows-based software
   c A database option for speedy data entry
   d A non-relational database field

12 What is a form field?
   a Part of a database specification
   b A field on a data entry form where data is entered
   c The area on a screen relating to the size of text input
   d A field for identifying the data type

13 Which of the following are part of the data dictionary?
   a Single data entry
   b Description of field
   c Multiple data entry
   d Screen input form

14 What is a special field?
   a A non-relational database field
   b A field that holds special data such as the time
   c Part of applications software allowing the input of graphical images
   d Part of a relational database holding special relationships between input data

15 Which of the following is included in a relational database structure?
  a Repeating data elements
  b Records and fields in an array
  c Entity relationship diagram
  d Data dictionary

16 Which of the following are special fields?
  a Form fields
  b Date fields
  c An output field
  d Data fields

17 A report layout may consist of *all but which one* of the following?
  a Screen prints
  b Print-outs
  c Input specification
  d Output specification

18 In a relational database a secondary key
  a Is the same as a primary key
  b Can only work in conjunction with a primary key
  c Modifies the data dictionary
  d Can also be used as a foreign key when joining tables to answer a query

19 Data types such as numeric, character and date are contained in a database
  a Screen input form
  b Data dictionary
  c DBMS
  d Special field

20 What is a query?
  a Part of a data structure
  b A database asking the user if the input is correct
  c A question posed to a database in SQL form
  d Part of a database form

21 What does SQL stand for?
  a Structured Query Language
  b Structured Question Language
  c Statutory Query Language
  d Statutory Question Language

22 What does QBE stand for?
  a Query by Endings
  b Query by Example
  c Query by Entity
  d Query by Enquiry

23 SQL allows trained users to enter
  a Text
  b Speech
  c English-type queries into a database
  d English-type instructions into a database

24 QBE is
  a An old-style database
  b A term that refers to any common relational database application software
  c An english-type queries in a database to obtain information
  d Simpler way of entering queries than SQL

25 In a data dictionary, currency and date/month/year information are described as
  a Data entry fields
  b Format
  c Special fields
  d Validation checks

26 Instruction fields are used to
  a Enter data for a QBE
  b Enter data for a SQL
  c Inform the user how to perform operations
  d Enter special fields

27 Additional information at the bottom of a database screen relating to data in a database is known as a
  a Closer
  b Footer
  c Pagination
  d Data grouping

28 Data can be made clearer by
  a Data grouping
  b SQL
  c QBE
  d Pagination

29 What is a pen that can provide input by pointing on a computer screen?
  a Laser pen
  b A light pen
  c Bar code reader pen
  d A touch screen pen

30 What do circuit breakers do?
  a Replace the fuse in a plug
  b Protect the user from electrocution and the computer from damage
  c Provide electricity to the computer
  d Stop the fuse from blowing

The harnessing of IT, whether in business organisations or for the public service, almost always relies on development projects to plan, design and implement new systems. Benefits for every section of the community arise from those systems. Project work in IT is therefore more than important: it is indispensable to competitive endeavour, and to raising the standard of life.

This unit gives you opportunities to explore the structure and operation of project teams:

- *Chapter 26 (Element 8.1) wants you to examine project planning and structure, and methods of planning and controlling projects.*
- *Chapter 27 (Element 8.2) involves you in the*

planning process by helping to formulate project objectives, and the roles and responsibilities of the project team; and to think about ways of improving your own performance as a member of the team.

- *Chapter 28 (Element 8.3) asks you to look at ways of recording comments on the operation of a project team, and to consider how improvements to the performance of the team might be introduced.*

If you are in a team that is tackling a realistic project, albeit a fairly small one, you will derive most benefit. Your tutor might decide that a project based on work you have completed earlier in the course would be useful.

Unit 8 does not include an external unit test.

Explore information technology team projects

Companies install and run computer systems so as to derive benefits for their businesses. Those benefits may be substantial, and of real importance to them. We saw examples earlier – banks, airlines and manufacturing firms – where the businesses could not compete with their rivals or, indeed, function at all, without extensive use of IT.

You must remember, though, that it is only applications systems that are running properly and are in full use that can confer those benefits. Systems being planned, under development, under test or withdrawn for any reason represent only costs.

In considering IT projects it is helpful to distinguish between three separate parties. They are *the Investor, the Customer,* and *the Implementer.* The Investor, representing the owners of the business, makes the financial decision to invest the firm's money in the launch of a particular project. The Customer is the department or individual that will use the new system which will arise from the project when it has been installed, and who therefore sets the specification of exactly what is wanted. The Implementer is the team responsible for building, documenting and testing a new system.

Although we are primarily concerned in this chapter with the work and management of the project team, namely the Implementer, we do need to keep in mind the interests of the two other parties. To take a specific example, suppose a major international oil company wanted to have a new computer-based system to control the movements around the world

of the ships in its tanker fleet. The main board would allocate funds for the project which would create the necessary application system, the shipping director would issue the specification of the desired system, and the project team within the IT department would build the application system.

What, then, is a project? It is a group of tasks which, taken together, result in a permanent change of some kind; which fulfils some explicit aim; which consumes certain resources; and which has a definite end. A project can be considered as a contained endeavour, in contrast to any process such as the regular running of an application which is a continuing one.

After studying this chapter you should be able to:

1 describe the *purposes of planning* activities
2 describe *project organisation activities*
3 explain *project scheduling,* with examples
4 explain *methods of controlling projects,* with examples.

Special note

There is only one evidence indicator project for this element. It is at the end of the element on page 333.

Before embarking on the first of these, let us narrow the field we shall be thinking about. Let us assume that the project teams are within their own companies, rather than being in software or

consulting firms. And, further, let us assume that prospective projects have been assessed through some kind of preliminary studies, that the financial case has been established, that the specifications have been drawn up and that the *go* signal to start whatever project we are considering has been given.

The purposes of planning activities

Controlling resources

We first consider the main resources, apart from *time* which we look at separately opposite under 'Meeting deadlines', that have to be provided for an IT project. These resources – accommodation, equipment, finance, material, people and software – although different from each other in obvious ways are linked by their importance to a project.

In one way or another each represents part of the total cost of a project, and taken together they account for most or all the cost. The size of that cost has to be assessed before a project is given the go-ahead. The individual costs are then reflected in the project budget.

The economic viability of a project depends on meeting the budget, and therefore the consumption of *all* the resources must be observed and controlled. The emphasis is placed on 'all' because failure in the planned deployment of any of the resources is likely to lead to an increase in the costs associated with others. For example, if the software turns out to be inappropriate or defective the equipment may stand idle, and the accommodation and the people will be needed for longer than planned.

Accommodation

Project teams cannot produce good work unless their accommodation is suitable. There must be enough space for individuals to do the work they have been given, and to store their reference material and other papers. They should be able to consult their immediate superior without having to go to another site. The temperature, lighting and levels of noise must be acceptable. There must be adequate administrative backup so that professional staff do not have to waste time on unskilled tasks like queuing for the photo-copier or fax machine, or having to walk miles to get a cup of coffee.

In some instances there may be a case for team members to work from home. This will be successful only if suitable communication links are installed, and users trained to use them.

 Did you know?

F International, the large profitable consultancy company, built its operations wholly on professional staff working at home. The company invested enough in training and supervision to gain a high reputation for quality and punctuality.

Equipment

Project development will be helped by providing teams with PCs that are reasonably up to date, powerful enough and with enough memory, and in all probability networked so that issues of loading and maintaining software, and of security, can largely be entrusted to a network manager. Printers should be sufficiently plentiful to allow individuals to have access to them when needed. Tables or desks, chairs and computer screens must encourage rather than discourage long spells on the job.

Finance

The Investor must be ready to commit enough money to give the project a good chance of success, even if things go wrong. We shall be looking below at the steps that might be taken if a project starts to run late or to exceed its budget. Few IT projects run exactly as planned, for many reasons, and there may be disadvantages in the project team members living on their nerves from the first day, fearing that the Investor might abandon the project because the budget had been exceeded.

Material

This topic covers all items that need to be supplied to support the team fully, including manuals for hardware and software, racks for diskettes and training aids.

People

The team members for an IT development project should all have the appropriate level of training and experience. IT projects are difficult undertakings: they should not be hampered by being starved of the human resources they need.

The appointment of a suitable project manager is vital. That person must have the technical ability and reputation to command respect within the project team, and to be able to make informed decisions on technical issues; and must also have the interpersonal skills to deal authoritatively with the Customer, and to generate and maintain enthusiasm in the team.

Software

There are three kinds of software that a project team will probably need. They are the software modules that are to be integrated into the new applications suite; language processors to turn source code into machine code together with utilities; and what is sometimes known as a 'project workbench', that is a computer-based facility for keeping records of every aspect of progress on a project.

Specifically, a project workbench is a software product that is fed with details of task completion, changes in estimates of time required for unfinished tasks, details of new tasks introduced and others deleted, and any alterations in the relationships between activities or tasks. On demand the project workbench will display graphically and numerically the state of the project, draw attention to critical areas and report on the loading on individual team members.

In addition, on large projects a CASE tool may be used. CASE stands for computer-aided software engineering. The purpose of CASE tools is to help maintain consistency across many development activities. They build up and keep a dictionary of data items, and support the design and construction of databases. They contain drafting software for producing diagrams of database structure.

Value for money

Before the Investor assigns money for a project the financial risks of the project will have been weighed against the expected benefits. The project is undertaken because the Investor believes that on balance advantage is likely to flow from it.

The planning by the Implementer, the project team, must be aimed at providing the required system, built to specification, within time and within budget. If those three goals are met the project should have provided value for money.

We say 'should have', because there are reasons why projects which do meet those goals can still lead to

failure as far as the Customer and the Investor are concerned. They are:

- the wrong objectives for the system may have been set
- the system may have been incorrectly specified
- the requirement may have changed during the life of the project
- the system may exactly match the specification, but for some operational reason such as a change of business practice, it may not yield the hoped-for benefits.

The Implementer's planning is not primarily directed at these issues, but the project team can none the less look out for them.

Meeting deadlines

All projects except the smallest are likely to have milestones – points at which certain measurable progress will have been made. The success or otherwise in meeting these intermediate targets gives early warning of departure from plan.

Whether progress is at the planned rate or not, the milestones provide occasions at which the Customer can be told how the project is going. If the Customer discovers only on the planned completion date that there is to be a great delay, confidence will be shattered.

The planning should be based on achieving all deadlines. Failure to meet them has immediate and obvious financial consequences. It may also have corporate penalties that the Implementer does not know anything about. For example, a delay in introducing a new accounting system scheduled for the start of the financial year may mean that its introduction has to be held back for twelve months, with the consequent delay in obtaining the intended benefits.

Securing consensus

Consensus and harmony throughout all the people involved in any endeavour helps to achieve a good outcome and to avoid nasty surprises. In the context of an IT project much the most important field for securing consensus is in the relationship between the Customer and the Implementer.

These parties will have worked together in drawing up the project specification, in estimating the timescales and in forecasting costs. They will need to work closely over defining the acceptance criteria for the completed project, and in constructing test data. It is to be hoped that consensus prevails throughout these activities. It is also vital that the parties keep in close touch with each other during the development phases of the system so that the Implementer keeps the Customer's confidence at all times.

Did you know?

Almost every large organisation is at present grappling with the 'Year 2000' project. Hardly any administrative systems, apart from those designed since about 1995, have taken proper account of the effects of the change of the senior digit in the year date from '1' to '2' at the end of the decade.

This problem sounds trivial but, as many companies are now discovering, it is extensive. The use of dates, both current and future, pervade practically every business system. The problem of changing all these systems to work correctly with dates later than 31 December 1999 is proving to be massive. The work involved really does have to be done by the deadline. No government or industrial corporation, however powerful, can negotiate a postponement of the millennium.

Project organisation activities

Role definition

The IT industry is young compared with many industries. One effect of this youth is that job categories are ill-defined and fluid. Titles in common use are programmer, systems engineer, programmer-analyst, analyst-programmer, systems analyst and analyst-designer; and within these titles are grades, also not accepted as standard, such as trainee programmer, junior programmer, programmer, senior programmer, consultant-programmer, and chief programmer. Further, in the Civil Service and some public bodies the IT job titles are related to the seniority scales used across the organisation.

Labels can thus be a distraction rather than a help in thinking generally about the needs of a project team. What is certain is that a number of tasks always have to be undertaken. Those tasks are management, customer liaison, design, analysis, programming, documentation, testing and administration.

The organisation within which a project team is operating will have its own standard titles for the appointments that need to be filled for any IT project, and may have job descriptions that are published for all to see: in this way uncertainty is avoided.

Role assignment

The Project Manager has a duty to ensure that everyone in the team is appropriately experienced and trained so that, collectively, they can fulfil all the jobs that have to be done. This is a changing scene, because the balance of requirements alters as the project advances. The need for design skills diminishes, and the need for programming followed by documentation and testing expands, though the need for management and customer liaison stays essential throughout.

In assigning individuals to tasks the manager, in addition to considering technical competence, will want to take account of personal preferences, ability to work with others in a group and what is commonly known as 'intellectual honesty'. This last term may sound insulting, but it is none the less often used to refer to the natural and widespread inclination of IT development people to indulge in a degree of wishful thinking. Intellectual honesty is crucially important in project work where, for example, to say that some test was successful, or that some job had been completed, when such was not the case, is sure to have undesirable consequences by hiding from management the true position.

Team building

Building the perfect project team is not easy. The people wanted for a team, even when they have been identified, may not be available. Yet the success of the team's work depends on how effectively all members co-operate.

Individuals do not change much. Someone who recently gave an enthusiastic and capable performance on some job is likely to do well next time. Anyone who works easily with others is similarly likely to remain a good person to have in a group. A person who works well under pressure is especially valuable, because the chances are that before a project is finished there will be moments, if not weeks, when great exertion is called for from members of the team.

An important part of the management role is to recognise the different strengths that individuals can bring to the team. Some like to display initiative, others flourish in a closely defined environment;

some like to stick to their own speciality, others to take a broader view; some are painstaking finishers, others want to get on with the next job.

In a large project there will be opportunities for staff other than the manager to exercise managerial functions, so a core of people to whom this would be congenial would be useful in making up the numbers.

But regardless of anything else, maintaining high morale in the team is the pearl of greatest price.

Planning

We have looked at the purposes of planning a project's activities. There must clearly be a plan before work starts: but planning is a continuing process. Performance against plan has to be reviewed regularly and fairly frequently; and revisions made to the plan. Revisions have to be plausible. Little is as dispiriting as being set a task that is seen at once to be impossible.

Planning is part of the manager's job. It cannot be delegated. We look below at methods of scheduling project tasks once the plan or the revision has been made. The schedules ought to have a wide distribution, so that all involved in any way with the progress of the project are brought and kept up to date.

If revisions have to be made to a plan often, because progress falls further and further behind the original schedule, it is possible that the schedule was too ambitious for the team and the resources available to it. Whenever this occurs the details must be recorded and examined at the end of the project so that lessons can be learned to improve planning in the future.

Design

The process of design, whether system design or program design, should be governed by an established methodology: there should be no need to work it out each time. The methodology should be defined and contained in the organisation's standards manual or equivalent document. Members of the implementation team will follow the methodology and thereby be free to concentrate on solving the problems of their particular project rather than on trying to work out how to address those problems. If the design is clear and sensible they will be able to move forward in an orderly way.

The design objectives for most IT projects, beyond seeing that all the functional requirements are met, are to

- make the system robust;
- make it easy to maintain and enhance;
- make it no more demanding on resources than necessary;
- ensure that training to use it is no harder than necessary; and
- furnish users, maintenance staff and technicians with full documentation.

Task assignment

Task assignment follows on from role assignment. Part of the output from the design process is the segmentation of the project requirement into smaller tasks. These tasks will be given to individuals or groups for completion. Each task will have defined inputs and outputs, be allotted resources and given a target finishing date.

Other things being equal, people will be given tasks for which they are well fitted and with which they are happy. If tasks have from time to time to be given to staff who are not fully equipped to undertake them, allowance must be made in assessing their performance.

Tasks should be assigned in a way that engenders a spirit of competition between the individuals or groups to whom they have been given. This aim might lead to a deliberate strategy of trying to make all tasks represent approximately the same amount of work.

Evaluation

When a new system has been satisfactorily handed over to the Customer there should be formal evaluation of the project. There should be a further evaluation after, say, a year, by which time the users' reactions to their new system will be available, and the teething troubles might be over.

The main purpose of the first evaluation is for the organisation to learn lessons from the project history and thus improve the planning and execution of future projects.

Questions that the evaluation could seek to answer include the following:

- Was the decision to go ahead correct?
- Were the estimates of time and cost sound?
- Was the specification right?

- Were the right people deployed on the project, and did they work well together as a team?
- Were the project control procedures efficient?
- Did the acceptance process go smoothly?
- Was full documentation provided with the completed system?

The outcome of this evaluation, and of any subsequent ones, must be documented. Any action that is needed must be taken.

Project scheduling and examples

Task analysis

We have said that a task is a piece of work small enough to be completed by an individual or group in a fairly short time. Some writers define a task more closely by saying that it should consist of an amount of work that one person can finish in a week.

There is nothing wrong with a tight definition of this kind, but it is unnecessary. What matters is that everyone involved is clear about the specification of the task, and about its inputs and the required outputs. In programming tasks it will not otherwise be possible to devise thorough testing of modules arising from the tasks after they are linked together.

Tasks can be defined for any stage of the development process, but are likely to be most successful in systems analysis, which is itself structured in a way that encourages the breaking down of the work into tasks, and in programming where task definitions may map conveniently on to the program module structure. In system design and program design there is likely to be difficulty in identifying individual component tasks.

When the project is evaluated there would be merit in looking carefully at some of the tasks to see if they were sensibly structured. Was there, for example, overlap between tasks that was not needed? Or were they either too big or too small for greatest efficiency?

Work study

If new computer-based systems are to justify the cost and risk of providing and installing them they must show undoubted advantage over the systems they replace. In order to compare new with old there is a need to record some features of the old system before it vanishes.

Work study is the name generally given to the identification and recording of such features. They could include the (identification and movement of pieces of paper, the number and size of files, the frequency of access to those files, the number of people engaged in running the system, and the levels of errors.

Direct comparisons can be made between these features of the old and new systems, and a judgement formed on the net benefit of the new one.

You should note the limitations of work study comparisons. They do not take into account any of the wider issues which might justify the project, such as the intended merger of two companies or the decision to enter a new overseas market or the launch of a new family of products.

Time and cost estimating

Estimating the time that building a system will take, and the cost that doing so will incur, is difficult. To give a close estimate is almost impossible.

The chief reason is that the estimate relates to work that has not previously been done. If it had already been done there would be no need to do it again. So we are trying to forecast the outcome of a piece of research. It is usually not quite as hard as asking in the year 1930 when penicillin would be invented; but it has something of the same flavour.

The most useful guide to time and cost is to find out what happened when something similar was done previously, and make adjustments for the differences. Beyond that there are techniques such as gauging complexity on some scale, taking note of the number of files that have to be accessed, allowing for the size of the job and employing a factor based on the number of branch points there will be in programs.

Other matters bear on the time and cost of a project. For example:

- the commitment and morale of the team
- the novelty of the work
- the ability of the team members
- the quality of the management.

All in all, although having estimates is essential, making them is bound to be hard.

Mileposts

Mileposts, or milestones, mark points in a project plan where progress can be accurately measured.

There need to be enough milestones to provide everyone with a reasonably accurate perception of the progress of a project, but not so many that looking at progress occupies a high proportion of the time and energy that would otherwise be devoted to actually making progress.

Critical paths

Let us look here at critical path methods as a means of displaying a plan. We shall return to the subject below. The technique is best explained by an example.

Suppose you were embarking on a project to build and install a new business computer system. One of the activities you have to undertake is the conversion of existing files to their new computer-based counterparts. First you would list the activities that would be necessary for this file conversion, and then arrange them, with the expected duration of each, in chronological order. You number each activity, and provide a column to show any activities that must be completed before any others can begin. Your list is shown in Figure 26.1.

No.	Activity	Duration (days)	Must follow activity no.
1	Plan conversion	2	–
2	Inspect data	2	1
3	Recruit person	2	1
4	Train person	5	3
5	Select software	5	1
6	Select hardware	3	1
7	Obtain hardware	10	6
8	Install hardware and software	5	5, 7
9	Establish test	3	2, 4
10	Carry out data entry	4	4, 8
11	Test conversion	3	9, 10

Figure 26.1 File conversion activities

We now have the information for drawing a critical path diagram, although we do not at this stage know what is critical about it (see Figure 26.2). All Figure 26.2 does is to highlight the relationships between activities, and to record the duration of each. You should note that when there are two activities that need to be completed before another is started the duration is shown on both.

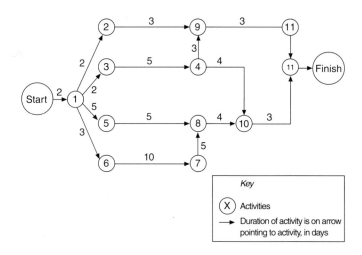

Figure 26.2 Critical path diagram – file conversion activities

Calendar of events

The diagram in Figure 26.2 says nothing about when the activities are to start and when they should finish. To display that information there has to be a calendar of what is due to occur when. For a large project many events can fall due on each day. Later we look at ways of combining the calendar with a planning and control chart.

Order of events

In Figure 26.2 we arranged the events into order without any difficulty because the job we had given ourselves was small. In a big project the inter-relationships between activities will be more numerous and will probably be harder to discern. Furthermore, as the project progresses there may be changes as a result of activities getting held up or, alternatively, racing ahead, meaning that the order would have to be monitored and adjusted.

Managing slippage

You will by now have taken in the message that projects often run late. If you were in charge of a project that was falling behind schedule, what would you do?

In practice you do not have many options. Here are the main ones:

- Try to get the specification reduced so you have less to do.
- Bring in extra people to help.
- Exhort your team to work harder, for longer hours, perhaps over weekends, possibly with extra money.

None of these is likely to solve your problems unless you detected the slippage at a very early stage. Getting the specification reduced really means that you have failed, which no one likes, and in any case is most unlikely to be agreed.

Any extra people you bring in will be new to the project and perhaps to the team members as well; and they may not be familiar with the standards you are following. Weeks will pass before they are fully productive on your project.

Exhortation to supreme effort can work for a short time if morale is high. If only some of the team are willing there is immediate disarray. In any case, there may be no money to pay for the overtime.

The project is safest if it never gets late!

Methods of controlling projects and examples

Co-ordination

Co-ordination is aligning the knowledge those concerned have of the project, and the canvassing of views. On big projects there are formal meetings at which progress is reviewed, usually by a 'steering committee' which would have amongst its members a representative of the Customer and possibly the Investor. The steering committee may call for action, following a meeting.

There are also likely to be team meetings at which local issues can be aired and technical decisions taken. The whole team should be invited, and should take part. Everyone must feel involved and recognise that each suggestion for furthering the cause of the project is welcome.

Team meetings form an important part of the co-ordination of the work of a project team. Meetings should be formal to the extent of distributing the agenda to all team members in advance of every meeting, even if much of the agenda is made up of items that regularly appear; and writing and distributing minutes and action points within a day or two of each meeting. Chairing of team meetings

by someone able to accomplish the necessary business speedily and yet attract all worthwhile contributions from team members is the goal.

Cost control

Some companies have extremely complicated schemes of measuring and controlling costs on each project. They put a price on every hour of every team member, on the use of rooms and computers, and on other details. That is one extreme, and one that is expensive to employ unless some standard approach has been introduced.

The other extreme is to make no effort to measure and control costs. That cannot be satisfactory. Any business has to find out what a project costs as it goes along so that if the cost gets out of hand the Investor can stop the project. Assuming the project runs its course all the parties are going to want to know how the finances worked out.

This means that records have to be kept of which individuals were working on the project, for which days and what their expenditure was on resources. The Project Manager always has to keep records of this kind.

Recording

In addition to records kept for financial purposes, the following types of recording are usual:

- steering committee minutes
- team meeting minutes
- progress reports
- proposals, memos, letters.

Reactions from the Customer are useful to keep. All these documents may be helpful when the project is evaluated.

Charting

There are several ways of charting plans and progress. Two are shown here. Figure 26.2 is initially a planning chart. It can be developed to show progress by issuing a modified version when progress has been measured. It can be used to show which individuals are involved in each of the activities or tasks.

Figure 26.3 represents high-level planning. In practice a project of this duration would have a hierarchy of lower-level planning charts, allowing control at several levels.

No.	Activity	Quarters Months	Q1			Q2			Q3			Q4			Q5			Q6			Q7			Q8													
			1	2	3	4	5	6	7	8	9	10	11	12	1	2	3	4	5	6	7	8	9	10	11	12											
01	Start project		✗																																		
02	Recruit team			✗	✗		✗	✗																													
03	Check physical stock			✗	✗																																
04	Training				✗	✗	✗	✗	✗																												
05	System analysis					✗	✗	✗	✗	✗																											
06	System design						✗	✗	✗	✗	✗	✗																									
07	Program design								✗	✗	✗																										
08	Programming									✗	✗	✗	✗	✗	✗																						
09	Testing											✗	✗	✗	✗	✗																					
10	Acceptance														✗	✗																					
11	Convert stock file																✗																				
12	Reconcile physical stock																	✗																			
13	Document conversion																✗	✗																			
14																																					
15																																					
16																																					
17																																					
18																																					
19																																					
20																																					

Schedule for: SAMPLE STOCK CONTROL PROJECT   Date: 16 Feb xx   No. 1

Figure 26.3 Typical schedule of activities

A second type of chart is called a Gannt chart, illustrated in Figure 26.4. This is essentially a bar chart of scheduled activities. It too can be used to record progress, but in this case on the same chart. There is less room for detail, but there is advantage in being able to show progress against each activity.

You may have come across the term 'PERT chart'. PERT stands for Project Evaluation and Review Technique. It was developed in 1958 for the US Navy for the control of the thousands of industrial and scientific activities which made up the *Polaris* development programme. PERT offers a highly formalised method of applying critical path procedures to large projects. It can be applied to projects of any size but its requirements and outputs are likely to seem top-heavy for any project that is not substantial. Several software vendors offer PERT packages.

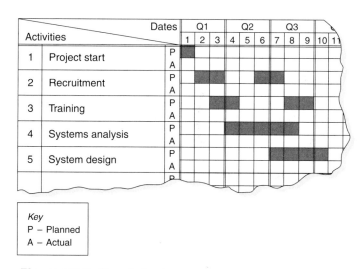

Figure 26.4 Gannt chart

Critical path analysis

If you now look back to Figures 26.1 and 26.2, you will see that we did not make use of the information about the duration of each activity. If we use those figures we will find that some of the routes through the network are quicker than others. The time for the whole job – assuming all the estimates are accurate – will be the time taken to follow the slowest path.

The start-to-finish route 1–6–7–8A–10A–11A, which is the route that will occupy the most time, takes 25 days. This is therefore the least time that the project can take. All other routes can be made up to 25 days by inserting dummy activities denoted by 'A' after their activity numbers. These dummy activities provide 'float' times with the durations shown on Figure 26.5. Float time is the time that can be used up on a route through the diagram without affecting the completion date.

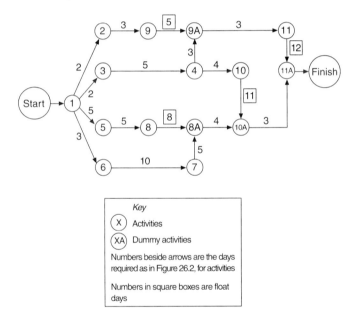

Figure 26.5 Full critical path diagram showing float times

Evidence indicator project

This project has been designed to cover all the evidence indicators related to Chapter 26 (Element 8.1). It has been designed to be carried out at the end of the element.

*Performance criteria:*1–4

Key skills:	Communication	3.2, 3.4
	Application of number	–
	IT	3.1, 3.2, 3.3

Write a report that:

1 discusses the reasons for planning activities
2 discusses project organisation activities
3 explains what project scheduling is, using at least one example from the range we have dealt with in this chapter
4 explains each of the different ways of co-ordinating projects and making sure they can finish on target. You should include at least one example for each item in the range we have dealt with in this chapter.

Chapter 27

Contribute to an information technology team project

This element differs from the other two elements in Unit 8, which are covered in Chapters 26 and 28, in one particular respect. It is directed at the contribution that you personally can and should make to aspects of an IT project: Chapter 26 (Element 8.1) and, to a lesser extent, Chapter 28 (Element 8.3), address issues which hold good for IT projects in general as well as some with which you yourself can identify.

There is none the less much overlap between the ground covered in this chapter and that in Chapter 28. To avoid repetition, we point out in this chapter places where topics relevant to this chapter are actually made in Chapter 28 (Element 8.3). To that extent you will find it helpful to face the two chapters together.

As the thrust of this element is your own contribution to a project you should try to see yourself as one of the members of a team which is charged with the successful completion of that project. You will be helping to achieve that result for a project forming part of your course, perhaps while doing so fulfilling a variety of roles in the team as the project moves forward.

After studying this chapter you should be able to:

1   contribute to defining the project *objectives* and *roles and responsibilities* of the project team
2   record personal and colleagues' *performance* on the project
3   obtain and record comments on personal *performance* from teachers/tutors and colleagues
4   improve personal *performance* following critical comment.

Special note

There is only one evidence indicator project for this element. It is at the end of the element on page 339.

The project on which you are to be working may have arisen from material you covered earlier in the course, or it may have been set by your college or school, or you and the rest of your team may have been able to choose it yourselves. Whatever the source of the project, let us assume that it has some commercial purpose, as opposed to an industrial or scientific purpose, and that it results in the creation of a new computer-based system.

You should, of course, imbue the conduct of your project with importance, as if much rode on a successful outcome. We looked at what success for a project entailed in Chapter 26 (Element 8.1).

The size of the project you tackle as part of your GNVQ course has to be limited: you have on average only about 20 to 25 hours to devote to each element. You should, though, see if you can picture how your involvement would differ if the project were much bigger, engaging more people, taking longer to finish and consuming an organisation's hard-earned money. The more you are able, by talking to staff and to knowledgeable individuals outside your institution, to learn about larger-scale IT projects, the more you will benefit.

Defining the project objectives and roles and responsibilities of the project team

Objectives

The objectives of a project will usually the principles of those listed in a feasibility study report which will have been issued before a project begins. Feasibility studies were discussed in Chapter 17 (Element 5.1) which dealt with the principles of systems analysis.

Let us now revisit those objectives in a different order, so that we conform with the specification of this element, and suggest how you, as a team member, might contribute to them.

Product (goods/services)

The main purpose of the project is, we shall say, to do with the manufacture or supply or warehousing of goods; or the supply of services; or, possibly, to do with accounting for such matters. The broad scope of your project, based on these possibilities, has to be set at the start. You will have an opportunity to influence the choice by drawing attention to the scale of the project that it implies, the extent to which it makes use of earlier work and its realism.

Time-scale

To arrive at an estimate of the time needed for the completion of the entire project, the team will have to make estimates of the time that they think will be required for each part or activity, and add them together. You will have views on some of these estimates, based either on experience or on common sense, which you can put forward to help the team reach agreed or compromise figures.

IT projects worldwide have a reputation for over-running their forecasts of the time they will need. When you try your hand at making estimates of the time necessary for analysis, design, programming, testing, documentation and acceptence, and then observing how closely they are met, even for a tiny project, you are likely to see what a tricky job it is.

Costs

In the outside world the largest direct cost of a project is almost sure to be the salaries of the professional staff working on the project, though in many cases as completion slips the opportunity costs will overtake the direct costs. Opportunity costs are those which arise from the postponement or reduction of the flow of benefits upon which the project was justified.

In your case you will have to obtain from your tutor the assumptions you should make about the notional costs of team members, equipment, software, electronic communications, accommodation, furniture, materials, and heating and lighting. On these assumptions the team can estimate project costs, using the estimates of time discussed above.

As before, you can contribute to the process of estimating by relying on your experience, outside help, and common sense.

Did you know?

The Inland Revenue's scheme of self-assessment for taxpayers, introduced in 1996, rested on a massive software project, and was justified by the expectation of large, progresssive staff savings. Perhaps you can imagine the opportunity cost to the government of any serious delay.

The automatic settlement and registration systems for the London Stock Exchange did suffer major delays. The opportunity costs to member firms, and to London's reputation as one of the world's largest and most efficient capital markets, have been heavy.

The Channel Tunnel, though not principally an IT project, was late opening at least partly because software was not ready. The opportunity cost of this delay will be felt for many years because the whole profile of increasing income from fares has been shifted back.

Specifications

The detailed description of what a new system produced by an IT project is to do is usually called the 'functional specification', or simply the 'specification'. This specification will contain all the information on input, processing, data storage and output that the team will need in order to fulfil their commitment.

You will be able to contribute to the wording of the specification by scrutinising it in draft form and suggesting improvements. You might spot inaccuracies, ambiguities or procedures that could be carried out more easily or more cheaply, on which you could base your suggestions.

Methods

The methods to be followed by the project team in developing a new system ought to be laid down in a procedures manual or standards manual. As someone trying to follow the prescribed methods you are well placed to comment on inconsistencies and procedures that are awkward. You might also be able to propose additions to the documentation to make the development activity quicker and more reliable.

Roles and responsibilities

We separate the roles from the responsibilities. Each member of the team will gain experience by moving from role to role, though there may not be time for everyone to undertake each role, and there certainly will not be enough people in the team for anyone to carry out one role to the exclusion of all the others: each member of the team will have to spread his or her effort across two or more roles. The responsibilities associated with each role stay the same during the life of the project.

As you act out a role you should concentrate on the requirements of that role, and notice what strengths and weaknesses you have in relation to the role. At the same time you should observe the performance of other members of your team fulfilling their roles, and note their strengths and weaknesses.

The strengths you should look out for in yourself and exhibited by others in the team are those that promote achievement and team cohesion.

Roles

Accountancy

The accountancy role for the project is to keep records of expenditure, including the expenditure of time, and of decisions affecting costs, and to provide the information on time to the Project Manager. Arising from this requirement is the evident need for the person in the role to be good with figures and a meticulous record-keeper.

Administration

The role of administration is to support in every practicable way the creative work of the project team. It could include the provision of good working conditions, the supply of manuals and other materials needed for the job, and as far as possible the protection of the team from unnecessary chores such as filling up forms or queueing for any facilities they need. Someone should be appointed to look after the administration for the team. Administration calls for that person to be a competent organiser, a lucid communicator and sensitive to the needs of team members.

Development

Development, in the context of this element, concerns carrying out the preparatory stages of the project, including the investigation and analysis of the field to be addressed by the project, and the testing and selection of alternative approaches. One or more members of the team will be assigned to development. The skills wanted here are the ability to think about problems broadly, in an unstructured way, to display initiative and creativity, and to be strong at devilling for information.

Design

This covers system design and program design. The smooth running of the remainder of the implementation of the system depends to a great extent on the competence with which the design is done. Design also ensures that the production methodology is appropriate for the tasks to be undertaken. When design has been completed the team may wish to review their initial estimates of time. Someone has to be in charge of the design. Like development, that person needs skill in thinking about a variety of solutions to a problem, and to be confident enough to select one.

Production

Production embraces the programming, testing and documentation of the new system. Collectively these activities consume the most time and the most members of the team. This role, above others, demands that all those involved work together comfortably. The skills needed for those in the production group are the technical ability to conduct the programming work quickly and reliably, without much supervision, and to be a dependable and amicable member of the group.

Management

The role of manager is distinctive. In a business setting the manager is in the 'hot seat'. The future prospects of the person appointed will be governed by how well the team performs on satisfying its objectives. The qualities that a manager should possess are discussed in Chapter 28 (Element 8.3). The outlook for the team member acting temporarily as manager on your project is not so precarious; but you do need to recognise that a project manager is the person in charge.

Responsibilities

The responsibilities of the person leading each of the roles on your project include the following:

- *Accountancy*: Finding out exactly what financial and time-keeping information is wanted, and devising ways of capturing it; and then ensuring that it is submitted punctually.
- *Administration*: Taking whatever steps are necessary to fulfil the role. This might mean being prepared to pester staff in the institution to try to sweep away petty bureaucracy which is hampering the productivity of the project team.
- *Development*: Planning the technical realisation of the project, and giving the manager details of the skills that will be needed at each stage of the project; and providing documentation setting out the plan.
- *Design*: Working closely with the development

leader and the production leader, producing, and, if necessary, revising, designs for the new system and for the programming structure.

- *Production*: Assigning tasks to the production group, keeping tight control over their progress, establishing and enforcing quality control procedures, and reporting progress to the manager.
- *Management*: The project manager must plan all facets of the project, calling for the information needed to do so; taking every technical decision; safeguarding quality; maintaining good internal communications within the team; and establishing high morale.

Activity

Imagine yourself as someone with no head for figures who has been assigned to the accountancy role. What steps do you think you could take to prepare yourself for the job with a view to doing it as well as possible?

Did you know?

Hundreds of millions of pounds of European Union money earmarked for government IT projects in UK are sitting unused because local authorities are failing to come forward with proposals for projects. This is an inversion of the usual situation in which organisations have difficulty funding projects they desperately want to carry out.

On this occasion there seem to be opportunities missed by top management.

Record personal and colleagues' performance

In Chapter 28 (Element 8.3) we shall be looking at the performance of the project team. Here, under similar headings we focus on the performance of individual team members, including yourself. As we shall see in Chapter 28 (Element 8.3) you should try not to take personally judgements made on your performance.

You may feel that you have been made in a particular way and that there is no point in criticism because you are not susceptible to change. That is true up to a point: no amount of determination will enable you to change the natural colour of your hair, or your height, or, for that matter, your tendency to be introverted or extrovert, or your predisposition to be diligent or slapdash. However there are areas where changes that are in your interests, and in the interests of any team you join, can be developed. They include

- aspects of personal communication
- knowledge, skill and understanding
- willingness to try hard to help secure common goals
- an awareness of the broad economic purpose of IT projects.

Let us consider these one by one to suggest how performance of your colleagues and yourself might be recorded.

In recording the performance of colleagues, you need help from them so that you can note down facts rather than opinions. You want to know about the problems they faced, and what they did well.

In thinking about your own performance try to recognise your own strengths and weaknesses, without being too critical of yourself, but being open and fair. Note any causes of difficulty you experienced in your work on your project, and how you could avoid or overcome those difficulties next time. You should also make a note of how well your skills were applied to the project tasks, and what you learned about what you found you could do well.

A form to record your response to all these issues could be devised:

- *Interpersonal skills*: How do you rate his or her co-operation with others? To what extent does he or she exhibit qualities of leadership? Is he or she enthusiastic about the work to be done? How adaptable is the person? When you get to the next chapter you will find a discussion on adaptability and on the qualities of leadership.
- *Technical knowledge and skill*: What are the areas on which he or she is especially well informed? Does he or she take steps to increase his or her knowledge and skill? Is he or she able to pass on that knowledge and skill in lucid written and oral communication?
- *Effort*: Is he or she willing and able to make a sustained effort to achieve some end? If so, does he or she make the effort with a good grace in a way that helps to sustain the spirits of other team members? Does the quality of his or her work stay at a high standard after prolonged spells of work?
- *Economic perspective*: Does he or she show an interest in, and a comprehension of, the economic issues of a project? Is he or she

337

resourceful in the sparing use of resources? Is he or she prudent in the use of time?

Obtain and record comments on personal performance from teachers/tutors and colleagues

The performance of individuals, and indeed every aspect of them as people, can look totally different to different observers, depending on the observers' standpoint. The strengths and weaknesses of politicians, for example, look markedly different to their supporters and their opponents. The impression created by a manager on subordinates may be unrecognisable to a superior.

It follows that the same form may be used to record the comments of both peers in the project team, and tutors and other colleagues, but the entries on the form are likely to reflect the different perspectives.

Below we touch on the way you can deal with critical comment. Here we just emphasise that comment on the performance of an individual, whether from staff or peers, must be sincere and constructive if it is to be helpful rather than damaging.

Improve personal performance following critical comment

Let us take the word 'critical' in the sense of censorious rather than in the sense of perceptive. How are you going to react to critical comment of your performance? If it is unexpected, or aggressive, you are likely to be resentful: most people would be. If, however, you uncouple what has been said from how it was said, and make yourself believe that the remarks were made with a sincere and disinterested purpose, you will find that you can after a short while become disposed to derive benefit from them.

If you want to use the comments to help you improve your personal performance, particularly on IT project work, you will find that you can extract the greatest advantage from them by.

■ after an interval, discussing them with their author. Surprisingly often people will say something like 'I am afraid I did not express myself very clearly. What I really meant was . . .'.

Also, if you reveal that you were upset by the remarks, the writer will probably express surprise, and may well even apologise. You must remember that not everyone is gifted with the knack of being both accurate and tactful

■ talking over what was written and then what was said by the author of the comments, with a friend. That could be both calming and constructive

■ finally, looking again at the comments, and matching them against the four headings in the section on recording performance, above. If you then review each aspect of performance against the comments you will probably identify areas where you believe that you could improve matters. You might feel it desirable, after a further interval, to return to the writer of the comments for a further chat.

Once you have agreed that there are particular areas in which you could improve your performance you should develop a plan for achieving that improvement. For example, if you realise that your ability to keep to deadlines is not what it might be you could adopt techniques of time management to set about overcoming the problem.

Activity

Devise a program for making improvements in two areas. If you felt that you needed to be more familiar with methods of program testing and with the main types of LAN management software, for instance, how would you plan an organised way of becoming better informed?

Evidence indicator project

This project has covers all the evidence indicators related to Chapter 27 (Element 8.2). It has been designed to be carried out at the end of the element.

Performance criteria: 1–4

Key skills: Communication   3.1, 3.4
Application of number –
IT   –

You should relate the evidence you present for this element to the project on which you have been working. Remember that the evidence you produce must show that it represents your own knowledge, skill and understanding; not just that of your project team as a whole.

You need to demonstrate to your tutor that you can:

■ contribute to the definition of the project objectives, roles and responsibilities of the project team, covering the range, all of which is discussed above, in this chapter
■ improve your personal performance following critical comment.

You need to show records that you have kept on:

■ personal and colleagues' performance on the project, covering the range, all of which is discussed above, in this chapter
■ the comments obtained from teachers/tutors and colleagues on personal performance on the project.

Evaluate an information technology team project

In Chapter 26 (Element 8.1), we discussed evaluation as an activity that should form part of the management of an IT project. We now return in this chapter to consider evaluation more fully. We shall do so by looking at the project team as a whole; and at the project, as an entity, throughout its implementation.

Project teams in IT vary in size from a single individual to many hundreds, the duration of projects can lie anywhere between a few days and several years, and the money spent and at risk can be up to tens of millions of pounds. Here we are not going to be looking at the extremes but shall be concentrating on medium-sized projects such as are to be found at any time in large numbers of organisations of all kinds. We assume that a project's objective is to build an IT system.

The conduct of evaluation is not that of the confessional, although it may provoke humility on occasion: its purpose is to place on record the major characteristics of a project that has been completed, with a view to the organisation learning useful lessons from what happened. Individual members of a project team will benefit from the review of the team's performance on a recently completed project. Every project should benefit from the evaluation process carried out on predecessor projects.

After studying this chapter you should be able to:

1 obtain and record *evaluative comments* on a team project
2 produce *constructive comments* on the *performance* of the project team
3 make suggestions for *areas of improvement* to the team project.

Special note

There is only one evidence indicator project for this element. It is at the end of the element on page 344.

Obtain and record evaluative comments

In Chapter 26 (Element 8.1) we saw that there should be project control procedures for keeping records of the progress of tasks at stages of the project, and for comparing actual progress with the progress that had been planned. This information must be kept so that it can be fed into the evaluation process, but it is not enough on its own to provide a full evaluation.

The evaluation will draw on the recollections and impressions of team members and others, as well as making use of facts recorded during the life of the project. For this reason evaluation should take place as soon as practicable after the system that was developed in the project has been handed over.

There ought to be subsequent evaluations, as we noted in Chapter 26 (Element 8.1), to review the reputation of the system after a period of use, to record whatever teething troubles had dogged the new system, and to note the maintenance load that had been placed on the project team after they had handed over the system. In this chapter you will be looking at the main evaluation only, and not any subsidiary evaluations that might be undertaken later.

The terms *the Investor, the Customer* and *the Implementer* will be used here, as they were earlier in this unit, to denote the three parties principally concerned with the commissioning and outcome of a project.

This first performance criterion is about obtaining answers to questions that need to be asked and answered for the evaluation to be made. We therefore present the subject-matter in the form of questions.

Quality

- Was the project brief clear, and issued in time for preparations to be made?
- Was the system specification clear, and had it been wholly agreed with the Customer?
- Was the team made up of suitably experienced and trained people?
- Were all the team members available when needed?
- Were standards embodying development methodology available, and understood by all team members?
- Were documentation standards similarly available?
- Did the software and documentation forming the system delivered to the Customer exhibit the quality called for by the standards?

- Were the arrangements for acceptance of the system by the Customer agreed with the Customer?
- Did the system perform exactly as required by its specification in terms of function, speed, use of computing resources and ease of operation?

Cost

- Has the project been completed within its cost budget?
- How did the project perform financially against each cost head – for instance salaries, equipment, software, electricity, telephone, external services – in the budget?
- Were the rules and procedures for determining and recording costs straightforward?
- Were there any unexpected costs?

Time taken

- Was the completed system delivered on time? Was it delivered early?
- How well did time forecasts for activities such as planning, design, programming, documentation, testing, acceptance and hand-over match the time actually taken for each?
- Was any obligation to pay for overtime, or to give time in lieu of extra hours worked, incurred?

Project organisation

- Was there an organisational structure that was clear to all team members?
- Were responsibilities allocated clearly?
- Was the performance of individuals recorded for use during staff appraisal sessions?
- Were changes to the project organisation, when they became necessary, handled competently?
- Was liaison with the Customer continuous and useful?

Methods used

- Was the development methodology followed closely? If not, why not?
- Were any new techniques or procedures adopted? Were they documented?
- Were other standards complete and unambiguous? Were they followed closely? If not, why not?

- Were the administrative procedures efficient and unobtrusive?

Interpersonal relationships

- Was the development of the system generally free from strife?
- Were there any instances of groups working together so effectively that the collective result exceeded 'the sum of the parts'?
- Have any lessons been learned about the selection of people to work within a project team?

Did you know?

The efficient control of projects from the smallest to the largest is always important to the organisations for which they are being run. Government has to carry out some of the biggest IT projects. To try to ensure that they are competently managed they published a document called *Guidelines for Directing Information Systems Strategy.*

Produce constructive comments on performance

You will not know until you have made comments on the performance of your project team whether or not they are considered to be constructive. What is important is that when you have been part of a project team you do make comments when invited to do so, and that you *intend* what you say to be constructive. Your remarks, whether written or oral, should be as follows:

- *Clea,* so that they cannot be misinterpreted.
- *Objective* because if you base them on prejudice or wishful thinking you will very soon be rumbled, and what you say will be ignored.
- *Accurate* because, by the same token, once it is discovered that what you said was not accurate little attention will be paid to what you say thereafter.
- *Concise* because you do not want to be accused of speaking just to enjoy the sound of your own voice. The impact of your words could be inversely proportional to the number of them.

You must develop ways of making comments so that they do not cause offence, even if they have to be critical. Likewise, you have to learn not to become upset by criticism of work that you have done on a project. It is constructive to think of the giving and receiving of comments as a professional activity carried out in the interests of a project as a whole, and to try not to become emotionally involved yourself.

The performance issues upon which you will be commenting include the following.

Co-operation

For the project to be successful there must be good co-operation at several levels. Team members must co-operate with each other in working together, and they must also do so with specialists they need to consult and with their immediate superiors. The team as a whole must co-operate with the Customer and, as required, with the Investor.

Leadership

The way the team is led and managed is crucial to success. Leadership is difficult to define, but if the members of the team do their work with energy and commitment they are probably being well led.

Enthusiasm

Enthusiasm is infectious. An enthusiastic team is a joy for those within it, and for those who deal with it from the outside; and it is almost sure to be an effective team.

Support

Support of one team member by another, and by the manager, creates a learning environment which can be valuable, as well as lubricating the progress of the work. You can assess the support provided to you by the Project Manager and the team members by thinking about how ready they were to listen to your queries and worries; whether they responded in a way that was helpful to you, rather than by showing off their knowledge; and whether they left you feeling that you could approach the same individuals again without the risk of being humiliated. You can also watch to see what support is provided to other team members and, indeed, how you yourself feel about giving support.

Adaptability

For the members of any group or team to work together effectively a degree of give and take is necessary. Individuals need to be adaptable to work constructively with one another. Adaptability is an abstract quality, but one you notice if it is absent. If a team member is obstinate in refusing to change his or her ways in order to fit in with the team's method of working it is apparent to you at once; and you are reminded of it every time the person's obstinacy causes difficulty.

Activity

Try to think of some task you could take on as a group of three or four to show up quickly anyone who is not able or willing to be adaptable. If you fasten on something physical – you do not actually have to do it – like having to transport a full bucket of water over a mile of hilly ground in 20 minutes, having only two poles to help you, slopping as little as possible, you may have something suitable.

Communication

The Project Manager will lay down which matters have to be communicated on paper or by email, and which can rely on word of mouth. In a well-knit team, where all members trust each other, and all enjoy the same perception of the goals, information, requests and instructions transmitted by the spoken word often suffice and, incidentally, save time.

Technical

The technical prowess of the team is a proper field for comment. The project is a technical endeavour. The knowledge, skill and problem-solving ability of the team must be adequate for the work that has to be done.

Effort

The effort applied by the team shows itself in the volume of work generated, the quality of that work and the compliance with the schedules and their deadlines. The sustained effort of the team is indispensable to a successful project. We saw in Chapter 26 (Element 8.1), the importance of establishing and maintaining high morale. This is where its benefits are seen.

Economic

Care must be taken to conserve the resources used, and the time spent, on each aspect of the project. The consumption of these expendable commodities will have been estimated before the project began, and using more than had been estimated will hurt the profile of the project and may be seriously damaging.

Make suggestions for areas of improvement

Let us now look at areas of the project where there might be scope for improvement, and then at how you might make suggestions to help realise this improvement.

Accountancy

Accountancy is an area where a project team might expect support from the relevant department in the organisation. The project team should provide details of their activities when sought, and receive promptly reports of financial performance against budget.

Administration

We saw in Chapter 26 (Element 8.1) the importance of appropriate administrative support for the project team, which would protect team members from spending unnecessary time on clerical and administrative tasks to the detriment of their professional and technical work.

Development

The efficiency of the development activity is hard to gauge because of its essentially innovatory nature. There are, however, pointers in, say, the investigation and analysis activities, to the competence of the team. Standards and techniques should have been observed, documentation should be of a high standard and those who will have to work with the output from the activities should be helped to understand exactly what has been done.

Activity

Look back at the recording and charting forms we considered in Chapter 26 (Element 8.1). How do you think they could be used to help you identify areas of possible improvement in the development process?

Design

In the same way the efficiency of design work is hard to calibrate: often the competence of a design is apparent only after the system incorporating it has been completed and can be assessed. A design for an IT system, in both the planning and preparatory stages, should be exposed to the scrutiny of all those whose work will be affected by it.

Production

Production is at the heart of the project. The extent and the quality of the resources allocated to the project will affect the team's productivity; and, conversely, the effectiveness of the use made of those resources that are provided will also bear on productivity. Amongst the resources will be the software tools provided to assist the system-building process. Ultimately, productivity will be assessed by comparing performance against schedule: it is to be hoped that the schedule itself had been accepted as achievable before it was used as a yardstick and publicity given to the verdict on productivity.

Management

Management of the highest quality is an ideal the Investor would like for every IT project in order to limit the financial risks as far as possible. The feedback on the quality of project management is important to an organisation's top management. Most of this feedback will be apparent to observers outside the project, and team members should not be encouraged to make observations about their own manager.

Indications of effective management can be seen in the high morale and enthusiasm displayed by the team, pointing to strong leadership, and also in the success of the manager in protecting the team from interference by people outside the team. The quality, content, and punctuality of communication of all kinds with the project team also say something about the way the project is being managed. Finally, the method of reaching decisions and the quality of the decisions themselves are vital to the success of the project.

Let us consider each of the six areas to identify how suggestions for improvement might be made. All suggestions should be capable of being expressed in writing, for the Project Manager, and normally they should be positive and constructive. Each suggestion made in writing should be answered in writing, saying what can be done to satisfy it.

Examples of possible suggestions are as follows:

- *Accountancy*: Could we have financial performance reports once every two weeks?
- *Administration*: Could our expense claims be dealt with more quickly?
- *Development.*: Could there be more copies of the standards manuals, so that there are enough for every team member to have one?

- *Design*: Could we have sessions with designers at an earlier stage of the design process so that everyone's ideas are canvassed and considered?
- *Production*: Could we be given some measure of our productivity and some way of comparing it with the productivity of other organisations?
- *Management*: Could we have a talk from our manager's manager on how our project relates to other activities throughout the organisation?

Evidence indicator project

This project has been designed to cover all the evidence indicators related to Chapter 28 (Element 8.3). It has been designed to be carried out at the end of the element.

Performance criteria: 1–3

Key Skills:		
	Communication	3.2
	Application of number	–
	IT	3.1, 3.2, 3.3

If you are able to see a project team at work in a commercial organisation you will find the presentation of evidence easier. If that is not possible you should base what you write on any project work you have done during your course, on help from your tutor and on your reading.

You need to provide records, or a report, which covers:

- evaluative comments obtained on a team project
- constructive comments on the performance of the project team
- appropriate suggestions for areas of improvement to the team project.

You will have to cover the range for this element in writing your records or report.

Answers to unit tests sample questions

Information Technology Systems: Unit Test 1

1	c	7	a	13	c	19	a	25	b
2	d	8	c	14	c	20	d	26	d
3	c	9	c	15	a	21	d	27	d
4	b	10	a	16	a	22	c	28	a
5	b	11	c	17	c	23	d	29	d
6	d	12	b	18	d	24	c	30	a

Using Information Technology: Unit Test 2

1	a	7	a	13	c	19	a	25	d
2	b	8	c	14	c	20	d	26	a
3	b	9	b	15	a	21	b	27	d
4	d	10	d	16	c	22	c	28	c
5	b	11	c	17	d	23	b	29	a
6	b	12	b	18	b	24	c	30	c

Organisations and Information Technology: Unit Test 3

1	b	7	c	13	d	19	d	25	d
2	d	8	d	14	c	20	a	26	b
3	b	9	c	15	a	21	b	27	d
4	d	10	a	16	a	22	d	28	b
5	c	11	c	17	b	23	c	29	b
6	a	12	b	18	d	24	b	30	b

Communications and Networking: Unit Test 4

1	c	7	a	13	d	19	c	25	a
2	d	8	c	14	a	20	a	26	d
3	d	9	b	15	c	21	a	27	c
4	b	10	b	16	d	22	b	28	d
5	a	11	b	17	b	23	a	29	b
6	b	12	b	18	d	24	b	30	c

Systems Analysis: Unit Test 5

1	a	7	c	13	a	19	a	25	c
2	a	8	c	14	b	20	b	26	c
3	a	9	a	15	b	21	b	27	c
4	d	10	c	16	d	22	d	28	a
5	a	11	b	17	b	23	b	29	c
6	d	12	a	18	c	24	b	30	c

Software: Unit Test 6

1	c	**7**	c	**13**	c	**19**	c	**25**	b
2	c	**8**	d	**14**	a	**20**	b	**26**	d
3	b	**9**	c	**15**	b	**21**	d	**27**	c
4	a	**10**	b	**16**	b	**22**	b	**28**	b
5	c	**11**	c	**17**	c	**23**	c	**29**	a
6	b	**12**	d	**18**	c	**24**	c	**30**	c

Database Development: Unit Test 7

1	c	**7**	d	**13**	b	**19**	c	**25**	c
2	c	**8**	c	**14**	b	**20**	c	**26**	c
3	d	**9**	a	**15**	d	**21**	a	**27**	b
4	b	**10**	c	**16**	b	**22**	b	**28**	a
5	d	**11**	a	**17**	d	**23**	c	**29**	b
6	a	**12**	b	**18**	b	**24**	d	**30**	b

KEY SKILLS TRACKING SHEET FOR COMMUNICATION LEVEL 3

Evidence assignment for element:	Unit 1				Unit 2				Unit 3				Unit 4			
	1.1	1.2	1.3	1.4	2.1	2.2	2.3	2.4	3.1	3.2	3.3	3.4	4.1	4.2	4.3	4.4
Communication Element 3.1 1	✓	✓				✓		✓	✓	✓		✓				
2	✓	✓	✓			✓			✓	✓		✓				
3	✓	✓	✓			✓			✓	✓		✓				
4	✓	✓				✓			✓	✓		✓				
5	✓	✓	✓			✓			✓	✓		✓				
Communication Element 3.2 1		✓	✓	✓		✓			✓		✓	✓	✓	✓	✓	
2		✓		✓		✓	✓	✓	✓		✓	✓	✓	✓	✓	
3		✓				✓	✓	✓	✓		✓		✓	✓	✓	
4		✓				✓	✓	✓	✓		✓		✓	✓	✓	
5		✓				✓			✓	✓	✓	✓			✓	
Communication Element 3.3 1			✓			✓		✓	✓				✓		✓	
2			✓			✓		✓	✓				✓		✓	
3			✓	✓		✓		✓	✓				✓			
Communication Element 3.4 1		✓				✓	✓	✓		✓			✓	✓		
2		✓				✓	✓	✓		✓			✓	✓		
3		✓				✓	✓	✓		✓			✓	✓		
4		✓				✓	✓			✓			✓	✓		

KEY SKILLS TRACKING SHEET FOR COMMUNICATION LEVEL 3

Evidence assignment for element:	Unit 5 5.1	5.2	5.3	Unit 6 6.1	6.2	6.3	Unit 7 7.1	7.2	7.3	Unit 8 8.1	8.2	8.3
Communication Element 3.1 1	✓	✓									✓	
2	✓	✓		✓							✓	
3	✓	✓		✓							✓	
4	✓	✓		✓							✓	
5	✓	✓		✓							✓	
Communication Element 3.2 1	✓	✓	✓		✓	✓	✓	✓	✓	✓		✓
2	✓	✓	✓		✓	✓	✓	✓	✓	✓		✓
3	✓	✓	✓		✓	✓	✓	✓		✓		
4	✓	✓	✓	✓	✓	✓	✓	✓		✓		
5	✓	✓	✓	✓		✓	✓	✓		✓		✓
Communication Element 3.3 1	✓	✓	✓				✓					
2	✓	✓	✓				✓					
3	✓	✓	✓				✓					
Communication Element 3.4 1		✓	✓	✓	✓		✓	✓	✓	✓	✓	
2		✓	✓	✓	✓		✓		✓	✓	✓	
3		✓	✓	✓	✓	✓	✓		✓	✓	✓	
4		✓	✓	✓		✓	✓			✓	✓	

KEY SKILLS TRACKING SHEET FOR APPLICATION OF NUMBER LEVEL 3

Evidence assignment for element:		Unit 1				Unit 2				Unit 3				Unit 4			
		1.1	1.2	1.3	1.4	2.1	2.2	2.3	2.4	3.1	3.2	3.3	3.4	4.1	4.2	4.3	4.4
Number Element 3.1	1										✓						
	2					✓	✓	✓			✓						
	3					✓	✓	✓									
	4					✓	✓	✓									
	5					✓	✓	✓			✓						
	6						✓	✓	✓		✓						
	7							✓	✓		✓						
Number Element 3.2	1					✓	✓	✓	✓		✓						
	2					✓	✓	✓	✓								
	3					✓	✓	✓									
	4					✓	✓	✓	✓						✓		
	5					✓	✓	✓	✓						✓		
	6					✓		✓	✓								
	7					✓		✓	✓								
	8							✓			✓						
	9								✓								
Number Element 3.3	1						✓	✓			✓						
	2						✓	✓			✓						
	3					✓	✓	✓			✓						
	4					✓	✓	✓			✓						
	5						✓	✓			✓						

KEY SKILLS TRACKING SHEET FOR APPLICATION OF NUMBER LEVEL 3

Evidence assignment for element:	Unit 5 5.1	5.2	5.3	Unit 6 6.1	6.2	6.3	Unit 7 7.1	7.2	7.3	Unit 8 8.1	8.2	8.3
Number Element 3.1 1												
2												
3												
4												
5												
6												
7												
Number Element 3.2 1					✓							
2					✓							
3												
4					✓							
5					✓							
6					✓							
7												
8												
9												
Number Element 3.3 1												
2					✓				✓			
3					✓				✓			
4												
5					✓							

KEY SKILLS TRACKING SHEET FOR IT LEVEL 3

Evidence assignment for element:	Unit 1 1.1	1.2	1.3	1.4	Unit 2 2.1	2.2	2.3	2.4	Unit 3 3.1	3.2	3.3	3.4	Unit 4 4.1	4.2	4.3	4.4
IT Element 3.1 1	✓	✓	✓	✓	✓	✓	✓	✓	✓	✓	✓			✓		✓
2	✓	✓	✓	✓	✓	✓	✓	✓	✓		✓			✓		✓
3	✓	✓	✓	✓	✓	✓	✓	✓	✓		✓			✓		✓
4	✓	✓	✓	✓	✓	✓	✓	✓	✓		✓			✓		✓
5	✓	✓	✓	✓	✓	✓	✓	✓	✓		✓			✓		✓
IT Element 3.2 1	✓	✓	✓		✓	✓		✓		✓	✓			✓		✓
2	✓	✓			✓	✓		✓			✓			✓	✓	✓
3	✓	✓			✓	✓		✓			✓			✓	✓	✓
4	✓	✓	✓	✓	✓	✓		✓	✓	✓	✓			✓	✓	✓
5	✓	✓	✓		✓	✓					✓			✓		✓
6	✓	✓			✓	✓			✓		✓			✓		✓
7	✓	✓	✓		✓				✓							✓
IT Element 3.3 1	✓	✓	✓	✓	✓	✓	✓		✓	✓	✓		✓	✓	✓	✓
2	✓	✓	✓		✓	✓	✓		✓	✓	✓		✓	✓	✓	✓
3	✓	✓	✓		✓	✓	✓		✓	✓	✓		✓	✓	✓	✓
4	✓	✓	✓	✓	✓	✓	✓		✓	✓	✓		✓	✓	✓	✓
5	✓	✓	✓		✓	✓	✓			✓	✓	✓		✓	✓	✓
6	✓				✓	✓	✓			✓		✓		✓	✓	✓
IT Element 3.4 1	✓					✓		✓		✓	✓			✓	✓	
2	✓				✓	✓		✓		✓	✓	✓		✓	✓	
3	✓	✓						✓		✓	✓	✓		✓	✓	
4	✓					✓		✓		✓	✓	✓		✓	✓	✓
5	✓			✓				✓	✓	✓				✓	✓	
6	✓			✓				✓	✓	✓				✓	✓	

KEY SKILLS TRACKING SHEET FOR IT LEVEL 3

Evidence assignment for element:	Unit 5			Unit 6			Unit 7			Unit 8		
	5.1	5.2	5.3	6.1	6.2	6.3	7.1	7.2	7.3	8.1	8.2	8.3
IT Element 3.1 1	✓		✓	✓		✓	✓	✓		✓		✓
2			✓	✓		✓	✓	✓		✓		✓
3			✓	✓		✓		✓		✓		✓
4			✓			✓		✓				✓
5			✓			✓		✓				✓
IT Element 3.2 1	✓					✓			✓	✓		✓
2						✓			✓	✓		✓
3						✓			✓			
4			✓	✓	✓	✓			✓			
5	✓			✓		✓			✓			
6	✓			✓		✓			✓			
7				✓		✓			✓			
IT Element 3.3 1	✓		✓	✓	✓	✓		✓	✓	✓		✓
2	✓		✓	✓		✓		✓	✓	✓		✓
3				✓		✓		✓	✓	✓		✓
4					✓	✓	✓		✓	✓		✓
5					✓	✓	✓		✓	✓		✓
6					✓	✓	✓		✓	✓		✓
IT Element 3.4 1				✓		✓			✓			
2				✓		✓			✓			
3						✓			✓			
4					✓	✓			✓			
5						✓						
6						✓						

Further reading

- Bowman, J. S. (ed.) (1996), The *Practical SQL Handbook* 3rd edn., Addison Wesley Developers Press

- Britton, C. & Doake J. (1996), *Software Systems Development* 2nd ed., McGraw-Hill

- Burgess, R. S. (1988), *Structured Program Design Using JSP* 2nd ed., Stanley Thornes

- Carter, R. (1996), *Information Technology Made Simple* 2nd ed., Butterworth Heinemann

- Chartered Institute of Management Accountants. (1996), *CIMA Study Text Stage 1: Business Environment and Information Technology*

- Corbitt, T. (1994), *Information Technology and its Applications* 2nd ed., Addison-Wesley Longman Higher Education

- Croucher, P. (1995), *Communications and Networks*, Sigma Press

- Date, C. J. (1994), *An Introduction to Database Systems* 6th edn., Addison-Wesley

- Doyle, S. (1996), *Information Systems For You* Revised ed., Stanley Thornes

- Eaglestone, B. M. (1991), *Relational Databases*, Stanley Thornes

- Fry, T. F. (1983), *Data processing*, Butterworth Heinemann

- Gosling, P. (1994), *Macmillan Master Series (computing): Mastering Spread Sheets* 2nd ed., Macmillan Press

- Hunter, P. (1993), *Local Area Networks*, Addison-Wesley

- Kernighan, B. W. & Ritchie, D. M. (1988), *The C Programming Language* 2nd ed., Prentice Hall US

- Murray, W. H. & Pappas, C. H. (1993), *Windows 3.1 Programming*, Osborne McGraw-Hill

- Needham, D. & Dransfield, R. (1995), *Business Advanced* 2nd ed., Heinemann Educational

- Philippakis, A. S. & Kazmier L. J. (1991), *Comprehensive Cobol: Advanced Cobol Programming (Chapters 14-26) Vol II*, McGraw-Hill Publishing Company

- Pidd, M. (1992), *Computer Simulation in Management Science* 3rd ed., John Wiley and Sons

- Prigmore, C. (1989), *Practical Information Technology*, Arnold

- Reed Business Publishing, *Computer Weekly*, Journal/Magazine published weekly

- Sargent, D. (1991), *An Introduction to Program Design*, McGraw-Hill International

- Schildt, H. (1992), *Turbo C/C++ The Complete Reference* 2nd edn., Osborne McGraw-Hill

- Senn, J. A. (1989), *Analysis & Design of Information Systems* 2nd edn., McGraw-Hill Publishing Company

- Sharp, J. A. & Howard, K. (1996), *The Management of a Student Research Project* 2nd ed., Gower Publishing Group

- Shelley, J. & Hunt, R. (1984), *Computer Studies: A First Course* 2nd ed., Addison-Wesley Longman Higher Education

- Simpson, A. (1990), *Understanding dBase IV 1.1* 2nd ed., Sybex

- Simpson, A. (1992), *Understanding dBase IV 1.5 for DOS* 3rd ed., Sybex

- Simpson, A. (1993), *Understanding dBase IV for Windows*, Sybex

- Tanik, M. M. & Chan, E. S. (1991), *Fundamentals of Computing for Software Engineers*, Van Nostrand Reinhold International

- Willis, N. (1992), *Computer Architecture and Communications* 2nd ed., Alfred Waller

Index